CURRENT TOPICS IN PLANT PHYSIOLOGY:
AN AMERICAN SOCIETY OF PLANT PHYSIOLOGISTS SERIES

With this volume, the American Society of Plant Physiologists continues its series of publications on timely topics in plant physiology. Publication of proceedings devoted to focus areas, such as the present one on carbon partitioning and source-sink interactions in plants, is designed to share information from plant science symposia with other scientists. This book is the thirteenth in the series "Current Topics in Plant Physiology: An American Society of Plant Physiologists Series." It is the wish of the Publications Committee and the Executive Committee of the Society to make these publications as useful as possible. To this end, copies of this publication and publications from previous years are available at an affordable price from the American Society of Plant Physiologists, 15501 Monona Drive, Rockville, Maryland 20855, telephone 301-251-0560.

The ASPP Publications Committee: Stanley Roux, Chair;
Samuel I. Beale; Judy Callis; Richard Dixon; Mary Schuler   June 1995

Current Topics in Plant Physiology:
An American Society of Plant Physiologists Series
Volume 13

Carbon Partitioning and Source-Sink Interactions in Plants

Edited by

Monica A. Madore

William J. Lucas

Proceedings

17th Annual Riverside

Symposium in Plant Physiology

January 19-21, 1995

Department of Botany and Plant Sciences
University of California, Riverside

Published by:
American Society of Plant Physiologists
15501 Monona Drive
Rockville, Maryland 20855-2768 U.S.A.

Printed in the United States of America.

Library of Congress Cataloging in Publication Data

Main entry under title:

Carbon Partitioning and Source-Sink Interactions in Plants

Current Topics in Plant Physiology:
An American Society of Plant Physiologists Series
Volume 13.

Includes bibliographies and index.

      1. Carbon Partitioning—Congresses. 2. Source-Sink Interactions—Congresses. 3. Carbon Partitioning in Plants—Congresses. 4. Source-Sink Interactions in Plants—Congresses.

      I. Madore, Monica A., 1955-. II. Lucas, William J., 1945- III. University of California, Riverside, Dept. of Botany and Plant Sciences. IV. Title.

Library of Congress Catalog Card Number: 95-077643.
ISBN 0-943088-30-5.

CONTRIBUTORS

M. D. Adcock

A. J. Anderson

Raphael Anguenot

Owen Atkin

Markus Bachmann

Suchandra Balachandran

Miguel A. Ballicora

Gerard F. Barry

A. Battistelli

Stephen D. Blakeley

K. A. Blee

Christopher S. Brown

Camilo Canel

Claudio Cantini

Muriel Chaumont

Wan-Hsing Cheng

Prem S. Chourey

Mark A. Conkling

T. M. DeJong

David T. Dennis

John D. Everard

Sylvie Ferrario

Karsten Fischer

Ulf-Ingo Flügge

Christine Foyer

Wolf B. Frommer

Ying-bin Fu

Michelle Gadush

Donald R. Geiger

Glena Gilbert

Y. L. Grossman

Rebecca Grumet

Hanping Guan

Edith Haritatos

Karin Herbers

Joseph A. M. Holtum

Joan L. Huber

Steven C. Huber

Richard J. Hull

Kyung H. Im

Canan Inan

Shigeo Katoh

Felix Keller

Diana Klein

Karen E. Koch

Anne Krapp

Hans Lambers

Mary J. Laughlin

Frank-Roman Lauter

Richard C. Leegood

Wayne H. Loescher

William J. Lucas

Monica A. Madore

Mara O. Massel

Andrew J. Maule

Robert W. McMichael, Jr.

S. Moscatello

Erik Murchie

Hyacinthe N'tchobo

Nathalie Galtier

Olaf Ninnemann

Kurt D. Nolte

Christine E. Offler

Thomas W. Okita

Amnon A. Olesinski

C. Barry Osmond

William H. Outlaw Jr.

John W. Patrick

Matthew Paul

D. Mason Pharr

Jack Preiss

Binh Nguyen Quoc

Raymond L. Rodriguez

Ursula Röper-Schwarz

Monica M. Sanwo

Renate Scheibe

Wen-Jang Shieh

Mirta N. Sivak

Alison M. Smith
Uwe Sonnewald
Mark Stitt
Tod Stoltz
Johan M. H. Stoop
Monika E. Studer Feusi
Earl W. Taliercio
Masaaki Terashima
Bruce R. Thomas
Robert Turgeon
Laszlö I. Técsi
Yoash Vaadia
Hong Li Wang
Andreas Weber
Ingo Wilke
John D. Williamson
Clyde Wilson
Shmuel Wolf
Yuri T. Yamamoto
Serge Yelle
Neil C. Yorio
Xiao-Min Yu

EDITORS' INTRODUCTION

Plant productivity is determined by a complex series of events leading from carbon dioxide fixation in the chloroplasts, formation of phloem-mobile and storage metabolites, and delivery of these to sink tissues. We are only just beginning to understand the extent of these complexities. In recent years, attention has turned to the techniques of molecular biology in an attempt to elucidate the mechanisms controlling carbon partitioning in plants. A key aspect considered in the organization of this Symposium was, therefore, to bring together a diverse group of scientists interested in all aspects of source-sink physiology. The 17th Annual Symposium in Plant Physiology, *Carbon Partitioning and Source-Sink Interactions in Plants*, which was held January 19-21, 1995, at the University of California at Riverside, we believe, did just that.

International scientists, active in areas of carbon partitioning, transport, and source-sink interactions, including agronomists, biochemists, cell biologists, geneticists, molecular biologists, and plant physiologists, gathered for discussion of state-of-the-art research in the areas of chloroplast metabolism, carbohydrate synthesis, phloem loading, carbohydrate transport pathways, and carbohydrate storage and catabolism. Many of these scientists had also been participants in the previous Symposium held in January 1985 on this same topic and were able to provide interesting updates of the advances in their particular research fields since that time. In the first session, an overview of our progress in the past decade was provided by the speakers in that session. This was followed by a session pointing out the importance that molecular biological approaches have had on furthering our understanding of the complex biochemical reactions occurring which result in the final pattern of carbon partitioning that is seen in the plant. The third session examined the important, but still poorly understood, role of transport pathways in source-sink interactions, while the fourth session covered the metabolism and transport of raffinose oligosaccharides and polyols, the "carbohydrates far more interesting than sucrose," for which carbon partitioning mechanisms have still to be elucidated. And finally, the fifth session focused on sink tissues, the ultimate destination of many of the carbon compounds synthesized and transported in the plant.

It is exciting to see that such progress has been made at the cellular, molecular, and physiological levels in our understanding of carbon partitioning in plants, even in the relatively short period since this topic was last covered at a Riverside Symposium. Hopefully, the next decade will be as productive, or even more so.

ACKNOWLEDGMENTS

We gratefully acknowledge the superb organization of this Symposium by Cindi McKernan of the Department of Botany and Plant Sciences at the University of California at Riverside. The success of the Symposium was greatly due to the painstaking care she took to make sure that all the organizational details were worked out well in advance of the Symposium. We also acknowledge Patti Fagan for the excellent job she has done in the technical editing of this volume and for her willingness to put in long hours preparing the camera-ready manuscripts.

We respectfully thank the following sponsors for their financial support for the Symposium and the Proceedings: the United States Department of Agriculture, Cooperative State Research Service; the National Science Foundation; the University of California Systemwide Biotechnology Research and Education Program; the Department of Botany and Plant Sciences, UCR; Michael T. Clegg, Acting Dean of the College of Natural and Agricultural Sciences, UCR; and The American Society of Plant Physiologists.

Finally, we thank the distinguished speakers, poster presenters and participants who came from near and far to attend the Symposium. The Symposium could not have succeeded without them.

Monica A. Madore
William J. Lucas

This volume is dedicated to the memory of Michele L. Gottlieb (1963-1994), a graduate student in the Department of Botany and Plant Sciences. Her presence at this symposium was sorely missed.

CONTENTS

Opening Remarks

Session I - Regulation of Carbon Partitioning in Photosynthetic
Tissues - 10 Years of Progress

Concluding Remarks

ABBREVIATIONS

$A_{0.5}$	concentration of activator giving 50% of maximal activation
A6PR	aldose 6-phosphate reductase
AGPase	ADP-glucose pyrophosphorylase
Amy	α-amylase gene
BE	branching enzyme
BS	bundle sheath
CaMV	cauliflower mosaic virus
CCCP	carbonyl cyanide m-chloro-phenolhydrazone
CMV	cucumber mosaic virus
CS	citrate synthase
CW	cell wall
DAP	days after pollination
DiT1	2-oxoglutarate/malate translocator
DiT2	glutamate/malate translocator
EAS	5-epi-aristolochene synthase
FBP	fructose-1,6-bisphosphate
FBPase	fructose-1,6-bisphosphatase
FTR	ferredoxin/thioredoxin reductase
FW	fresh weight
G6PDH	glucose-6-phosphate dehydrogenase
GAPDH	glyceraldehyde 3-phosphate dehydrogenase
GBSS	granule-bound starch synthase
GGT	galactan:galactan galactosyltransferase
GOGAT	glutamate synthase
GPDH	glyceraldehyde-3-phosphate dehydrogenase
GS	glutamine synthetase
GSyn	galactinol synthase
HATS	high-affinity transport system
$I_{0.5}$	concentration of inhibitor giving 50% inhibition
Ivr	acid invertase gene
LATS	low-affinity transport system
LED	light-emitting electrode

M	mesophyll
M6PR	mannose 6-phosphate reductase
MALDI	matrix-assisted laser desorption ionization mass spectroscopy
MDH	malate dehydrogenase
MP	movement protein
MTD	mannitol dehydrogenase
NiR	nitrite reductase
NR	nitrate reductase
PEP	phosphoenolpyruvate
PEPcase	phosphoenolpyruvate carboxylase
PFK	ATP-dependent phosphofructokinase
PFP	PPi-dependent phosphofructokinase
PGA	phosphoglycerate
3PGA	3-phosphoglycerate
PK	pyruvate kinase
PK_c	cytosolic pyruvate kinase
PK_p	plastid pyruvate kinase
PR	pathogenesis-related
PRK	phosphoribulose kinase
PVY	potato virus Y
QTL	quantitative trait line
rbcS	small subunit of ribulose-1,5-bisP carboxylase oxygenase
RCMV	red clover mottle comovirus
RFO	raffinose family oligosaccharide
RS	raffinose synthase
Ru1,5bisP	ribulose-1,5-bisphosphate
RUBP	ribulose bisphosphate
SE-CCC	sieve element-companion cell complex
SEL	size exclusion limit
SPS	sucrose phosphate synthase
SS	sucrose synthase
STS	stachyose synthase
Sus	sucrose synthase gene

TCHO	total carbohydrate concentration
Td	thioredoxin
TFP	trifluoroperazine
TMV	tobacco mosaic virus
TMV-MP	tobacco mosaic virus movement protein
TPT	triose phosphate/phosphate translocator
trioseP	triose phosphate
ts	temperature sensitive
UDPG	UDP-glucose
VSP	vegetative storage proteins
WT	wild type

The Revolution in Carbon Partitioning and Source-Sink Interactions in Plants From the Perspective of CAM

Joseph A. M. Holtum and C. Barry Osmond

Department of Botany and Tropical Agriculture, James Cook University of North Queensland, Townsville, QLD 4810, Australia (J.A.M.H.); and Research School of Biological Sciences, Institute of Advanced Studies, Australian National University, Box 475, Canberra, ACT 2601, Australia (C.B.O.)

Partitioning presupposes compartmentation and source-sink interactions presuppose transport between compartments, processes which have long been central to our understanding of photosynthetic physiology and biochemistry in and between cells of CAM and C_4 plants. As CAM plants were the focus of our participation in previous Riverside symposia, there seems to be no good reason to change the focus, only the context. Furthermore, if the need to know is a priority, then the huge gaps in our understanding of these processes in CAM and C_4 plants deserve mention at this meeting. There is another good reason to discuss these problems in Riverside. Every time we begin to generalize about CAM, Irwin Ting serves us another significant exception! Against this background, we shall set out a series of conundrums in compartmentation and source-sink relations in CAM and C_4 plants, while also attempting to respond to the commissions of W.J. Lucas.

UNDE VENISTIS?

"...it would seem essential that you reflect on where we were 10 years ago..."

Ten years ago, one was justifiably impressed by what seemed to be a mature understanding of the biochemistry of carbon partitioning at source during leaf photosynthesis. This understanding was built on the traditional approaches of interspecific comparisons, analysis of mutants, developmental differences, and environmental responses. The definitive reviews were in preparation. Tom ap Rees (1987) was arguing that the metabolism of plants was uniquely compartmented, and used the compartmentation of sucrose metabolism in leaves during photosynthesis as his prime illustration. He did not mention CAM. Heldt and Flügge (1987) were cataloguing the metabolite transporters of cell and organelle membranes that made for effective compartmentation of photosynthetic carbon metabolism. They dealt with sucrose synthesis and photorespiratory metabolism in C_3 photosynthesis, briefly with C_4 photosynthesis, and acknowledged that the massive metabolite fluxes of the biggest organelle of all, the vacuole of CAM plants, "has still to be elucidated." Stitt *et al.* (1987) were addressing the control of photosynthetic sucrose formation in all three higher plant photosynthetic systems, integrating knowledge of the coarse and fine control of enzymes with knowledge of translocators and compartmentation. They noted how thin this was so far as CAM was concerned, by reference to Edwards *et al.* (1982), a review in the first of the Riverside symposia to be published. Clearly, a decade ago, we were relatively well founded in leaves of C_3 and C_4 plants, but foundering in CAM.

In comparison, a decade ago our understanding of mechanisms of source-sink interactions was relatively poor. Although *Annual Reviews* of this time contained articles on cell membrane ATPases (including those that transported sugars), the dynamics of vacuolar compartmentation, and on phloem loading and unloading, these topics then had little in common. Some of the most important processes underlying plant source-sink interactions, the unique relationships of the apoplasm and symplasm, were still anchored in the elegant theoretical and structural contexts of the previous decade.

Perhaps confidence in the concepts of fine tuning of complex systems, of exclusive compartmentation and specific function, was too highly developed in the mid 80's. In our enthusiasm, we may have overlooked the fact that plant life is nonhomeostatic, and that even within the best husbanded agricultural systems, plants confront daily extremes of biotic and physical environments that demand flexibility so far as carbon partitioning and source-sink relationships are concerned. Acceptance of this flexibility in compartmentation and of concurrent multiple forms of enzyme regulation now seems more commonplace. Thus, at the dawn of the first decade of the revolution in plant molecular biology, we were well prepared to exploit techniques that could target the amount and/or properties of soluble proteins, and address the structure-functional relationships of membrane-carrier proteins—targets that were vital to further understanding of carbon partitioning and source-sink interactions.

UBI ESTIS?

"...you would then identify the high points of scientific advancement achieved over the ensuing decade...."

These high points are already summarized in the titles of the papers of this symposium, and the details are most competently elaborated in the papers that follow. Indeed, these titles reveal one paramount advance; today, one finds experts ranging from molecular genetics, through mechanisms of catalysis, metabolic flux control and metabolite transport, compatible solutes, to those with a stomatal complex fetish, all on the same program. Some of the big questions in plant cell physiology have found new hope in a common approach—the ability to perturb the levels and properties of particular proteins through targeted molecular intervention. Mercifully, this meeting will not deal with the technologies themselves, only with the progress in understanding of the big issues in plant biology. In an analogy apposite in California, it seems we are not so interested in the jeans themselves (i.e. in the Levi Strauss outcomes of the goldrush), but in the nuggets. This is an old fashioned view of the socioeconomic impact of goldrushes, but one that endures.

The maturation in plant cell physiology has thus taken place as (and because) appropriate molecular technologies have become available and have been deployed alongside traditional disciplines. We have seen the structure and function of plasmodesmata yield to a range of physiological and biochemical approaches (Lucas *et al.*, 1993). In one volume of *Annual Reviews* (1991), we find progress in chloroplast translocators, the pH and ionic status of the apoplast, and fructan metabolism. In another volume of *Annual Reviews* (1993), we see progress in plasma membrane and tonoplast transport energetics, phloem loading, sugar transporters, and compatible solutes. All of these advances have contributed to our present understanding of carbon partitioning and source-sink interactions. What better illustration of the continued need for traditional disciplines could we have than the painstaking studies of subcellular volumes and metabolite concentrations by Winter *et al.* (1993)?

UBI DATA SUNT?

(Discourse on some of the low points of the last decade was not in the brief for these Opening Remarks, but neither was it excluded!).

To some extent, progress in carbon partitioning and source-sink relationships in CAM and C_4 plants over the last decade has been a casualty of the above successes. However, the sheer perversity of some of the problems and the prevalence of paradox in the data deserves some attention here. In what follows, we shall consider a few examples from studies of CAM and C_4 plants over the last decade that, though still unresolved, illustrate three mechanisms of carbon partitioning, namely:

♦ intracellular compartmentation and organelle transporters;

♦ coarse and fine control of metabolic pathways;

♦ intercellular compartmentation and symplasmic transport.

Conundrums of Carbon Partitioning in CAM

Photosynthetic cells of CAM plants exhibit diversity and tight regulation of carbon partitioning. Although different species show diverse patterns of storage of different carbohydrates in different compartments, all CAM plants, each day, have to secure 75% of the carbohydrates synthesized from decarboxylation of malic acid, in whatever chemical form or compartment, for the following period of nocturnal CO_2 fixation. Up to 20% of the total carbon in CAM cells may be involved in these transfers, a demand that places unique constraints on carbon partitioning and source-sink relationships in these plants.

The evidence suggests that the local carbohydrate-recycling demands of nocturnal CO_2 fixation in photosynthetic tissues of CAM take priority over export. Labelling studies (Mayoral and Medina, 1985) show:

♦ that there is minimal export of carbohydrate derived from deacidification of CO_2 fixed into malate in the dark. About 25% of this carbohydrate is lost each day.

♦ that nearly all of the carbohydrate derived from CO_2 fixation after deacidification is exported or respired within 16 h.

These authors further confirmed local priority for carbohydrate partitioning in the course of subsequent source-sink manipulations (Mayoral *et al.*, 1991). Increased sink strength (shading all but one leaf) did not alter the malate to glucan transfer, but did reduce the extent of transient soluble sugar accumulation during deacidification. Reduced sink strength (removal of young leaves or girdling) enhanced soluble sugar and glucan pools, doubling the extent of malate-glucan interconversion. The accumulation of soluble sugars led to a complete loss of CO_2 fixation in the light by C_3 photosynthesis following deacidification.

Kalanchoe pinnata, the species used in the above experiments, is a malic enzyme-CAM plant (Osmond and Holtum, 1981; Leegood *et al.*, 1995) in which the carbohydrate for the next night's CO_2 fixation is secured as glucan in the chloroplast during the light. In these plants, the chloroplast is evidently "force-fed" with triose under conditions of saturating CO_2 during deacidification (Fig. 1). Chloroplasts of these CAM plants contain all the enzymes and

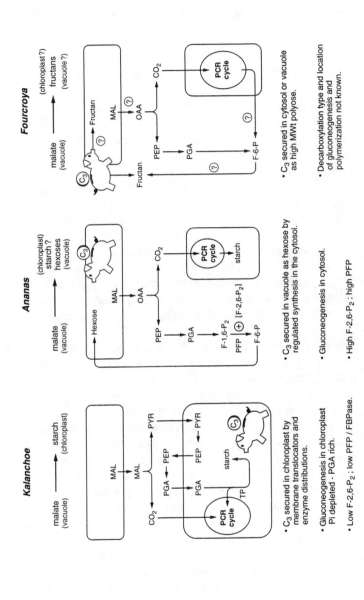

Figure 1. Carbon partitioning and source sink regulation in three subtypes of CAM plants. The need to "bank" 3-C units during deacidification in the light (i.e. to retain this carbon in leaves during C$_3$ photosynthesis) for subsequent PEP carboxylation and malic acid synthesis in the dark evidently occurs in different compartments in each of the three subtypes, differentiated also by the principal storage carbohydrate in each case. Some key regulatory processes of carbohydrate metabolism are also indicated.

translocators of a C_3 chloroplast *and* a mesophyll chloroplast of C_4 plants (Demmig and Winter, 1983; Neuhaus *et al.*, 1988). Taken together, the absence of enolase in the chloroplast, and the presence of pyruvate-Pi, diki-nase, the pyruvate translocator, and the high phosphoenolpyruvate (PEP)-affinity Pi translocator, seem to ensure that pyruvate formed by malate decar-boxylation in the cytosol is quantitatively secured by gluconeogenesis in the chloroplast. This process seems to be metabolically impervious to concurrent C_3 photosynthesis that assimilates CO_2 produced by malate decarboxylation and generates soluble sugars potentially available for translocation and respira-tion. Diurnal variations in the regulatory metabolite F-2,6-P_2 seem to be such as to facilitate this process (Fahrendorf *et al.*, 1987). One cannot avoid asking whether *Kalanchoe* chloroplasts are differentiated with respect to these activi-ties, a question that may remain unanswered until quantitative antibody-label-ing microscopy is undertaken.

There are some striking parallels between carbohydrate partitioning in *Kalanchoe* chloroplasts during deacidification and chloroplasts of transgenic potato plants with 20 to 30% lower activities of the Pi translocator (Heineke *et al.*, 1994a). Compared to wild type under the same conditions, the trans-formed plants show double the amount of glucan accumulation and much higher nocturnal glucan hydrolysis. These studies with tobacco add plausibil-ity to the notion that the significantly different translocator specificities of chloroplasts in *Kalanchoe* and metabolically related CAM plants may dominate the processes of "force-feeding" the chloroplast to secure carbon substrates for nocturnal acidification.

Ananas comosus (pineapple), the principal CAM crop, exemplifies the other extreme, so far as securing carbohydrate for local nocturnal CO_2 fixation is concerned. This PEP carboxykinase-CAM plant secures hexoses and glu-cans during deacidification. It seems that in bright light, hexoses alone (fructose and glucose) are sufficient to accommodate malate synthesis in the following night, but glucans also can be mobilized under some conditions (Carnal and Black, 1989; Medina *et al.*, 1993). Carbohydrate partitioning in these leaves is more enigmatic and may well depend on "force-feeding" the vacuole with hexoses or sucrose (Fig. 1). There is little doubt that cytosolic gluconeogenesis from PEP arising from malate decarboxylation is facilitated by high activities of PPi-PFK, reinforced by the effector F-2,6-P_2 which remains at high concentration during deacidification in these plants (Fahrendorf *et al.*, 1987). Thus, coarse and fine control of cytosolic enzymes dominate this mechanism of carbohydrate partitioning. However, it is difficult to explain how a quantitative relationship between C_4 acid loss and hexose recovery in the vacuole can be sustained in parallel with sucrose synthesis and translocation. Perhaps it is not strictly regulated, because glucans are often mobilized as well, and perhaps some precarious compromise may be involved.

There are also some striking parallels between carbohydrate partitioning in pineapple cells during deacidification and in leaf cells of transgenic potato and tobacco expressing yeast invertase (Heineke *et al.*, 1992, 1994*b*). Cells of these plants, with either vacuolar or apoplasmic invertase, show higher vacuolar and/or apoplasmic hexose concentrations than wild type and provide evidence for direct vacuolar uptake of glucose and fructose. Thus, these studies add plausibility to the notion that "force-feeding" of the vacuole with hexoses is a component of the processes that secure carbohydrate for nocturnal acidification in *Ananas*.

We know relatively little about other mechanisms of carbohydrate compartmentation in other CAM plants, especially in those that accumulate acids other than malate and carbohydrates other than glucans and hexoses. One interesting variation in *Agave* and *Aloe* involves quantitative interconversion of malate and hexose polymers, including fructans and mannose/galactose polymers. In these, it is tempting to suggest that during deacidification the cytosol and/or vacuole may be "force-fed" to retain soluble carbohydrate polymers whose size exceeds the exclusion limits of plasmodesmata (Fig. 1). Thus, malate synthesis in *Fourcroya* is quantitatively related to decrease in fructan hexose equivalents (Olivares and Medina, 1990), and the process is accompanied by a decrease in the extent of polymerization of the fructans (from average of approximately 43 to approximately 24). Such a process leading to carbohydrate retention in photosynthetic tissues seems to be the flip side analogy of one path for symplasmic phloem loading, based on the polymerization trap mechanism (Turgeon and Gowan, 1990). The location of the fructans in these CAM plants is unknown, but in other monocotyledons, fructans and the enzymes involved in their hydrolysis are located in the vacuole (Wagner and Weinken, 1986). Clearly, these CAM plants present a number of conundrums for which we have few plausible models.

The Paradox of Sucrose Inhibition of Photosynthesis in CAM, C_4, and C_3 Plants

As mentioned above, girdling of *Kalanchoe* petioles leads to the retention of the 25% of malate carbon that can be exported as sucrose, and of any sucrose formed by C_3 photosynthesis in phase 4 of CO_2 fixation. Within 48 h, there is a complete cessation of C_3 photosynthesis in this phase, but little effect on nocturnal CO_2 fixation (Mayoral *et al.*, 1991). Cool block treatments of the petioles of C_4 *Amaranthus edulis* lead to a 5- to 10-fold increase in sucrose and soluble sugar concentrations and a 20 to 30% reduction in C_4 photosynthesis within 4 h (Blechschmidt-Schneider *et al.*, 1989). Rice varieties differ in the sensitivity of C_3 photosynthesis to the Dry Cold Dew Wind syndrome in southeast China. (Huang *et al.*, 1989). Retention of sucrose in leaves during the first chilling (10°C) night and subsequent cool bright days (23°C) leads to a rapid (20-40%) decline of canopy photosynthesis within 1 h on the 1st d, followed by a slower further decline of 40 to 60% after 3 d.

Although we now have elegant studies of the effects of low temperature on the structure of the sucrose translocating systems (Gamalei et al., 1994), biochemical interpretations remain enigmatic. So far as we can discover, none of the fine control mechanisms for the regulation of the rate of sucrose synthesis, or for the regulation of sucrose versus starch synthesis, satisfactorily explain the rapid feedback inhibition of C_3 photosynthesis, let alone C_4 photosynthesis, when sucrose is caused to accumulate in leaves following such source-sink manipulations. A close reading of Stitt et al. (1987) and Foyer (1987, 1988) tends to favor interpretations based on cytosolic (C_3) and intercellular (C_4), Pi limitations in the chloroplast, that should be accompanied by hexose and hexose-P accumulation (Sharkey and Vanderveer, 1989; Sawada et al., 1992). The slower responses of photosynthesis to cold-accumulated hexoses and sucrose may involve coarse control via effects of sucrose and hexoses on gene expression (Krapp and Stitt, 1994). However, Hurry et al. (1994) and others continue to observe marked increases in Rubisco and sucrose phosphate synthase (SPS) in the presence of high cytosolic sucrose during cold hardening. These enigmas demand resolution.

QUO VADIS?

"...this would lead you to the most challenging part of the presentation, namely the 'crystal ball' and where things will be in the year 2005."

From the few examples above, it is clear that we can learn much from further research on curious wild plants in controlled environments, if this research can be allowed to continue alongside research with transgenic plants (Schulze, 1994). Already, we have burned our fingers by not taking the environmental context seriously enough when using transgenic plants to evaluate flux control. Thus, we need to constantly refer to earlier, hard-won data from wild plants as we devise tests for hypotheses using transgenic plants. For example, given the difficulties we have with understanding sucrose feedback inhibition of photosynthesis, girdling and low temperature studies of existing transgenic C_3 plants might be a constructive place to begin (Krapp and Stitt, 1994; Sonnewald et al., 1994). The development of efficient transformation systems for C_4 dicotyledons (Chitty et al., 1995) seems imminent, and if native tissue-specific regulation of gene expression is robust, we can expect a suite of transgenic plants that will help understand the sucrose inhibition of C_4 photosynthesis. Of course, it is the C_4 monocotyledons that hold greatest interest. Transformation of these continues to be notoriously inefficient and some objectives raise questions. Thus, we wonder if Saccharum officinale, which has held a plateau of 16% fresh weight sucrose despite decades of breeding, can be engineered to hold much higher concentrations (16% =

approximately 0.5 M, long a pragmatic optimum for organelle isolation and presumably cytosolic function). However, what one might do by substituting other compatible solutes (and with sugarcane architecture) is another challenge altogether, a challenge that will require all the expertise we can muster.

This audience scarcely needs to be reminded that natural selection will continue to work on the integrated physiology of the whole organism. Although most of the single-gene interventions have, thus far, given us further insights into this physiological integration, most have reduced the fitness, or the usefulness, of the target plants. This may be just as well because, in the present socioeconomic climate, a super tobacco plant may be the last thing we need. Thus, although the revolution in biology already allows us to amplify the physiological and biochemical noise we cherish as plant biodiversity, progress will be greater if we can sustain a partnership between researchers with traditional and transgenic perspectives.

We are, in fact, engaged in an enterprise best described as "ecotypic engineering," in which progress depends as much on past experience from plant ecophysiology and biochemistry as it does on future developments. We have proven that continued successful resolution of the big questions in biology depends on sustaining traditional skills in biochemistry and cell physiology. However, we are confronted by the fact that much of modern biochemistry and physiology has been put on hold by the diversion of very limited resources for research in the direction of molecular technology. As much as one can justify this diversion, we now have to cope with the shortfall of a generation of biochemists and physiologists, just when we can least afford *"to waste this opportunity by failing to get the practice right through ignorance of biochemical methods and physiological pitfalls"* (ap Rees and Hill, 1994). Thus, it seems obvious to us that continued research on the clever, and still unresolved, patterns of carbon-partitioning and source-sink priorities in CAM and C_4 plants (and no doubt many still to be examined C_3 plants—especially woody plants) will be a valuable complement to studies with transgenic plants over the next decade. Indeed, we need to take steps now to foster a renaissance of interest in, and opportunities for research in, environmental plant physiology and biochemistry. If we do not, we may simply lose the skills necessary to recognize and evaluate some of the most interesting transgenic plants.

ACKNOWLEDGMENTS

This work is being resurrected by an Australian Research Council grant to J.A.M.H., and by collaboration between RSBS-ANU and JCUNQ. We are grateful to R. Dunn and C. Büchen-Osmond for advice on the Latin translations of W.J. Lucas' not overly short commissions.

9

LITERATURE CITED

ap Rees T (1987) Compartmentation of plant metabolism. *In* DD Davies, ed, The Biochemistry of Plants, Vol 12. Academic Press, New York, pp 87-115

ap Rees T, Hill SA (1994) Metabolic control analysis of plant metabolism. Plant Cell Environ **17**: 587-599

Blechschmidt-Schneider S, Ferrar P, Osmond CB (1989) Control of photosynthesis by the carbohydrate level in leaves of the C_4 plant *Amaranthus edulis L.* Planta **177**: 515-525

Carnal NW, Black CC (1989) Soluble sugars as the carbohydrate reserve for CAM in pineapple leaves. Plant Physiol **90**: 91-100

Chitty JA, Furbank RT, Marshall JS, Chen Z-H, Taylor WC (1995) Genetic transformation of the C_4 plant, *Flaveria bidentis.* Plant J (in press)

Demmig B, Winter K (1983) Photosynthetic characteristics of chloroplasts isolated from *Mesembryanthemum crystallinum*, a halophyte plant capable of Crassulacean acid metabolism. Planta **57**: 66-76

Edwards GE, Foster JG, Winter K (1982) Activity and intracellular compartmentation of enzymes of carbon metabolism in CAM plants. *In* IP Ting, M Gibbs, eds, Crassulacean Acid Metabolism. Amer Soc Plant Physiol, Rockville, pp 92-112

Fahrendorf T, Holtum JAM, Mukherjee U, Lazko E (1987) Fructose-2,6-bisphosphate, carbohydrate partitioning and Crassulacean acid metabolism. Plant Physiol **84**: 182-187

Foyer CH (1987) The basis for source-sink interaction in leaves. Plant Physiol Biochem **25**: 649-657

Foyer CH (1988) Feedback inhibition of photosynthesis through source-sink regulation in leaves. Plant Physiol Biochem **26**: 483-492

Gamalei YV, van Bel AJE, Pakhomova MV, Sjutkina AV (1994) Effects of temperature on the conformation of the endoplasmic reticulum and on starch accumulation in leaves with the symplastic minor-vein configuration. Planta **194**: 443-453

Heineke D, Kruse A, Flügge U-I, Frommer WB, Riesmeier JW, Wilmitzer L, Heldt HW (1994*a*) Effect of antisense repression on the chloroplast triose-phosphate translocator on photosynthetic metabolism in transgenic potato plants. Planta **193**: 174-180

Heineke D, Sonnewald U, Büssis D, Gnter G, Leidreiter K, Wilke I, Raschke K, Wilmitzer L, Heldt HW (1992) Apoplastic expression of yeast-derived invertase in potato. Plant Physiol **100**: 301-308

Heineke D, Wildenberger K, Sonnewald U, Wilmitzer L, Heldt HW (1994*b*) Accumulation of hexoses in leaf vacuoles: studies with transgenic tobacco plants expressing yeast-derived invertase in the cytosol, vacuole or apoplasm. Planta **194**: 29-33

Heldt HW, Flügge UI (1987) Subcellular transport of metabolites in plant cells. *In* DD Davies, ed, The Biochemistry of Plants, Vol 12. Academic Press, New York, pp 49-85

Hurry VM, Malmberg G, Gardeström P, Öquist G (1994) Effects of short-term shift to low temperature and long-term hardening on photosynthesis and ribulose-1,5-bisphosphate carboxylase/oxygenase and sucrose phosphate synthase activity in leaves of winter rye (*Secale cereale* L.). Plant Physiol **106**: 983-990

Huang LK, Wong SC, Terashima I, Zhang X, Lin D-X, Osmond CB (1989) Chilling injury in mature leaves of rice. I. Varietal differences in the effects of chilling on canopy photosynthesis under simulated "Dry Cold Dew Winds" conditions experienced in South-East China. Aust J Plant Physiol **16**: 321-337

Krapp A, Stitt M (1994) Influence of high carbohydrate content on the activity of plastidic and cytosolic isoenzyme pairs in photosynthetic tissues. Plant Cell Environ **17**: 861-866

Leegood RC, von Caemmerer S, Osmond CB (1995) Metabolite transport and photosynthetic regulation in C_4 and CAM plants. *In* DT Dennis, DH Turpin, DB Layzell, eds, Plant Physiology, Biochemistry and Molecular Biology. Longmans, Burnt Mill (in press)

Lucas WJ, Ding B, van der Schoot C (1993) Plasmodesmata and the supracellular nature of plants. New Phytol **125**: 435-476

Mayoral ML, Medina E (1985) ^{14}C- translocation in *Kalanchoe pinnata* at two different stages of development. J Exp Bot **36**: 1405-1413

Mayoral ML, Medina E, Garcia V (1991) Effect of source-sink manipulations on the Crassulacean acid metabolism of *Kalanchoë pinnata*. J Exp Bot **42**: 1123-1129

Medina E, Popp M, Olivares E, Janett H-P, Lüttge U (1993) Daily fluctuations of titratable acidity, content of organic acids (malate and citrate) and soluble sugars of varieties and wild relatives of *Ananas comosus* L. growing under natural tropical conditions. Plant Cell Environ **16**: 55-63

Neuhaus HE, Holtum JAM, Lazko E (1988) Transport of phosphoenolpyruvate by chloroplasts from *Mesembryanthemum crystallinum* L. exhibiting Crassulacean acid metabolism. Plant Physiol **87**: 64-68

Olivares E, Medina E (1990) Carbon dioxide exchange, soluble carbohydrates and acid accumulation in a fructan accumulating plant, *Fourcroya humboldtiana* Trel. J Exp Bot **41**: 579-585

Osmond CB, Holtum JAM (1981) Crassulacean acid metabolism. *In* MD Hatch, NK Boardman, eds, The Biochemistry of Plants, Vol 8. Academic Press, New York, pp 283-328

Sawada S, Usuda H, Tsukui T (1992) Participation of inorganic orthophosphate in regulation of ribulose-1,5-bisphosphate carboxylase activity in response to change in photosynthetic source-sink balance. Plant Cell Physiol **33**: 943-949

Schulze E-D (ed) (1994) Flux Control in Biological Systems. Academic Press, San Diego, 494 pp

Sharkey TD, Vanderveer PJ (1989) Stromal phosphate concentration is low during feedback limited photosynthesis. Plant Physiol **91**: 679-684

Sonnewald U, Lerehe J, Zrenner R, Frommer W (1994) Manipulation of sink-source relations in transgenic plants. Plant Cell Environ **17**: 649-658

Stitt M, Huber S, Kerr P (1987) Control of photosynthetic sucrose formation. *In* MD Hatch, NK Boardman, eds, The Biochemistry of Plants, Vol 10. Academic Press, New York, pp 327-409

Turgeon R, Gowan E (1990) Phloem loading in *Coleus blumei* in the absence of carrier mediated export of sugar from the apoplast. Plant Physiol. **92**: 1244-1249

Wagner W, Weinken A (1986) Properties and subcellular localization of fructan hydrolase in the leaves of barley (*Hordeum vulgare* L. cv Gerbel). J Plant Physiol **123**: 429-439

Winter H, Robinson DG, Heldt HW (1993) Subcellular volumes and metabolite concentrations in barley leaves. Planta **191**: 180-190

Light Modulation of Stromal Enzymes

Renate Scheibe

*Pflanzenphysiologie, Fachbereich Biologie/Chemie
Universität Osnabrück, D-49069 Osnabrück,
Federal Republic of Germany*

THE FERREDOXIN/THIOREDOXIN SYSTEM

It has been known for more than 20 years that ferredoxin (Fd) reduced by photosynthetic electron flow not only donates electrons for NADP reduction via Fd/NADP reductase, for nitrite reduction via nitrite reductase, for sulfite reduction via sulfite reductase, and for the reductive generation of glutamate from oxoglutarate via glutamate synthase (GOGAT), but also for the reduction of the thioredoxin (Td) via Fd/Td reductase (FTR) (for review see: Knaff and Hirasawa, 1991). The components of this latter system have been purified and characterized, and amino acid sequences are also available now. FTR is composed of two different subunits. Subunit A is rather variable between organisms, and subunit B is more conserved and contains an Fe-S cluster, but it is not a flavoprotein as is Fd/NADP reductase (Tsugita *et al.*, 1991; Falkenstein *et al.*, 1994). The Tds are small, ubiquitous, heat-stable proteins occurring in all organisms and in many compartments, and even in the chloroplast various isoforms (Td_m, Td_f) of differing primary structure and specificity are present (for review see: Eklund *et al.*, 1991). Td_m is thought to primarily activate NADP-dependent malate dehydrogenase (NADP-MDH), and to inactivate the chloroplast glucose-6-phosphate dehydrogenase (G6PDH), while Td_f preferentially activates the chloroplast fructose-1,6-bisphosphatase (FBPase), phosphoribulose kinase (PRK), NADP-dependent glyceraldehyde-3-phosphate dehydrogenase (NADP-GAPDH), and the chloroplast coupling factor (CF_1) (for review see: Buchanan, 1991). Whether this pattern of specificities, however, holds true for the *in vivo* situation with its extremely high protein concentration still remains to be established.

It is only until recently that we view the light/dark modulation of chloroplast enzymes not only as an on/off switch, but also as a means to fine-tune enzyme activities in the light (Scheibe, 1991). The basis for such a function is the fact that due to the high O_2 concentration in the chloroplast (Steiger *et al.*, 1977), there is continuous reoxidation of the cysteines generated by Td-mediated electron flow to the target enzymes. Thus, the light-modulated enzymes exist as two interconvertible forms that are subjected to covalent modification (reduction and reoxidation of cystine/cysteine residues) comparable to those enzymes that are subject to protein phosphorylation/dephosphorylation (Scheibe, 1990). In both cases, energy is consumed to drive the cycle between the two forms, but photosynthetic electron flow providing the energy to drive the redox-cycle for the chloroplast enzymes is easily available in the light.

As a prerequisite for this type of covalent regulatory principle, the target enzymes, as well as the chloroplast Td, are characterized by the very negative midpoint redox potentials of their regulatory cyst(e)ines (Faske *et al.*, 1994). Thus, for NADP-MDH, FBPase, and PRK, these are around -380 mV, similar to that of the nonphysiological reagent DTT, and even more negative than for Td_m and Td_f (-350 mV; see Gilbert, 1984). All these redox potentials, however, are more negative than those of NADP(H) (-320 mV), and glutathione (-260 mV), indicating that reduction of these special protein thiols cannot be achieved by cellular reductants other than reduced Fd. It became evident, however, that the formation of an intramolecular disulfide bridge is not involved in all cases, but either exclusively or in addition to this, mixed disulfides are formed with low-mol-wt thiols such as glutathione (Ocheretina and Scheibe, 1994). In these cases, less electron pressure is required to generate the free cysteine, and it is feasible that, at least sometimes, the modification serves for protection of these thiols. The fact that certain chloroplast proteins are present in their oxidized forms is rather unique, since generally, only extracellular proteins exhibit this property (Fahey *et al.*, 1977). However, for chloroplast enzymes, it is this specific property which is the basis for a very flexible regulatory system, as will be shown here.

TARGET ENZYMES

The light/dark-modulated chloroplast enzymes are characterized by their unusually negative redox potentials. As a result of this, they are only in the reduced state when electrons of very negative redox potential from Fd are available in the light; otherwise, they relax to their oxidized state. The redox potentials, however, are affected by specific metabolites, mostly the substrate or the product of the respective enzyme reaction. These metabolites are also known to act as effectors of the reductive and/or the oxidative part of the redox cycle. At equilibrium (with the redox buffer, *in vitro*) or at steady-state (*in vivo*), the combined action of the effectors results in a more or less pronounced shift of the ratio between oxidized and reduced enzyme form in a concentration-dependent manner (Faske *et al.*, 1994). While the effector ATP does not significantly influence the ratio between oxidized and reduced PRK, there is a strong dependence of the NADP-MDH activity in a redox buffer upon the NADPH/(NADPH + NADP) ratio and of the FBPase activity upon the FBP concentration, i.e. NADP-MDH or FBPase cannot easily be activated by DTT or in the light, in the presence of a low reduction state of the pyridine nucleotides or in the absence of FBP, respectively. The resulting regulatory patterns are a strict feedback inhibition of the MDH activation by NADP and a strict feedforward mechanism of the FBPase activation due to increasing FBP levels. PRK activation/inactivation does not appear to be under fine-control. This enzyme is subject to noncovalent regulation of its catalytic activity (Gardemann et al., 1983).

Oxidation of cysteines is a well-known reaction occurring upon folding and secretion of proteins, often assisted by the action of Td-like proteins as protein-disulfide isomerase (for review see: Loferer and Hennecke, 1994). However, these reactions are essentially irreversible and confer stability to the proteins in an oxidizing extracellular environment. The fact that intracellular proteins are oxidized in a reversible manner is rather unique. Oxidation is accompanied by drastic changes in enzymic parameters, such as V_{max}, K_m, and K_a. Thus, for NADP-MDH and PRK, oxidation results in a decrease in their maximal velocities (V_{max}) to essentially zero. For FBPase, oxidation causes a shift, of its substrate affinity, Mg^{2+}-requirement and of its pH optimum to higher values. Oxidized G6PDH is characterized by a strongly decreased K_m value for Glc-6-P such that only this form exhibits activity under physiological conditions (Scheibe et al., 1989). Oxidation of the coupling factor CF_1 and of NADP-GAPDH finally results in an increased requirement for the actual activators, i.e. ΔpH for ATPase (Mills and Mitchell, 1982) and the 1,3-bis-phosphoglycerate (1,3-bisPGA) concentration for NADP-GAPDH (Baalmann et al., 1994). In the latter case, the activator 1,3-bisPGA not only causes the decrease in K_m for the substrate 1,3-bisPGA, but is also responsible for the dissociation of the aggregated low-affinity form to generate the high-affinity heterotetramer (A_2B_2). The electron pressure required for the reduction of NADP-GAPDH and also of G6PDH is rather low when compared to the other redox-modulated enzymes, so that electron flow will never be limiting even at low light, thus providing an efficient means to enable the reductive step of the Calvin cycle to occur and the oxidative conversion of the fixed carbohydrates to be prevented, respectively, under all conditions.

From comparison with the primary structures of their nonregulatory counterparts, it became evident that the light/dark-modulated chloroplast enzymes not only exhibit high similarities, but in addition, possess unique sequences that are responsible for their regulatory properties (see Scheibe, 1990). The MDHs are all very conserved apart from the chloroplast-specific extra-sequences at the C- and the N-terminus. The 35 amino acid nature N-terminus carries the two cysteines that are involved in the redox-modification (Scheibe et al., 1991). Removal of that part of the sequence by limited proteolysis resulted in an enzyme that is as active as the intact enzyme, but still needs reduction (Ocheretina *et al.*, 1993). However, the oxidative modification of further cysteine(s) was shown to be due to the formation of mixed disulfides with low-mol-wt thiols, the reduction of which occurs at less electron pressure than required for the reduction of the N-terminal disulfide bridge, which therefore masks the additional reductive events in the protein (Ocheretina and Scheibe, 1994). In addition, the C-terminus appears to act as an "intramolecular inhibitor" (Jackson *et al.*, 1992) that can be removed from the active site by treatment with a carboxypeptidase (Fickenscher and Scheibe, 1988) or by low concentrations of guanidine hydrochloride (Ocheretina and Scheibe, 1994). It had been shown previously that limited proteolysis of chloroplast NADP-GAPDH with the endoprotease V8 from *Staphylococcus aureus* leads to the removal of the extra-sequence at the C-terminus of subunit B, which is unique to the light-modulated chloroplast enzyme, and to concomitant dissociation of the hexadecamer (Zapponi *et al.*, 1993). We could show that due to this reaction, the active, high-affinity tetrameric form is irreversibly generated, thus indicating that this extra-sequence is involved in the inactivation of the chloroplast enzyme (R. Scheibe, E. Baalmann, B. Warner, C. Rak, submitted).

PHYSIOLOGICAL CONSEQUENCES

As can be predicted from the results obtained for the purified enzymes, both electron pressure driving the redox cycle and metabolite concentrations, reflecting the metabolic situation, will determine the actual activation state of each of the light-modulated enzymes. That this is true has been shown for isolated intact chloroplasts exposed to various light intensities and to intermediates or inhibitors of metabolism added to the medium (S. Holtgrefe, C. Kitzmann, V. Emmerlich, A. Emmerlich, S. Rattmann, C. Harms, and R. Scheibe, manuscript in prep.).

Thus, the actual enzyme activities in isolated chloroplasts achieved at various light intensities will strongly depend upon the metabolic situation (Fig. 1). The actual NADP-GAPDH activity is at 100%, even at the lowest light intensity (10 μE) when ATP and 3PGA are added. Apparently, in the presence of bicarbonate (control), ATP and/or 3PGA are not saturating for the conversion of the low-affinity oligomer to the highly active heterotetramer (E Baalmann, JE Backhausen, S Vetter, R Scheibe, submitted), thus enabling only a partial conversion and a partial activation even in high light. If the stromal 1,3-bisPGA level is further decreased by the addition of tentoxin (to decrease the ATP level), only the activation level is obtained which results from the activity of the oligomer under standard assay conditions. *In vivo*, this activity will be even much lower due to the lack of substrate (1,3-bisPGA) and due to

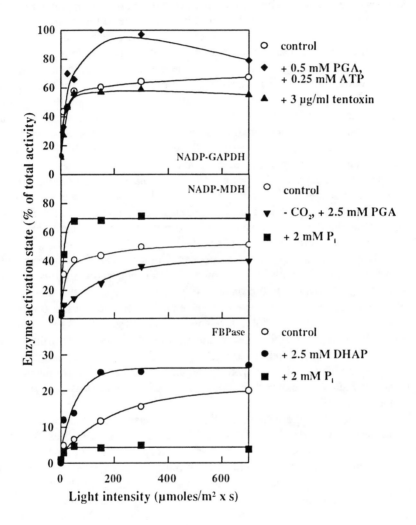

Figure 1. Light saturation curves for various light-modulated enzymes in isolated chloroplasts subjected to different metabolic conditions. Intact chloroplasts were isolated from spinach leaves as described in Backhausen et al. (1994). The actual enzyme activations were determined after 4 min illumination. Full activation of the enzymes were achieved upon incubation with 50 mM DTT (in the presence of 1,3-bisPGA for NADP-GAPDH and of Ca^{2+}/FBP for FBPase).

the inorganic phosphate present in the stroma which shifts the reaction equilibrium in the opposite direction (E Baalmann, JE Backhausen, S Vetter, R Scheibe, submitted). NADP-MDH is activated even in low light, when by addition of inorganic phosphate, the intermediate 3PGA will be drained out of the chloroplast, and the NADPH level is increased due to the lack of electron acceptors. In contrast, less activation of the enzyme is achieved in the presence of 3PGA which results in decreased NADPH levels. Finally, FBPase at low light is activated significantly only in the presence of additional dihydroxyacetone phosphate that is converted into the positive effector FBP inside the chloroplast. If phosphate addition has depleted the stroma from triose phosphates, no activation is obtained at all up to very high light intensities. During CO_2 fixation (control conditions), apparently both an increasing electron pressure and a concomitantly increasing FBP level in the stroma will lead to a light-dependent rise in the actual enzyme activity.

These relationships will enable us to extrapolate to the situation in the whole leaf, where the determination of stromal metabolite levels is almost impossible. The correlations of light intensity and photosynthetic electron transport on the one hand, and stromal enzyme activities on the other, have already been analyzed in a number of studies (Harbinson *et al.*, 1990; Sassenrath-Cole *et al.*, 1994). In some cases, a more or less positive correlation was found. But in others, as at low O_2 or CO_2 concentration, this did not appear to be the case (Harbinson and Foyer, 1991; Sassenrath-Cole *et al.*, 1994). This discrepancy, however, can be explained by the fact that under the chosen conditions, the metabolite levels will also be drastically altered, thus in turn, shifting the activation states of the enzymes at a given thylakoid redox state. Therefore, it is important to include both electron pressure and metabolite levels into models of photosynthetic regulation, since the redox potential of the isolated enzyme alone does not reflect the dynamic situation *in vivo* (Kramer *et al.*, 1990).

Taken together, the differential light- and metabolite-dependent modulation of each of the enzymes provides the basis for an extremely flexible fine-tuning. In isolated chloroplasts, this mechanism has been shown to establish a strict hierarchy between all reactions consuming light-generated electrons, so that no competition between the various pathways will occur (Backhausen *et al.*, 1994). Due to the differential affinity of the various electron acceptors for electrons from reduced Fd, the essential reactions such as NADP-reduction, nitrite reduction, and Td-dependent enzyme activation will preferentially occur under physiological conditions. The required ATP/NADPH ratio is adjusted by the action of the malate valve (Backhausen *et al.*, 1994). Only an excess of electrons will flow into the Mehler/ascorbate reaction and into cyclic electron flow (Steiger and Beck, 1981; Heber and Walker, 1992). In contrast, at higher concentrations the unphysiological electron acceptors H_2O_2 and nitrite

Table I. *Rate of Photosynthesis, Biomass Production and Malate Content as Dependent Upon the NADP-MDH Level in Transgenic Tobacco Plants*

Except where otherwise noted, all measurements were done with leaves of 5-week-old plants (almost fully expanded) after 6-8 h at 600 $\mu E/m^2 \cdot$ s. Each measurement is the mean $\pm$ SD for at least three individual plants.

NADP-MDH (expression level)	"Low"	"Control"	"High"
NADP-MDH activity[a]			
(μmol/mg Chl $\cdot$ h)	<40	200-300	>1500
(μmol/m$^2 \cdot$ s)	<15	50-100	> 150
Activation state			
(% of full capacity)	75 $\pm$ 25	95 $\pm$ 5	58 $\pm$ 3
Rate of photosynthesis			
(μmol/m$^2 \cdot$ s)	6.5 $\pm$ 0.15	7.5 $\pm$ 0.5	11.5 $\pm$ 0.2
Malate content			
(μmol/cm^2)	0.2 $\pm$ 0.04	0.47 $\pm$ 0.05	0.17 $\pm$ 0.05
Total biomass[b]			
(g fresh weight)	4.90 $\pm$ 0.25	5.46 $\pm$ 0.66	7.15 $\pm$ 0.35
(g dry weight)	0.45 $\pm$ 0.03	0.52 $\pm$ 0.22	0.74 $\pm$ 0.07

[a] Enzyme capacity in a growing leaf of a 2-week-old plant after full activation by incubation with 50 mM DTT. These measurements were performed in order to classify the plants into "Low", "Control", and "High" according to the NADP-MDH activity. [b] Plants were 2 weeks old.

can drain electrons from the Calvin cycle (Robinson *et al.*, 1980; Backhausen *et al.*, 1994) and thus inhibit photosynthesis.

From the experiments with isolated chloroplasts, it is clear that the malate valve, as controlled by the activation state of NADP-MDH, is of major importance during photosynthesis in C_3 plants (Scheibe and Beck, 1994). Thus, it was of significant interest to generate transgenic plants with changed levels of this enzyme (M Faske, M Sendker, R Scheibe, A von Schaewen, submitted). In preliminary experiments, it has been shown that indeed photosynthetic CO_2 fixation and, also as a result, biomass production can be increased when tobacco plants are transformed with a sense-construct of pea NADP-MDH leading to overexpression of the enzyme (JE Backhausen, A Grass, A von Schaewen and R Scheibe, in prep.). The malate levels in these leaves, however, are not significantly altered (Table I).

In conclusion, the results from these studies suggest that the increased growth rate might be a result of the increased efficiency of CO_2 fixation due to the action of the malate valve. The beneficial role of malate could, therefore, be in ATP formation in the mitochondria as required for sucrose synthesis in the cytosol (Krömer *et al.*, 1988), in reductant generation as required for cytosolic nitrate reduction (Rathnam, 1978), or in a combination of these factors.

LITERATURE CITED

Baalmann E, Backhausen JE, Kitzmann C, Scheibe R (1994) Regulation of NADP-dependent glyceraldehyde 3-phosphate dehydrogenase activity in spinach chloroplasts. Bot Acta **107**: 313-320

Backhausen JE, Kitzmann C, Schebe R (1994) Competition between electron acceptors in photosynthesis-regulation of the malate valve during CO_2 fixation and nitrite reduction. Photosyn Res **42**: 75-86

Buchanan BB (1991) Regulation of CO_2 assimilation in oxygenic photosynthesis: The ferredoxin/thioredoxin system. Arch Biochem Biophys **288**: 1-9

Eklund H, Gleason FK, Holmgren A (1991) Structural and functional relations among thioredoxins of different species. Proteins: Struct Funct Gen **11**: 13-28

Fahey RC, Hunt JS, Windham GC (1977) On the cysteine and cystine content of proteins. Differences between intracellular and extracellular proteins. J Mol Evol **10**: 155-160

Falkenstein E, von Schaewen A, Scheibe R (1994) Full-length cDNA sequences for both ferredoxin-thioredoxin reductase subunits from spinach (*Spinacia oleracea* L.). Biochim Biophys Acta **1185**: 252-254

Faske M, Holtgrefe S, Ocheretina O, Meister M, Backhausen JE, Scheibe R (1994) Redox equilibria between the regulatory thiols of light/dark-modulated chloroplast enzymes and dithiothreitol: fine-tuning by metabolites. Biochim Biophys Acta (in press)

Fickenscher K, Scheibe R (1988) Limited proteolysis of inactive tetrameric chloroplast NADP-malate dehydrogenase produces active dimers. Arch Biochem Biophys **260**: 711-779

Gardemann A, Stitt M, Heldt HW (1983) Control of CO_2 fixation. Regulation of spinach ribulose-5-phosphate kinase by stromal metabolite levels. Biochim Biophys Acta **722**: 51-60

Gilbert HF (1984) Redox control of enzyme activities by thiol/disulfide exchange. Meth Enzymol **107**: 330-351

Harbinson J, Foyer CH (1991) Relationships between the efficiencies of photosystem I and II and stromal redox state in CO_2-free air. Plant Physiol **97**: 41-49

Harbinson J, Genty B, Foyer CH (1990) Relationship between photosynthetic electron transport and stromal enzyme activity in pea leaves. Plant Physiol **94**: 545-553

Heber U, Walker D (1992) Concerning a dual function of coupled cyclic electron transport in leaves. Plant Physiol **100**: 1621-1626

Jackson RM, Sessions RB, Holbrook JJ (1992) A prediction of the three-dimensional structure of maize $NADP^+$-dependent malate dehydrogenase which explains aspects of light-dependent regulation unique to plant enzymes. J Computer-Aided Mol Design **6**: 1-18

Knaff DB, Hirasawa M (1991) Ferredoxin-dependent chloroplast enzymes. Biochim Biophys Acta **1056**: 93-125

Kramer DM, Wise RR, Frederick JR, Alm DM, Hesketh JD, Ort DR, Crofts AR (1990) Regulation of coupling factor in field-grown sunflower: A redox model relating coupling factor activity to the activities of other thioredoxin-dependent chloroplast enzymes. Photosyn Res **16**, 213-222

Krömer S, Stitt M, Heldt HW (1988) Mitochondrial oxidative phosphorylation participating in photosynthetic metabolism of a leaf cell. FEBS Lett **226**: 352-356

Loferer H, Hennecke H (1994) Protein disulfide oxidoreductases in bacteria. Trends Biochem Sci **19**: 169-171

Mills JD, Mitchell P (1982) Modulation of coupling factor ATPase activity in intact chloroplasts. Reversal of thiol modulation in the dark. Biochim Biophys Acta **679**: 75-83

Ocheretina O, Harnecker J, Rother T, Schmid R, Scheibe R (1993) Effects of N-terminal truncations upon chloroplast NADP-malate dehydrogenase from pea and spinach. Biochim Biophys Acta **1163**: 10-16

Ocheretina O, Scheibe R (1994) Cysteines of chloroplast NADP-malate dehydrogenase form mixed disulfides. FEBS Lett **355**: 254-258

Rathnam CKM (1978) Malate and dihydroxyacetone phosphate-dependent nitrate reduction in spinach leaf protoplasts. Plant Physiol **62**: 220-223

Robinson JM, Smith MG, Gibbs M (1980) Influence of hydrogen peroxide upon carbon dioxide photoassimilation in the spinach chloroplast. Plant Physiol **65**: 755-759

Sassenrath-Cole GF, Pearcy RW, Steinmaus S (1994) The role of enzyme activation state in limiting carbon assimilation under variable light conditions. Photosynth Res **41**: 295-302

Scheibe R (1990) Light/dark modulation: Regulation of chloroplast metabolism in a new light. Bot Acta **103**: 327-334

Scheibe R (1991) Redox-modulation of chloroplast enzymes. A common principle for individual control. Plant Physiol **96**: 1-3

Scheibe R, Beck E (1994) The malate valve: Flux control at the enzymic level. *In* ED Schulze, ed, Flux Control in Biological Systems. Academic Press, San Diego, pp 3-11

Scheibe R, Geissler A, Fickenscher K (1989) Chloroplast glucose-6-phosphate dehydrogenase: K_m shift upon light modulation and reduction. Arch Biochim Biophys **274**: 290-297

Scheibe R, Kampfenkel K, Wessels R, Tripier D (1991) Primary structure and analysis of the location of the regulatory disulfide bond of pea chloroplast NADP-malate dehydrogenase. Biochim Biophys Acta **1076**: 1-8

Steiger HM, Beck E (1981) Formation of hydrogen peroxide and oxygen dependence of photosynthetic CO_2 assimilation by intact chloroplasts. Plant Cell Physiol **22**: 561-576

Steiger HM, Beck E, Beck R (1977) Oxygen concentration in isolated chloroplasts during photosynthesis. Plant Physiol **60**: 903-906

Tsugita A, Yano K, Gardet-Salvi L, Schürmann P (1991) Characterization of spinach ferredoxin-thioredoxin reductase. Protein Seq Data Anal **4**: 9-13

Zapponi MC, Iadorola P, Stoppini M, Ferri G (1993) Limited proteolysis of chloroplast glyceraldehyde-3-phosphate dehydrogenase (NADP) from *Spinacia oleracea*. Biol Chem Hoppe-Seyler **374**: 395-402

Carbon Transport Across the
Chloroplast Envelope

Ulf-Ingo Flügge, Andreas Weber, and Karsten Fischer

Botanisches Institut der Universität zu Köln,
Gyrhofstr. 15, D-50931 Köln, Germany

During photosynthesis, light energy derived from the sun is used for the formation of carbon skeletons. This process is confined to the chloroplasts which are enclosed by two membranes, the outer and the inner envelope membranes. Both membranes are permeability barriers for the photosynthetic products and mediate the exchange of metabolites between the chloroplast and the cytosol. The outer envelope membrane possesses, like other organelles, pore-forming proteins called porins that allow, in the case of chloroplasts, the unspecific diffusion of hydrophilic solutes up to a molecular mass of 10 kD (Flügge and Benz, 1984). The inner envelope membrane, however, contains translocator proteins that are highly specific for particular compounds (Flügge and Heldt, 1991). The chloroplast triose phosphate/3-phosphoglycerate/ phosphate translocator (cTPT) mediates the export of fixed carbon as C_3-compounds in exchange for Pi. The exported photosynthates are then used for synthesis of sucrose which is then exported from the mesophyll cell and (actively) loaded into the phloem (Fig. 1). Photosynthates can also be used for starch synthesis within the chloroplasts. But most of this carbon pool is mobilized during the following dark period and exported from the chloroplasts either via the cTPT after phosphorolytic starch breakdown, or via the glucose translocator after hydrolytic starch breakdown. The resulting carbohydrates can then be used for respiratory processes or transformed to sucrose to supply heterotrophic tissues.

C_3-compounds exported from the chloroplasts can also serve as a source for the formation of α-keto acids (α-oxoglutarate), which are reimported into the chloroplasts for the fixation of ammonia (derived from nitrate reduction or photorespiration) via the glutamine synthetase/glutamate synthase pathway. The glutamate synthesized during this cycle is exported into the cytosol. Two different dicarboxylate antiport systems are involved in this process: the

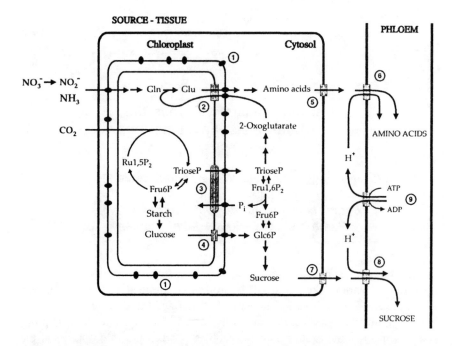

Figure 1. Processes involved in the transport of photoassimilates in leaves. The circled numbers refer to transporters or enzymes: (1) porins; (2) dicarboxylate translocator(s); (3) triose phosphate/phosphate translocator; (4) glucose translocator; (5) and (6) amino acid transporters; (7) and (8) sucrose transporters; (9) ATPase associated with the sieve element-companion cell complex. Fru6P, fructose-6-phosphate; Fru1,6P$_2$, fructose-1,6-bisphosphate; Glc6P, glucose-6-phosphate; Gln, glutamine; Glu, glutamate; Ru1,5P$_2$, ribulose-1,5-bisphosphate; TrioseP, triose phosphate.

2-oxoglutarate/malate translocator (DiT1) transporting 2-oxoglutarate into the chloroplasts and a glutamate/malate translocator (DiT2) exporting glutamate. Since both translocators use malate as the substrate for counterexchange, the resulting 2-oxoglutarate/glutamate transport proceeds without net malate transport (Woo *et al.*, 1987, Flügge *et al.*, 1988). Glutamate and other amino acids can then be further loaded into the sieve tubes via specific amino acid transporters (Fig. 1).

PORINS OF THE OUTER ENVELOPE MEMBRANE

We have recently succeeded in the identification and molecular characterization of voltage-dependent, anion-selective channels from pea root and maize root plastids (Fischer *et al.*, 1994*b*). These porins have molecular masses of

29,596 D (276 amino acid residues) and 29,977 D (277 amino acid residues), respectively, and are 58% homologous on the protein level. Sequence comparison revealed low homology (20-25%) to mitochondrial porins from fungi and humans. On the secondary structure level, however, the plant porins contain 16 antiparallel transmembrane β-strands that are also present in porins from other organism. To verify the function of the cloned genes, the coding region of the cDNA coding for the pea porin (pspor8; Fischer *et al.*, 1994*b*) was subcloned into the bacterial expression vector pQE-60 (Diagen, Hilden, Germany). An *E. coli* clone harboring the plasmid pQE-pspor8 overexpressed the 30-kD protein which was deposited as inclusion bodies. The protein produced represented approximately 15% of the total cellular *E. coli* protein and could be easily isolated and purified from the bacteria. Measurements of the pore-forming activity of the renatured recombinant protein in planar lipid bilayers revealed single channel conductances and voltage dependences almost identical to the authentic 30-kD protein [1.5 and 3 nS (1 M KCl); data not shown]. Thus, we could demonstrate that the plant porin produced in bacteria can be functionally reconstituted in artificial membranes. It is worth noting that the electrophysiological characterization of the plant porins revealed a remarkable similarity to mitochondrial porins indicating that both organelles, nongreen plastids and mitochondria, obviously possess closely related porin proteins. This conclusion is corroborated by direct alignments of porin sequences from plant mitochondria (U. Schmitz, pers. commun.).

Although the primary sequences of the first plastidial porins have now been elucidated, the identity of the chloroplast porin remains unknown. Figure 2 shows a Western blot analysis of different plant mitochondria and plastidial membranes probed with an antibody directed against the yeast mitochondrial porin. This antibody recognizes the porins from mitochondria isolated from green or etiolated pea leaves, and the porin from pea root amyloplasts, respectively, but not the porins from chloroplasts or cauliflower bud plastids. This result again supports the assumption that mitochondria and amyloplasts contain homologous porins, whereas green plastids possess different porins.

THE TRIOSE PHOSPHATE/PHOSPHATE TRANSLOCATOR: TRANSPORT CHARACTERISTICS

The plastidial TPTs serve different functions: in C_3-chloroplasts, it mediates the export of the fixed carbon in the form of triose phosphate (trioseP) and 3-phosphoglycerate for the synthesis of sucrose and amino acids. In C_4-mesophyll chloroplasts, phosphoenolpyruvate (formed by pyruvate, phosphate dikinase) is exported by the C_4-TPT for carboxylation to oxaloacetate via PEP carboxylase. The second product of this reaction, Pi, has to be reimported into the chloroplasts. One function of the C_4-TPT is, therefore, to mediate an

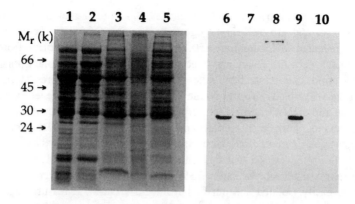

Figure 2. Western blot analysis of different plant mitochondrial and plastidial membranes probed with an antibody directed against the yeast mitochondrial porin. SDS-PAGE and analysis by Coomassie-staining (lanes 1-5) and Western blotting (lanes 6-10). Lanes 1 and 6, mitochondria from green pea leaves; lanes 2 and 7, mitochondria from etiolated pea leaves; lanes 3 and 8, envelope membranes from spinach chloroplasts; lanes 4 and 9, envelope membranes from pea root plastids; lanes 5 and 10, envelope membranes from cauliflower bud plastids.

exchange of phosphoenolpyruvate with Pi. In C_4-plants with a reduced PSII activity in the bundle sheath cells, the C_4-TPT of both cell types are involved in a trioseP/3-phosphoglycerate shuttle in order to provide the bundle sheath chloroplasts with reducing equivalents in the form of trioseP. Thus, the C_4-TPTs mediate in both phosphoenolpyruvate/phosphate and trioseP/3-PGA exchange.

Nongreen plastids of heterotrophic tissues are carbohydrate-importing organelles. Sucrose delivered from the source tissue is cleaved by either invertase or sucrose synthase. The resulting monosaccharides are converted into hexosephosphates. Since most heterotrophic plastids lack Fru-1,6-bisPase activity (Entwistle and ap Rees, 1988; Neuhaus *et al.*, 1993*b*), the key enzyme for the conversion of trioseP into hexosephosphates, these organelles rely on the import of hexosephosphates as precursors for starch biosynthesis. Transport measurements with intact organelles or reconstituted tissues from different plants suggest that this transport is mediated by a translocator that also transports hexosephosphates (Flügge and Heldt, 1991; Borchert *et al.*, 1993; Neuhaus *et al.*, 1993*a*; Flügge and Weber, 1994). The phosphate translocator from nongreen plastids of pea roots has been shown to transport only Glu-6-P, but not Glu-1-P (Borchert *et al.*, 1993). In cauliflower bud plastids and developing pea embryos, only Glu-6-P was able to sustain starch synthesis at significant rates (Hill and Smith, 1991; Neuhaus *et al.*, 1993*a*). On the other hand, plastids from wheat endosperm preferentially incorporate Glu-1-P into starch (Tyson and ap Rees, 1988; Tetlow *et al.*, 1994). However, measurements of reconstituted transport activities from this tissue demonstrated that wheat endosperm amyloplasts are capable of mediating only a Glu-6-P/phosphate exchange, but not a Glu-1-P/phosphate antiport (Flügge, 1995). Thus, Glu-1-P has to be imported into these plastids by a mechanism different from that of other heterotrophic tissues.

The primary sequences of the TPT from different C_3-plants, as well as those from the C_4-plant maize and the C_4-species *Flaveria trinervia*, have been elucidated (Fischer *et al.*, 1994a). The nature of their counterparts present in heterotrophic tissues is still unknown. The chloroplastidial translocators are almost exclusively expressed in photosynthetic tissues, but not in nongreen tissues (Schulz *et al.*, 1993; Flügge, 1995). It appears obvious that various plastids contain different phosphate translocators mediating an exchange of phosphate with other substrates, e.g. trioseP, phosphoenolpyruvate, or Glu-6-P. But it remains to be elucidated as to how diverse these translocators are with respect to their particular primary structures.

THE TRIOSE PHOSPHATE/PHOSPHATE TRANSLOCATOR: ITS PHYSIOLOGICAL ROLE *IN VIVO*

To elucidate the function of the cTPT *in vivo*, we have inhibited the expression of the TPT gene in potato (*Solanum tuberosum* L.) via antisense repression (Riesmeier *et al.*, 1993; Heineke *et al.*, 1994). Transgenic plants with a maximal reduction in transport activity by approximately 30% were obtained. There was almost no effect on photosynthetic activities under ambient CO_2 and light conditions. Likewise, growth and tuber development were not affected. A detailed analysis of the transgenic plants, however, revealed a strong alteration of leaf metabolism—most of the carbon assimilated during the day is directed into the synthesis of starch and deposited in the chloroplasts. Carbon export from source leaves to the sink tissues is substantially reduced. This is due to the reduction of trioseP export and phosphate import across the chloroplast envelope. How can the transgenic plants compensate for their deficiency in TPT activity? In contrast to wild-type plants, the photoassimilates in antisense plants are preferentially translocated from the leaves to the sink tissue during the night. Whereas, during the photosynthetic period, the assimilated carbon can only be exported via the TPT; at night, starch degradation yields either trioseP or glucose, and these products can be exported from the chloroplasts either via the TPT or, alternatively, via the glucose translocator (see Fig. 1). This ensures such an efficient provision of the heterotrophic tissues with photosynthetic products that the reduction of the TPT activity in the transformants had no obvious effect on the productivity of the plants.

THE DICARBOXYLATE TRANSLOCATOR

The DiT1 mediates the import of 2-oxoglutarate for the net synthesis of glutamate via the glutamine synthetase/glutamate synthase (GS/GOGAT) pathway. We have recently described the identification of this transporter as a 45-kD component of the inner envelope membrane (Menzlaff and Flügge, 1993). The purified protein was digested with endoproteases, and the amino acid sequence of a peptide obtained allowed the design of an oligonucleotide that was then used to screen a cDNA library. A full-length cDNA clone was obtained that codes for the entire 569 amino acid residues of the precursor protein corresponding to a relative molecular mass of 60,288 D (Weber et al., 1995). There is no detectable homology between this protein and any other known protein, not even to the mitochondrial 2-oxoglutarate/malate carrier which has similar transport characteristics to the DiT1 (Runswick et al., 1990).

ANALYSIS OF THE AMINO ACID SEQUENCE OF THE DiT1 PROTEIN

Both the overall polarity index of DiT1 (Capaldi and Vanderkooi, 1972) and the analysis of the hydrophobicity distribution (Fig. 3; Kyte and Doolittle, 1982) revealed the high hydrophobic nature of the translocator which extends through the whole sequence. An exception is the region containing the first 93 amino acid residues that represents the putative transit peptide. In contrast to the transit peptides of the cTPTs containing a positively charged amphiphilic α-helix that is common in mitochondrial presequences (Fig. 3, Flügge et al., 1989; Willey et al., 1991), the transit peptide of DiT1 possesses the typical features of nuclear-coded proteins destined for the chloroplast stroma. Both translocators are, however, correctly targeted to chloroplasts and inserted into the inner envelope membrane (Flügge et al., 1989, Weber et al., 1995). It could indeed be demonstrated that transit peptides of envelope membrane proteins possess a stroma-targeting function only, whereas the "envelope-insertion-domains" are contained in the mature parts of the proteins (Brink and Flügge, 1995).

The mature part of DiT1 contains 13 to 14 hydrophobic segments; 12 of which are long enough to span the membrane as transmembrane α-helices (Fig. 3). These helices are obviously arranged in such a way that a cluster of six helices each are separated by an intervening hydrophilic loop. This transmembrane topology resembles that of other transporters from prokaryotes and eukaryotes which may all function as monomers. DiT1 is the first example of an organellar translocator with such a 12-helix motif. All other organellar translocators known so far, including those from mitochondria, belong to the second group of transporters (Maloney, 1990) having 5 to 7 transmembrane helices like the chloroplast TPT (Fig. 3; Wagner et al., 1989, Wallmeier

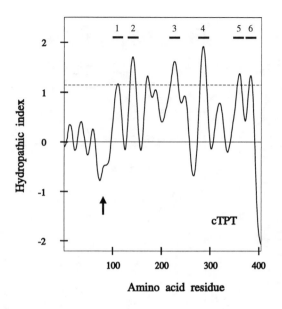

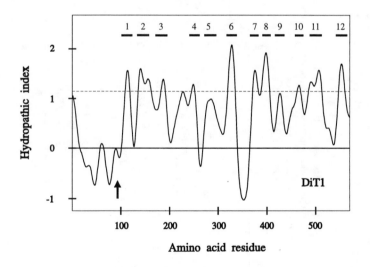

Figure 3. Hydrophobicity distribution analysis of the amino acid sequences of the triose phosphate/phosphate translocator (top, cTPT) and the dicarboxylate (2-oxoglutarate/malate) translocator (bottom, DiT1) from chloroplasts. Hydropathy was evaluated according to Kyte and Doolittle (1982) with a span setting of 11 amino acid residues (smoothed 11x2; hydrophilic: negative values; hydrophobic: positive values). Predicted membrane spanning segments are indicated by bars (cTPT: 1-6); DiT1: 1-12), and the processing sites by arrows.

Table I. *Measurement of the 2-Oxoglutarate/Malate Translocator From Chloroplasts by Functional Reconstitution Into Artificial Membranes*

Liposomes which had been preloaded with the substrates indicated were mixed with solubilized: (*i*) translocator protein purified from spinach envelope membranes (Menzlaff and Flügge, 1993); (*ii*) membranes from *Schizosaccharomyces pombe* cells containing the expressed translocator (Weber *et al.*, 1995); or (*iii*) tissue homogenate from spinach leaves (Flügge and Weber, 1994). Measurements of the reconstituted transport activities were performed as described (Flügge, 1992).

	$[^{14}C]$Malate Exchange Rates of:		
	Purified translocator protein	Recombinant protein (transformed yeast cells)	Tissue homogenate from spinach leaves
	nmol/mg protein x min	*nmol/mg protein x min*	*nmol/mg chlorophyll x min*
Liposomes loaded with			
Malate	263 (= **100%**)	0.8 (= **100%**)	82.3 (= **100%**)
2-Oxoglutarate	108 (**41%**)	0.35 (**44%**)	44.1 (**54%**)
Glutamate	26 (**10%**)	0.02 (**3%**)	16.9 (**21%**)
No substrate	2 (< **1%**)	0.01 (< **1%**)	10.2 (**12%**)

et al., 1992). These translocators probably function as homodimers with a "6+6" transmembrane helix pattern. Thus, the envelope membrane obviously possesses members of the two different types of transporters which may all have, in their functional state, a comparable number of membrane-spanning segments.

TRANSPORT CHARACTERISTICS OF THE DiT1 PROTEIN

To verify the identity of the cloned gene, the full-length cDNA sequence was expressed in the yeast *Schizosaccharomyces pombe*. This heterologous system has already been used to produce functional TPTs (Loddenkötter *et al.*, 1993; Fischer *et al.*, 1994*a*). It could be shown that yeast transformants harboring the DNA coding for DiT1 indeed displayed reconstituted malate transport activities at rates exceeding those of the endogenous transporters by at least two orders of magnitude (Weber *et al.*, 1995). For measuring the substrate specificities of the recombinant protein, yeast cell membranes were reconstituted into liposomes that had been loaded with different dicarboxylates, i.e. malate, 2-oxoglutarate or glutamate. Table I shows that the chloroplastidial DiT1 produced in yeast cells possesses almost identical transport characteristics to the translocator purified from envelope membranes. Transport of malate was strictly dependent on an exchangeable substrate as counter-ion and was only exchanged for 2-oxoglutarate and malate, but not for glutamate. The activity of the recombinant protein is thus in accordance with its proposed function as a supplier of the chloroplasts with 2-oxoglutarate for ammonia assimilation.

Since DiT1 mediates a strict counter-exchange of substrates, its activity should be ascertainable by directly reconstituting crude plant tissue homogenates in artificial membranes (Table I; Flügge and Weber, 1994). This method was developed to circumvent the necessity of isolating intact organelles and for the rapid screening of plant material for metabolite transport activities, e.g. in the case of transgenic plants with altered translocator activities. Table I demonstrates that crude tissue homogenates, tested for dicarboxylate transport, showed transport characteristics comparable to the purified or the recombinant DiT1, respectively. This method will be applied to analyze plants with an altered activity of the DiT1 protein.

ACKNOWLEDGMENTS

This work was supported by the Deutsche Forschungsgemeinschaft.

LITERATURE CITED

Borchert S, Harborth J, Schünemann D, Hoferichter P, Heldt HW (1993) Studies of the enzymatic capacities and transport properties of pea root plastids. Plant Physiol **101**: 303-312

Brink S, Flügge UI (1995) Intraorganellar sorting of chloroplast proteins. Proc Phytochem Soc Europe (in press)

Capaldi RA, Vanderkooi G (1972) The low polarity of many membrane proteins. Proc Natl Acad Sci USA **69**: 930-932

Entwistle G, ap Rees T (1988) Enzymatic capacities of amyloplasts from wheat (*Tritium aestivum*) endosperm. Biochem J **255**: 391-396

Fischer K, Arbinger B, Kammerer K, Busch C, Brink S, Wallmeier H, Sauer N, Eckerskorn C, Flügge UI (1994*a*) Cloning and *in vivo* expression of functional triose phosphate/phosphate translocators from C_3- and C_4-plants: Evidence for the putative participation of specific amino acid residues in the recognition of phosphoenolpyruvate. Plant J **5**: 215-226

Fischer K, Weber A, Brink S, Arbinger B, Schünemann D, Borchert S, Heldt HW, Popp B, Benz R, Link TA, Eckerskorn C, Flügge UI (1994*b*) Porins from plants. Molecular cloning and functional characterization of two new members of the porin family. J Biol Chem **269**: 25754-25760

Flügge UI (1992) Reaction mechanism and asymmetric orientation of the reconstituted chloroplast phosphate translocator. Biochim Biophys Acta **1110**: 112-118

Flügge UI (1995) Phosphate translocation in the regulation of photosynthesis. J Exp Bot (in press)

Flügge UI, Benz R (1984) Pore forming activity in the outer membrane of the chloroplast envelope. FEBS Lett **169**: 85-89

Flügge UI, Fischer K, Gross A, Sebald W, Lottspeich F, Eckerskorn C (1989) The triose phosphate-3-phosphoglycerate-phosphate translocator from spinach chloroplasts: nucleotide sequence of a full-length cDNA clone and import of the *in vitro* synthesized precursor protein into chloroplasts. EMBO J **8**: 39-46

Flügge UI, Heldt HW (1991) Metabolite translocators of the chloroplast envelope. Annu Rev Plant Physiol Plant Mol Biol **42**: 129-144

Flügge UI, Weber A (1994) A rapid method for measuring organelle-specific substrate transport in homogenates from plant tissues. Planta **194**: 181-185

Flügge UI, Woo KC, Heldt HW (1988) Characteristics of 2-oxoglutarate and glutamate transport in spinach chloroplasts. Studies with a double-silicone-layer centrifugation technique and in liposomes. Planta **174**: 534-541

Heineke D, Kruse A, Flügge UI, Frommer WB, Riesmeier JW, Willmitzer L, Heldt HW (1994) Effect of antisense repression of the chloroplast triose phosphate translocator on photosynthetic metabolism in transgenic potato plants. Planta **193**: 174-180

Hill LM, Smith AL (1991) Evidence that glucose 6-phosphate is imported as the substrate for starch synthesis by the plastids of developing pea embryos. Planta **185**: 91-96

Kyte J, Doolittle RF (1982) A simple method for displaying the hydropathic character of a protein. J Mol Biol **157**: 105-132

Loddenkötter B, Kammerer B, Fischer K, Flügge UI (1993) Expression of the functional mature chloroplast triose phosphate translocator in yeast internal membranes and purification of the histidine-tagged protein by a single metal-affinity chromatography step. Proc Natl Acad Sci USA **90**: 2155-2159

Maloney PC (1990) A consensus structure for membrane transport. Res Microbiol **141**: 374-383

Menzlaff E, Flügge UI (1993) Purification and functional reconstitution of the 2-oxoglutarate/malate translocator from spinach chloroplasts. Biochim Biophys Acta **1147**: 13-18

Neuhaus HE, Henrichs G, Scheibe R (1993*a*) Characterization of glucose-6-phosphate incorporation into starch by isolated intact cauliflower-bud plastids. Plant Physiol **101**: 573-578

Neuhaus HE, Thom E, Batz O, Scheibe R (1993*b*) Purification of highly intact plastids from various heterotrophic plant tissues. Analysis of enzyme equipment and precursor dependency for starch biosynthesis. Biochem J **296**: 495-501

Riesmeier JW, Flügge UI, Schulz B, Heineke D, Heldt HW, Willmitzer L, Frommer WB (1993) Antisense repression of the chloroplast triose phosphate translocator affects carbon partitioning in transgenic potato plants. Proc Natl Acad Sci USA **90**: 6160-6164

Runswick MJ, Powell SJ, Bisaccia F, Iacobazzi V, Palmieri F (1990) Sequence of the bovine 2-oxoglutarate/malate carrier protein: structural relationship to other mitochondrial transport proteins. Biochemistry **29**: 11033-11040

Schulz B, Frommer WB, Flügge UI, Hummel S, Fischer K, Willmitzer L (1993) Expression of the triose phosphate translocator gene from potato is light dependent and restricted to green tissues. Mol Gen Genet **238**: 357-361

Tetlow IJ, Blissett KJ, Emes MJ (1994) Starch synthesis and carbohydrate oxidation in amyloplasts from developing wheat endosperm. Planta **194**: 454-460

Tyson RH, ap Rees T (1988) Starch synthesis by isolated amyloplasts from wheat endosperm. Planta **175**: 33-38

Wagner R, Apley EC, Gross A, Flügge UI (1989) The rotational diffusion of the chloroplast phosphate translocator and of lipid molecules in bilayer membranes. Eur J Biochem **182**: 165-173

Wallmeier H, Weber A, Gross A, Flügge UI (1992) Insights into the structure of the chloroplast phosphate translocator protein. *In* DT Cooke, DT Clarkson, eds, Transport and Receptor Proteins of Plant Membranes. Plenum Press, New York, 77-89

Weber A, Menzlaff E, Arbinger B, Gutensohn M, Eckerskorn C, Flügge UI (1995) The 2-oxoglutarate/malate translocator of chloroplast envelope membranes: Molecular cloning of a transporter containing a 12-helix motif and expression of the functional protein in yeast cells. Biochemistry (in press)

Willey D, Fischer K, Wachter E, Link TA, Flügge UI (1991) Molecular cloning and structural analysis of the phosphate translocator from pea chloroplasts and its comparison to the spinach phosphate translocator. Planta **183:** 451-461

Woo KC, Flügge UI, Heldt HW (1987) A two-translocator model for the transport of 2-oxoglutarate and glutamate in chloroplasts during ammonia assimilation in the light. Plant Physiol **84:** 624-632

Carbon Partitioning and Source-Sink Interactions in Plants, *Monica A. Madore* and *William J. Lucas*, eds, Copyright 1995, published by The American Society of Plant Physiologists

Light Regulation of Sucrose Synthesis: Role of Protein Phosphorylation and Possible Involvement of Cytosolic [Ca^{2+}]

Steven C. Huber, Robert W. McMichael, Jr., Joan L. Huber, Markus Bachmann, Yuri T. Yamamoto, and Mark A. Conkling

United States Department of Agriculture, Agricultural Research Service, and Departments of Crop Science and Botany, (S.C.H.; R.W.M.; M.B.); Department of Horticultural Science (J.L.H.); and Department of Genetics (Y.Y.; M.C.), North Carolina State University, Raleigh, NC 27695, USA

It is becoming clear that phosphorylation plays a major role in regulation of several metabolic pathways in the plant cell cytoplasm, e.g. sucrose synthesis and nitrate reduction. In the sucrose synthesis pathway, control of sucrose phosphate synthase (SPS) by reversible seryl phosphorylation is the basis for light/dark modulation, feedback regulation, and osmotic stress activation (Huber *et al.*, 1995). In this article, we will summarize our current understanding of the phosphorylation of specific sites on the spinach SPS molecule. In addition, we will present evidence that implicates Ser-162 of maize SPS as a major regulatory site *in vivo*. Lastly, we will consider the possibility that, in certain species, cytosolic [Ca^{2+}] may modulate SPS phosphorylation as a result of activation of the requisite kinase(s).

MULTI-SITE PHOSPHORYLATION OF SPS

Several lines of evidence indicate that SPS is phosphorylated on multiple seryl residues *in vivo*, but that only one of the sites appears to play a major role in light/dark modulation of enzyme activity.

Ser-158 is the Major Regulatory Phosphorylation Site of Spinach SPS

Prior to identification of the specific amino acid phosphorylated, it was clear that one site was probably involved in regulation even though the enzyme was phosphorylated on multiple sites. A tryptic phosphopeptide (designated as

Phosphopeptide 7; Pp7) was qualitatively identified as containing the regulatory site (Huber and Huber, 1992), and it was subsequently shown that Ser-158 was the specific residue phosphorylated (McMichael et al., 1993). That Ser-158 is the primary, if not sole, regulatory site is suggested by several lines of evidence: (i) in a reconstituted system in vitro, labeling of Ser-158 (contained within Pp7) is sufficient to inactivate SPS (Huber and Huber, 1990b; Huber and Huber, 1992); (ii) labeling of Ser-158 (contained within Pp7) in situ correlates with inactivation of SPS (Huber and Huber, 1992); (iii) a synthetic peptide (15-mer) based on the phosphorylation site is a good substrate for SPS-kinase in vitro and competes effectively with native SPS for phosphorylation/inactivation (R.W. McMichael, Jr., M. Bachmann, and S.C. Huber, submitted); (iv) labeling of the regulatory site (Ser-158 in Pp7) occurs more rapidly in vivo compared to the other phosphorylation sites, presumably reflecting different rates of turnover (Huber et al., 1995); and (v) antibodies generated against a synthetic peptide based on the spinach phosphorylation site sequence preferentially recognize and immunoprecipitate highly activated dephospho-SPS as opposed to inactivated phospho-SPS (Weiner and Weiner, 1994). Presumably, phosphorylation of Ser-158 (either in vivo or in vitro) prevents binding of antibodies to epitopes containing that residue.

Identification of "Nonregulatory" Phosphorylation Sites

We have tentatively identified several other seryl residues that, unlike Ser-158, appear to be constitutively phosphorylated in vivo and, thus, do not play a direct role in light/dark modulation. However, phosphorylation/dephosphorylation of these sites could regulate SPS activity in response to other conditions or could have some other function, and thus the designation of these sites as "nonregulatory" must be tentative. The nonregulatory sites were identified by labeling of SPS in situ by providing [^{32}P]Pi via the transpiration stream, followed by extraction and immunopurification of ^{32}P-labeled SPS. The 120-kD subunit of the protein was digested with trypsin, and phosphopeptides were partially purified by affinity chromatography on Fe^{3+}-chelate chromatography as described previously (McMichael et al., 1993). The complex mixture of predominantly phosphopeptides was then subjected to HPLC reversed-phase chromatography, and distinct A230 peaks that contained ^{32}P (by Cerenkov counting) were subjected to automated Edman degradation. By this method, the sequences for two nonregulatory sites have been established. The amino acids surrounding the putative phosphorylated seryl residues are similar to one another and quite distinct from the recognition elements surrounding the regulatory site (R.W. McMichael, J. Kochansky, R.R. Klein, and S.C. Huber, unpubl. results). A protein kinase has been partially purified from spinach leaves that phosphorylates synthetic peptides (based on the two nonregulatory sequences) and may be involved in phosphorylation of these sites in vivo. As might be expected, the regulatory protein kinase (SPS-kinase) and the recently identified kinase are distinct proteins (S.C. Huber, unpubl. data).

Phosphorylation of Maize SPS *In Vivo*

Direct evidence (i.e. ^{32}P-labeling) for phosphorylation of SPS *in vivo* has thus far only been obtained with spinach. In addition, the identity of the regulatory phosphorylation site has only been established for spinach, although a homologous site has been identified in maize (Ser-162) and potato (Ser-150) based strictly on sequence comparisons (R.W. McMichael,Jr., M. Bachmann, and S.C. Huber, submitted). In order to expand the base of information to include additional species, studies were conducted with maize to establish the occurrence of phosphorylation *in vivo* and to determine whether Ser-162 in maize SPS was involved in the regulation by phosphorylation.

SPS was phosphorylated *in situ* by providing [^{32}P]Pi to excised leaves via the transpiration stream. We used leaves of maize as well as transgenic tobacco expressing the maize SPS gene driven by the rbcS promoter. In both systems, we could specifically analyze ^{32}P-labeled maize SPS because the monoclonal antibodies used (Bruneau *et al.*, 1991) recognize maize, but not tobacco SPS. The immunopurified maize SPS was further purified by SDS-PAGE, digested with trypsin, and subjected to two-dimensional mapping exactly as described for spinach SPS (Huber and Huber, 1992). ^{32}P-labeling of maize SPS was observed in both the light and dark; as expected, total labeling was greater in the dark. As shown in Figure 1, the peptide maps were complex, suggestive of multi-site phosphorylation, and the labeling pattern was similar when maize SPS was labeled in maize leaves (Fig. 1A) or in transgenic tobacco leaves (Fig. 1B). Unlike spinach, labeling of all the phosphopeptides was reduced in the light relative to darkness (data not shown); thus, any of the putative phosphorylation sites could be of regulatory significance.

In order to determine whether Ser-162 of maize SPS may be involved in regulation, a synthetic peptide corresponding to residues 154 to 166 of the maize sequence (Worrell *et al.*, 1991) was produced. The synthetic peptide (designated "Mz1") was readily phosphorylated *in vitro* by partially purified spinach leaf SPS-kinase. When the ^{32}P-labeled Mz1 peptide was subjected to two-dimensional mapping, essentially one labeled spot was detected (Fig. 1C) which co-migrated with one or more of the phosphopeptides labeled in native maize SPS (Figs. 1A and B).

Another line of evidence consistent with Ser-162 as the regulatory site is that the synthetic peptide Mz1 was a good substrate for maize leaf SPS-kinase *in vitro*. In fact, chromatography of a 5 to 12% polyethyleneglycol fraction on FPLC-ResourceQ resolved a single large peak of activity required for the ATP-dependent inactivation of maize SPS *in vitro* (Huber and Huber, 1990*a*). Importantly, an identical elution profile was observed for Mz1-kinase activity

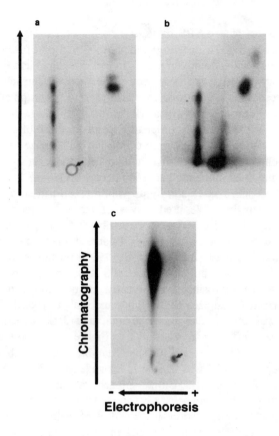

Figure 1. Evidence for multi-site phosphorylation of maize leaf SPS. Two-dimensional resolution of tryptic phosphopeptides. SPS was labeled *in vivo* by feeding [32P]Pi to excised leaves of maize (Fig. 1A) or transgenic tobacco (Fig. IB) expressing the maize SPS gene driven by the rbcS promoter. In Figure 1C, the synthetic peptide Mz1 (for sequence, see Table II) was labeled *in vitro* with [γ-32P]ATP and partially purified spinach leaf SPS-kinase. After labeling, residual ATP was removed by binding to Dowex AG 1X8 resin in 30% HOAc (Kemp *et al.*, 1975). After lyophilization, the 32P-peptide was digested with trypsin and processed exactly as peptides derived from labeled SPS. *In situ*-labeling conditions, immunopurification of 32P-labeled maize SPS (using monoclonal antibodies specific for the maize enzyme), digestion with trypsin, and thin layer electrophoresis/TLC was essentially as described previously (Huber and Huber, 1992). Peptides derived from approximately 5 μg of SPS (or 50 μg of peptide) were applied to the origin (marked with an arrow) as indicated in each panel.

(data not shown). Moreover, Mz1 could effectively compete with native maize SPS for phosphorylation/inactivation. These sequence-specific responses are consistent with Ser-162 as the regulatory site of maize SPS.

Maize SPS activity is strongly regulated by phosphorylation/ dephosphorylation *in vivo* in response to light/dark signals (Huber *et al.*, 1989); in maize, phosphorylation reduces both V_{max} activity (nonselective assay) and activity measured with limiting substrates plus Pi (selective assay) (see Table I). In contrast, tobacco leaf SPS activity is much less affected by light/dark transitions, although there was a slight decrease in SPS activity as measured in the selective assay (Table I) which is generally consistent with previous findings (Huber *et al.*, 1989). Interestingly, maize SPS expressed in transgenic tobacco also displayed considerable light/dark modulation of activity (Table I), indicating that the requisite kinases and phosphatases necessary for reversible modification of the maize enzyme are present in tobacco leaves. This result is significant because maize SPS, expressed in transgenic tomato, shows relatively little light/dark modulation *in vivo* (Table I, and see Galtier *et al.*, 1993). One explanation is that not all species contain endogenous protein kinases that can effectively recognize and phosphorylate the maize SPS protein.

Thus far, we know relatively little about the protein kinases from different species that function in the phosphorylation/inactivation of SPS. With many

---

Table I. *Light/Dark Modulation of SPS In Vivo in Leaves of Maize, Tobacco, and Transgenic Tobacco Expressing Maize SPS*

Leaves were harvested in liquid nitrogen in the light (800 μmol·m^{-2}·s^{-1} PAR) and after transfer to darkness for 30 min. Leaves were extracted and SPS activity was measured in the selective (Sel) and nonselective (Nonsel) assays as described earlier (Huber *et al.*, 1989). In the transgenic tobacco, expression of the maize SPS gene (Worrell *et al.*, 1991) was driven by the rbcS promoter.

| | Extractable SPS Activity (μmol·g^{-1}·h^{-1}) | | | |
| | Light | | Dark | |
Species SPS Assay:	Sel	Nonsel	Sel	Nonsel
Tobacco	22	48	17	49
Maize	120	150	30	75
Transgenic Tobacco (rbcS-maize SPS)	77	127	42	95
Transgenic Tomato (rbcS-maize SPS)	171	264	189	290

protein kinases, in particular the Ser/Thr-specific kinases, the primary amino sequence around the phosphorylated residue contains many of the "recognition elements" that target the kinase to the phosphorylation site (for review, see Kennelly and Krebs, 1991). Consequently, synthetic peptides are often good substrates for the requisite kinases *in vitro*, and peptide analogs of the native sequence can be used to identify which residues function as recognition elements. With spinach and maize SPS-kinase, it appears that the recognition sequence is Basic-X-X-Basic-X-X-*Ser*-X (R.W. McMichael and S.C. Huber, manuscript in prep.). However, if one compares activity of partially purified kinases from the two species with synthetic peptides based on the Ser-158 (SP1; spinach) and Ser-162 (MZ1; maize) sequences, significant differences are observed. First, the maize SPS kinase utilized the MZ1 peptide much more effectively than the SP1 peptide, whereas the spinach SPS-kinase phosphorylated the two peptides rather equivalently. Studies with peptide analogs of the spinach SPS phosphorylation sequence have indicated that while the two kinases share similar recognition elements (i.e. basic residues at P-3 and P-6), the exact position of acidic residues C-terminal to the phosphorylated serine may be critical. In Mz1, the aspartyl residue is at $P+1$, whereas in SP1, the glutamyl residue is at $P+2$. The critical feature appears to be position, not the identity of the residue (i.e. D versus E). Interestingly, an acidic residue at $P+1$ is not a positive recognition element (i.e. its replacement with an alanine residue does not have much effect), but an acidic residue at $P+2$ appears to be a negative factor (i.e. its replacement with an alanine residue does have a large effect). Apparently, the protein kinases in maize and spinach can tolerate an acidic residue at the $P+1$ versus $P+2$ positions to different extents. This raises the possibility that in some heterologous systems (i.e. transgenic plants expressing a 'foreign' SPS), the transgene may not be effectively phosphorylated by the endogenous protein kinase(s). This could explain why maize SPS is not light/dark modulated in transgenic tomato plants (Galtier *et al.*, 1993).

A second and more important point to note from Table II is that SPS-kinase is Ca^{2+}-*dependent* in maize but Ca^{2+}-*independent* in spinach. The lack of Ca^{2+}-dependence of spinach SPS-kinase has been reported previously (Huber and Huber, 1990*b*) and is confirmed here using the new synthetic peptide assay. Thus, it was most unexpected when we realized that all of the protein kinase activity in maize leaves that recognized SPS was strictly Ca^{2+}-dependent (R.W. McMichael and S.C. Huber, manuscript in prep.). These observations raise the intriguing possibility that cytosolic $[Ca^{2+}]$ may regulate sucrose biosynthesis, at least in some species. In this regard, it is known that cytosolic $[Ca^{2+}]$ is reduced in the light relative to the dark in algal cells (Miller and Sanders, 1987). Presuming that similar changes occur in higher plant mesophyll cells, this could be one of the factors contributing to light activation of SPS as a result of restriction of kinase activity in the light.

Table II. *Phosphorylation of Synthetic Peptides In Vitro by Protein Kinases Partially Purified From Maize and Spinach Leaves*

Kinases were partially purified by polyethyleneglycol fractionation followed by FPLC-ResourceQ chromatography as described (R.W. McMichael, Jr., M. Bachmann, and S.C. Huber, submitted). Assays (50 μM) contained kinase, 80 μg/mL synthetic peptide, 0.1 mM [γ-^{32}P]ATP (500 cpm/pmol) in 50 mM Mops-NaOH (pH 7.5), 10 mM $MgCl_2$ and 2 mM dithiothreitol. Sequences: SP1:GRMRRIS$\underline{S}$VEMMDNWANTFK; MZ1:KKKFQRNF$\underline{S}$DVTLWSDDNK

	Peptide-Kinase Activity (Relative Activity)		
Synthetic Peptide	EGTA	Maize	Spinach
SP1	-	0.20	0.87
	+	0.05	0.81
MZ1	-	1.00	1.00
	+	0.06	1.06

POSSIBLE REGULATION OF SUCROSE SYNTHESIS BY Ca²⁺

Use of Ca²⁺ Antagonists *In Situ*

It is generally recognized that the control of C-flux into sucrose involves the coordinated regulation of several enzymes, including cytosolic Fru-1,6-bisPase, SPS, and enzymes involved in metabolism of PPi (Stitt *et al.*, 1987; Stitt and Quick, 1989). Brauer *et al.* (1990) have considered whether physiological concentrations (i.e. submicromolar) of cytosolic Ca²⁺ might regulate sucrose synthesis in spinach leaves. As one experimental approach, the Ca²⁺ antagonists La³⁺, trifluoroperazine (TFP), and ruthenium red, were provided to excised barley leaves via the transpiration stream. All three Ca²⁺ antagonists selectively inhibited sucrose synthesis relative to starch synthesis (Brauer *et al.*, 1990). Detailed studies of leaf metabolites suggested that La³⁺ and Ca²⁺ inhibited cytosolic FBPase; TFP acted by inhibiting turnover of PPi; and ruthenium red reduced the activation state of SPS. Thus, it was postulated that cytosolic Ca²⁺ could control sucrose synthesis by regulating flux at one or more of three potential sites.

Ca²⁺ Antagonists *In Vitro*

Although Ca²⁺ does not have a direct effect on SPS activity *per se*, cytosolic [Ca²⁺] may control SPS activity indirectly by influencing the activity of the requisite interconverting enzymes, i.e. SPS-kinase and/or SPS-phosphatase. As already discussed, it appears that SPS-kinase may be a Ca^{2+}-dependent protein kinase, at least in some species (see Table II).

A problem with studies supplying Ca^{2+} antagonists *in situ* is the potential for side effects, i.e. the antagonists may directly affect other enzymes in addition (perhaps) to altering intracellular $[Ca^{2+}]$. With respect to SPS, we have attempted to address this point by looking at the effect of Ca^{2+} and Ca^{2+} antagonists on SPS-phosphatase *in vitro*. It is known that phospho-SPS is dephosphorylated/activated by a type 2A protein phosphatase *in vitro* (Siegl *et al.*, 1990). SPS-protein phosphatase was partially purified from spinach leaves by polyethyleneglycol fractionation followed by FPLC-MonoQ chromatography. The partially purified enzyme catalyzed the activation of phospho-SPS and, as expected for a type 2A protein phosphatase, the enzyme also catalyzed the release of radioactivity from ^{32}P-casein (labeled by protein kinase A). As shown in Table III, both phosphatase activities were inhibited by ruthenium red and La^{3+}. The direct inhibition of SPS-phosphatase by ruthenium red may explain the observed decrease in SPS activation state *in situ* (Brauer *et al.*, 1990).

CONCLUDING REMARKS

By identification of three phosphorylation sites on spinach SPS, we have provided the first direct evidence for multi-site phosphorylation of this important enzyme. As might be expected, distinct protein kinases target the regulatory site versus the nonregulatory sites. The major regulatory phosphorylation site of spinach SPS has been identified as Ser-158, and evidence has been obtained that the homologous site in maize (Ser-162) may also function in a regulatory manner. However, an important difference between the two species may concern the role of Ca^{2+}. In maize, all of the SPS-kinase activity is Ca^{2+}-dependent, whereas in spinach, the major form of SPS-kinase is strictly Ca^{2+}-independent. Thus, a new concept to emerge is that in some species

Table III. *Ca^{2+} Antagonists Inhibit SPS-Phosphatase and Casein Phosphatase (PP2A) In Vitro*

Additions	Relative Phosphatase Activity	
	^{32}P-Casein	Phospho-SPS
None	1.00	1.00
Ruthenium red (100 μg/mL)	0.35	0.10
La^{3+} (0.1 mM)	0.08	0.30

(e.g. maize), light/dark changes in cytosolic $[Ca^{2+}]$ may play a role in regulation of SPS phosphorylation status. It will be important to examine a wider range of species and also to determine whether changes in $[Ca^{2+}]$ actually occur *in vivo* and, if so, whether C-flux into sucrose is affected.

ACKNOWLEDGMENTS

Mention of a trademark or proprietary product does not constitute a guarantee or warranty of the product by the U.S. Department of Agriculture or the North Carolina Agricultural Research Service and does not imply its approval to the exclusion of other products that may also be suitable. This work was supported in part with funds from the U.S. Department of Energy (grant DE-AIO5-91ER-20031 to S.C.H.). M.B. was the recipient of a fellowship from the Swiss National Foundation. The synthetic peptide SP1 was purchased with funds from the Triagency Plant Biology Program on Collaborative Research (USDA-CSRS 92-37105-7675). The authors thank Dr. Monica Gervais (Roussel-Uclaf, Romainville, France) for supplying the mouse monoclonal antibodies against maize SPS and Dr. Toni Voelker (Calgene, Inc., Davis, CA) for supplying the maize SPS cDNA.

LITERATURE CITED

Brauer M, Sanders D, Stitt M (1990) Regulation of photosynthetic sucrose synthesis: a role for calcium? Planta **182**: 236-243

Bruneau JM, Worrell AC, Cambou B, Landou D, Voelker TA (1991) Sucrose phosphate synthase, a key enzyme for sucrose biosynthesis in plants. Protein purification from corn leaves and immunological detection. Plant Physiol **96**: 473-478

Galtier N, Foyer CH, Huber J, Voelker TA, Huber SC (1993) Effects of elevated sucrose-phosphate synthase activity on photosynthesis, assimilate partitioning, and growth in tomato (*Lycopersicon esculentum* var UC82B). Plant Physiol **101**: 535-543

Huber JL, Huber SC (1992) Site-specific serine phosphorylation of spinach leaf sucrose-phosphate synthase. Biochem J **283**: 877-882

Huber SC, Huber JL (1990*a*) Regulation of maize leaf sucrose-phosphate synthase by protein phosphorylation. Plant Cell Physiol **32**: 319-326

Huber SC, Huber JL (1990*b*) *In vitro* phosphorylation and inactivation of spinach leaf sucrose-phosphate synthase by an endogenous protein kinase. Biochim Biophys Acta **1091**: 393-400

Huber SC, McMichael RW Jr, Bachmann M, Huber JL, Shannan JC, Kang K-K, Paul M (1995) Regulation of leaf sucrose-phosphate synthase and nitrate reductase by reversible protein phosphorylation. *In* PR Shewry, ed, Protein Phosphorylation in Plants. Oxford University Press, Oxford, UK (in press)

Huber SC, Nielsen TH, Huber JLA, Pharr DM (1989) Variation among species in light activation of sucrose-phosphate synthase. Plant Cell Physiol **30**: 277-285

Kemp BE, Bylund DB, Huang T-S, Krebs EG (1975) Substrate specificity of the cyclic AMP-dependent protein kinase. Proc Natl Acad Sci USA **72**: 3448-3452

Kennelly PJ, Krebs EG (1991) Concensus sequences as substrate specificity determinants for protein kinases and protein phosphatases. J Biol Chem **266**: 15555-15558

McMichael RW Jr, Klein RR, Salvucci ME, Huber SC (1993) Identification of the major regulatory phosphorylation site in sucrose-phosphate synthase. Arch Biochem Biophys **307**: 248-252

Miller AJ, Sanders D (1987) Depletion of cytosolic free calcium induced by photosynthesis. Nature **326**: 397-400

Siegl G, MacKintosh C, Stitt M (1990) Sucrose-phosphate synthase is dephosphorylated by protein phosphatase 2A in spinach leaves. Evidence from the effects of okadaic acid and microcystin. FEBS Lett **270**: 198-202

Stitt M, Huber SC, Kerr P (1987) Control of photosynthetic sucrose synthesis. *In* MD Hatch, NK Boardman, eds, The Biochemistry of Plants, Vol 10, Photosynthesis. Academic Press, New York, pp 327-409

Stitt M, Quick P (1989) Photosynthetic carbon partitioning: its regulation and possibilities for manipulation. Physiol Plant **77**: 633-641

Weiner H, Weiner H (1994) Phosphorylation and regulation of potato tuber SPS. Plant Physiol **105S**: 91

Worrell AC, Bruneau JM, Summerfelt K, Boersig M, Voelker TA (1991) Expression of a maize sucrose phosphate synthase in tomato alters leaf carbohydrate partitioning. Plant Cell **3**: 1121-1130.

Carbon Partitioning and Source-Sink Interactions in Plants, *Monica A. Madore* and *William J. Lucas*, eds, Copyright 1995, published by The American Society of Plant Physiologists

End-Product Modulation of Carbon Partitioning With a View to Improved Biomass Production

Christine Foyer, Muriel Chaumont, Erik Murchie,
Nathalie Galtier, and Sylvie Ferrario

*Environmental Biology Department, IGER, Plas Gogerddan,
Aberystwyth, Dyfed SY23 3EB, UK (C.F.); and Laboratoire
du Metabolisme, INRA, Route de Saint-Cyr, 78026
Versailles cedex, France (M.C.; E.M.; N.G.; S.F.)*

Acclimation is an essential feature of plant metabolism. It is a prerequisite for survival in a dynamic environment. It is also a fundamental requirement for growth and development so that supply and demand for assimilates are in an appropriate balance. Acclimation is a multifactoral process involving short-term modulation of enzymes and other proteins together with longer-term changes in composition and metabolism that allow the plant to optimize available resources over a wide range of conditions. Growth, vigor, and biomass production in a given situation are all largely determined by the ability of the plant to modify its structure, physiology, and metabolism to take advantage of resources in situations where essential inputs, light, CO_2, water, and nitrogen, are plentiful and to compensate for deficits when one or more of these essential elements is in short supply. Foliar carbohydrate reserves, for example, provide a buffer against diurnal variations in the rate of photosynthetic carbon assimilation (Servaites *et al.*, 1989a, b). The type of carbohydrate stored in leaves varies between species. Some species preferentially store starch in their leaves, others store sucrose, and many accumulate both types of carbohydrate (Stitt *et al.*, 1987). When sucrose is stored, it is often accompanied by the synthesis of sucrose-derived oligosaccharides such as raffinose or long-chain fructans (Pollock and Chatterton, 1988). The different storage strategies may, to some degree, confer advantage in different environments, but the benefit of one accumulation strategy over another is largely obscure.

In contrast to the acclimatory phenomena associated with fluctuating exogenous factors, the metabolic regulation associated with endogenous supplies and demands for assimilates is not well-defined and only poorly understood. The source-sink interaction is an acclimatory response that matches supply and demand (Geiger, 1987). The productivity of a plant is fundamentally and inescapably related to the sum total of net photosynthesis throughout the growing season. Even in a perennial plant, such as the grapevine which has major vegetative and reproductive storage organs, some simple relationships between source leaf metabolism and sink activity can be demonstrated (Fig. 1). While the precise nature of the causal relationships involved remains to be elucidated, it is clear that defoliation results in decreased grape yield (Fig. 1A), and removal of fruit during the growing season, caused a pronounced, if temporary, inhibition of the rate of CO_2 assimilation in field-grown vines. Both of these interactions will involve complex hormonal and metabolic crosstalk. It is evident that substantial retranslocation of carbon reserves from woody storage tissues to the fruit does not occur following defoliation (Candolfi-Vasconcelos et al., 1994). Similarly, deprivation of an important sink cannot always be accommodated by diversion to other sinks and significant repercussions for photosynthesis can follow (Fig. 1B). Photosynthetic acclimation is suggested to be caused by accumulation of carbohydrates in the source leaves that directly or indirectly can result in feedback inhibition of photosynthesis (Ascón-Bieto, 1983; Bleshschmidt-Schneider et al., 1989). Negative photosynthetic adjustments of this type may occur as a result of any type of imbalance between sink and source organs that results in carbohydrate accumulation by the source leaves. Photosynthetic acclimation is observed occasionally in plants grown at elevated CO_2 (Stitt, 1991; Bowes, 1994). Carbon assimilation rates in almost all terrestrial plants are increased by even brief exposures to atmospheric CO_2 enrichment (Makino, 1994). In some species exposed to long periods of CO_2 enrichment, these elevated photosynthetic rates are not maintained because photosynthesis acclimates over a period of days or weeks (Besford and Hand, 1989; Yelle et al., 1989; Bowes, 1994). While the degree of photosynthetic adjustment varies considerably between species, such feedback repression can decrease the potential benefit that elevated CO_2 levels should afford (Stitt, 1991; Bowes, 1994; Makino, 1994). A better understanding of the metabolic regulation involved in source-sink relationships, together with the application of this knowledge to produce transformed plants, might lead to improved synthesis and translocation of sugars and amino acids toward economically important sinks (Foyer and Ferrario, 1994). It was with these aims in mind that the following studies were initiated.

MANIPULATION OF CARBON PARTITIONING

Photosynthetic carbon and nitrogen assimilation provide the building blocks for plant growth, development, and biomass production. The activities

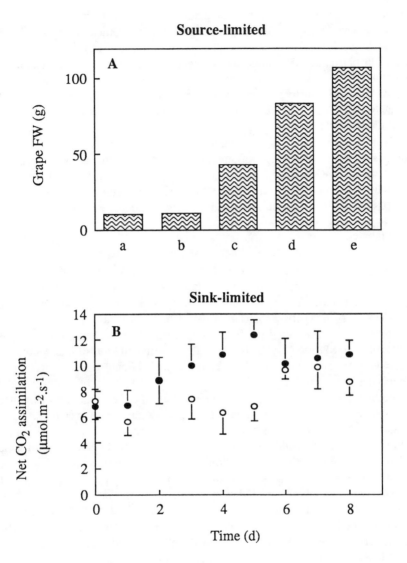

Figure 1. (A) The effects of defoliation on the yield of grapes on field-grown *Vitis vinifera* L. cv Pinot noir vines measured at the end of the growing season. Individual shoots were deprived of all of their leaves (a,b) or were left with one leaf (c), three leaves (d) or with the full complement of leaves (e) at fruit set. (B) The effect of fruit removal on the rate of CO_2 assimilation in field-grown *Vitis vinifera* L. cv Pinot noir vines. Photosynthesis was measured in the field on adjacent vines. Vines from which all grapes had been removed just subsequent to the measurement at day 0 (without fruit; o - o) were compared to controls where all fruit remained present (control; ●-●).

of enzymes involved in sugar metabolism are dominant factors in the determination of source capacity and sink strength (Stitt and Quick, 1989; Ho, 1988). The relative activities of sucrose phosphate synthase (SPS) and sucrose synthase in particular, determine the availability and distribution of assimilated carbon between the various plant organs. Photoassimilates produced by the source leaf are translocated toward different sinks for utilization or accumulation. The source leaves accumulate large foliar carbohydrate pools to buffer variations in the rate of photosynthesis and to liberate sufficient sucrose at night to ensure a more or less continuous supply of sucrose, which constitutes the major source of energy, for sink organs in many plant species (Servaites *et al.*, 1989*a*, *b*; Geiger and Fondy, 1991). The enzymes involved in sucrose synthesis have thus been the subject of considerable study and provide prime targets for genetic manipulation with a view to improved biomass accumulation.

SUCROSE PHOSPHATE SYNTHASE

Sucrose phosphate synthase is a putative major control point in the source-sink relationship. The arguments supporting this hypothesis are as follows: (*i*) the observed positive correlation between the capacity of a leaf to export sucrose and its SPS activity (Huber and Israel, 1982; Rocher, 1988); (*ii*) the induction of SPS activity in leaves following modulation of the source-sink ratio (Rufty and Huber, 1983); (*iii*) the complex regulation of this enzyme involving both direct metabolic regulation, *via* the levels of Glc-6-P and Pi (inorganic phosphate), and covalent modulation of the enzyme involving phosphorylation/dephosphorylation modifications responsive to metabolic signals (Doehlert and Huber, 1983; Sicher and Kremer, 1984; Stitt *et al.*, 1987; Huber *et al.*, 1989; Huber and Huber, 1991); and (*iv*) the precise coordination of photosynthetic carbon assimilation and sucrose synthesis involving regulation of SPS activity (Battistelli *et al.*, 1991). Thus, SPS is suggested to be responsive to metabolic regulation by both source (the rate of photosynthesis) and sink (sucrose import and utilization). Regulation of SPS also serves to maintain the level of metabolites in the stroma allowing optimal rates of Calvin cycle activity (Stitt and Quick, 1989; Battistelli *et al.*, 1991).

Transgenic tomato plants expressing both native SPS and an SPS gene from maize (Worrell *et al.*, 1991; Galtier *et al.*, 1993, 1995) were used to analyze the role of this enzyme in carbon assimilation and carbon partitioning. The transformed plants exhibited higher photosynthetic rates than untransformed controls both in air and in saturating CO_2, but at high CO_2, the stimulation of photosynthesis was more pronounced. Furthermore, there was a strong positive correlation between the increase in the ratio of sucrose to starch in the leaves and SPS activity (Galtier *et al.*, 1993, 1995). The marked increase in the maximum extractable SPS activity in these plants was suggested to be caused by the absence of complete regulation of the introduced SPS protein, for example, the introduced maize enzyme did not appear to be inactivated to a great extent in darkness (Worrell *et al.*, 1991; Galtier *et al.*, 1993, 1995).

Galtier *et al.* (1993) studied the SPS activity of different tissues within the tomato plants when the maize SPS gene was expressed under the control of the rbcS promoter. In this case, SPS activities were highest in the leaves, the total extractable SPS activity in roots and petioles being 10-fold less than that in the leaves. The level of SPS activity in the roots of the rbcS transformants was three times higher than in the untransformed controls. Galtier *et al.* (1995) also studied a second type of transgenic tomato plant where the maize leaf SPS cDNA construct was expressed under the control of the cauliflower mosaic virus (CaMV) 35S promoter. In this case, expression is considered to be constitutive (Williamson *et al.*, 1989). Improved rates of photosynthesis in air and at elevated CO_2, together with a modification in foliar carbon partitioning in favor of sucrose were common to all the transformed tomato plants expressing the maize SPS gene (Galtier *et al.*, 1993, 1995). These new characteristics are, therefore, not the result of somaclonal variation consecutive to tissue culture, but the result of increased SPS activity in the leaves.

Biomass accumulation in the rbcS lines 9 and 11 and the wild-type controls was similar in all cases (Fig. 2). This suggests that an increase in foliar SPS activity alone has little influence on total biomass production. In contrast, there was always a marked increase in biomass in the plants where the SPS activity was increased as a result of expression of the maize SPS under the control of the constitutive 35S promoter (Foyer and Galtier, 1995). Thus, constitutive expression of SPS may have a positive effect on dry matter accumulation. However, we must now confirm that enhanced biomass accumulation co-segregates with the constitutive expression of the inserted gene in crosses with the wild type. Independent studies with the rbcS line 9 have shown that, following this procedure, the resultant populations of transformed plants had equivalent biomass to the wild-type controls, confirming the observations reported here (Calgene Fresh Inc.; J.J. Van Oosten and R.T. Besford; pers. commun.). As yet, we do not have similar back-crossed lines arising from 35S-SPS line 13. Calgene Fresh are producing these lines for study. Until we have biomass data from these plants, the effect of constitutive expression of SPS on biomass accumulation remains equivocal.

NITRATE REDUCTASE (NR)

Nitrogen assimilation has been considered to be a limiting step for growth and biomass accumulation in plants. In CO_2-enriched environments, plants may have an even greater requirement for reduced nitrogen than in air. A major consequence of the increase in photosynthetic rate and in foliar carbohy-

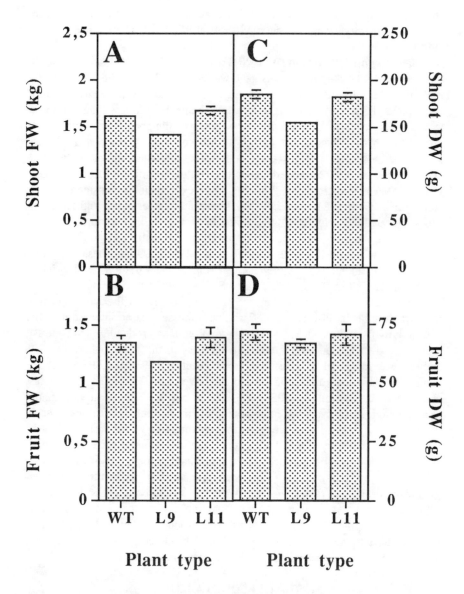

Figure 2. Biomass production in control wild type (WT) and high SPS expressors (lines 9, L9, and 11, L11) tomato plants grown in the greenhouse from May to October 1994 under natural irradiance. Plants were harvested when the fruit reached maturity. Ten plants were used for each line. Mean plus standard error values are given in all cases, but were frequently too small to be visible in the figure.

drate accumulation that occurs during CO_2 enrichment, is an increase in the carbon-to-nitrogen ratio. This is usually due to a lower total nitrogen content and has been interpreted as an increased nitrogen-use efficiency (Conroy, 1992). This could result from a modification of nitrogen allocation between nitrogenous compounds (Makino, 1994). Constitutive over-expression of NR, a key enzyme of the nitrogen assimilation pathway, in transgenic tobacco plants, has provided a novel opportunity for testing this hypothesis. Transformed *Nicotiana plumbaginifolia* plants, constitutively expressing an NR gene from *N. tabacum* (Vincentz and Caboche, 1991), were grown for 2 weeks in high CO_2 (1000 ppm). Subsequently, carbon and nitrogen metabolism, and growth were compared to those of the wild type (WT) in the same conditions. These transgenic plants have previously been extensively characterized (Foyer *et al.*, 1993, 1994a, b; Quilleré *et al.*, 1994). They have a two- to five-fold increase in total extractable foliar NR activity when grown in air with similar biomass production and photosynthetic metabolism to the untransformed controls. The foliar glutamine level is increased while the foliar NO_3^- contents are decreased (Foyer *et al.*, 1994a; Quilleré *et al.*, 1994).

After 2 weeks of exposure to elevated CO_2, the total foliar NR activity, measured *in vitro*, was much decreased in the transgenic line compared to the level found in leaves of plants grown in air. At this time, the differences in foliar NR activity and foliar nitrogen metabolism between the constitutive expressors and the wild type disappeared almost completely (Fig. 3). No

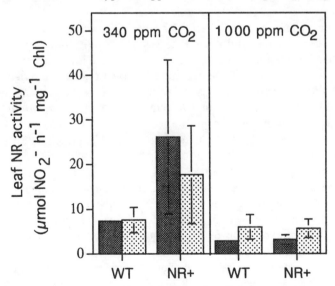

Figure 3. Leaf NR activity in wild-type (WT) and in transgenic *Nicotiana plumbaginifolia* constitutively expressing NR (NR +) after a period of 2 weeks growth at two levels of CO_2. The plants were 9 weeks old (shaded) or 6 weeks old (dotted) at the end of the experiment.

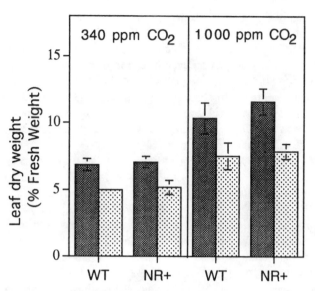

Figure 4. Leaf dry weight in wild-type (WT) and in transgenic *Nicotiana plumbaginifolia* constitutively expressing NR (NR +) after a growth period of 2 weeks at two levels of CO_2. The plants were either 9 weeks old (shaded) or 6 weeks old (dotted) at the end of the experiment.

significant differences were observed between NR activity at 1000 ppm and 340 ppm CO_2 for the wild type (Fig. 3). NR activity *in situ* was probably decreased since the total foliar amino acid pools were lowered in both types of plant. No significant modifications were observed for other enzyme activities such as glutamine synthase, phospho*enol*pyruvate carboxylase, and SPS. The specific effect of high CO_2 on NR activity in *N. plumbaginifolia* may be related to the lower NO_3^- content observed in these plants at 1000 ppm (Hocking and Meyer, 1991). The turnover of the NR protein is dependent on the NO_3^- concentration of the cell (Galangau *et al.*, 1988). This may explain the decrease in NR activity in the transgenic line at 1000 ppm CO_2. As a consequence of this decrease, similar patterns of carbohydrate and dry matter accumulation were observed in wild-type *N. plumbaginifolia* and the constitutive NR expressors grown in conditions of CO_2 enrichment. Therefore, constitutive over-expression of the NR gene did not modify the response of plants to atmospheric CO_2 enrichment (Fig. 4). Constitutive expression of NR activity does not lead to increased biomass production in these conditions. Similarly, when the constitutive NR-expressors were grown under conditions of nitrogen-deficiency, the foliar NR activity decreased to almost zero (Foyer *et al.*, 1994b; Ferrario *et al.*, 1995). Taken together, these results strongly suggest that in conditions of CO_2 enrichment or nitrogen-deficiency, posttranscriptional modification of NR can play a fundamental role in determining the level of activity of this enzyme.

ACKNOWLEDGMENTS

The experiments concerning the responses of transgenic *N. plumbagini-folia* to CO_2 enrichment were conducted in collaboration with M. C. Thibaud, P. Contard, and T. Betsche at CEA, Cadarache, France.

LITERATURE CITED

Ascón-Bieto J (1983) Inhibition of photosynthesis by carbohydrates in wheat leaves. Plant Physiol **73**: 681-686

Battistelli A, Adcock MD, Leegood RC (1991) The relationship between the activation state of sucrose-phosphate synthase and the rate of CO_2 assimilation in spinach leaves. Planta **183**: 620-622

Besford RT, Hand DW (1989) The effects of CO_2 enrichment and nitrogen oxides on some Calvin cycle enzymes and nitrite reductase in glasshouse lettuce. J Exp Bot **40**: 329-336

Blechschmidt-Schneider S, Ferrar P, Osmond CB (1989) Control of photosynthesis by carbohydrate level in leaves of the C_4 plant *Amaranthus edulis* L. Planta **177**: 515-525

Bowes G (1994) Facing the inevitable: Plants and increasing atmospheric CO_2. Annu Rev Plant Physiol Plant Mol Biol **44**: 309-332

Candolfi-Vasconcelos M, Candolfi MP, Koblet W (1994) Retranslocation of carbon reserves from the woody storage tissues into the fruit as a response to defoliation stress during the ripening period in *Vitis vinifera* L. Planta **192**: 567-573

Conroy JP (1992) Influence of elevated atmospheric CO_2 concentrations on plant nutrition. Aust J Bot **40**: 445-456

Doehlert DC, Huber SC (1983) Regulation of spinach leaf sucrose-phosphate synthase by glucose 6-phosphate, inorganic phosphate, and pH. Plant Physiol **73**: 989-994

Ferrario S, Valadier M-H, Morot-Gaudry J-F, Foyer CH (1995) Effects of constitutive expression of nitrate reductase in transgenic *Nicotiana plumbaginifolia* L. in response to varying nitrogen supply. Planta (in press)

Foyer CH, Ferrario S (1994) Modulation of carbon and nitrogen metabolism in transgenic plants with a view to improved biomass production. Biochem Soc Trans **22**: 909-915

Foyer CH, Galtier N (1995) Source sink interaction and communication in leaves. *In* E Zamski, AA Schafer, eds, Photoassimilate Distribution in Plants and Crops: Source Sink Relationships. Marcel Dekker, Inc, Publ, New York (in press)

Foyer CH, Lefebvre C, Provot M, Vincentz M, Vaucheret H (1993) Modulation of nitrogen and carbon metabolism in transformed *Nicotiana plumbaginifolia* mutant E23 lines expressing either increased or decreased nitrate reductase activity. *In* E White, PS Kettlewell, MA Parry, RP Ellis, eds, Aspects of Applied Biology, Vol 34, Physiology of Varieties. Assoc Appl Biol, Wellesbourne, Warwick, UK, pp 137-145

Foyer CH, Lescure JC, Lefebvre C, Morot-Gaudry JF, Vincentz M, Vaucheret H (1994*a*) Adaptations of photosynthetic electron transport, carbon assimilation and carbon partitioning in transgenic *Nicotiana plumbaginifolia* plants to changes in nitrate reductase activity. Plant Physiol **104**: 171-178

Foyer CH, Valadier MH, Ferrario S (1994*b*) Co-regulation of nitrogen and carbon assimilation in leaves. *In* N Smirnoff, ed, Environment and Plant Metabolism, Flexibility and Acclimation. Bios Scientific Publ, Guildford, UK, pp 17-33

Galangau F, Daniel-Vedele F, Moureaux T, Dorbe MF, Leydecker MT, Caboche M (1988) Expression of leaf nitrate reductase genes from tomato and tobacco in relation to light dark regimes and nitrate supply. Plant Physiol **88**: 383-388

Galtier N, Foyer CH, Huber J, Voelker TA, Huber SC (1993) Effects of elevated sucrose-phosphate synthase activity on photosynthesis, assimilate partitioning and growth in tomato (*Lycopersicum esculentum* var. UC28B). Plant Physiol **101**: 535-543

Galtier N, Foyer CH, Murchie E Alred, Quick P, Voelker TA, Thépenier C, Lasceve G, Betsche T (1995) Effects of light and atmospheric carbon dioxide enrichment on photosynthetic carbon assimilation and carbon/nitrogen ratios in tomato (*Lycopersicon esculentum* L.) plants over-expressing sucrose phosphate synthase. J Exp Bot (in press)

Geiger DR (1987) Understanding interactions of source and sink regions of plants. Plant Physiol Biochem **25**: 659-666

Geiger DR, Fondy BR (1991) Regulation of carbon allocation and partitioning: status and research agenda. *In* HA Monney, W Winner, EJ Pell, eds, Response of Plants to Multiple Stresses. Academic Press, New York, pp 1-9

Ho LC (1988) Metabolism and compartmentation of imported sugars in sink organs in relation to sink strength. Annu Rev Plant Physiol Plant Mol Biol **39**: 355-378

Hocking PJ, Meyer CP (1991) Effects of CO_2 enrichment and nitrogen stress on growth, and partitioning of dry matter and nitrogen in wheat and maize. Aust J Plant Physiol **18**: 339-356

Huber JL, Huber SC, Nielsen TH (1989) Protein phosphorylation as a mechanism for regulation of spinach leaf sucrose-phosphate synthase activity. Arch Biochem Biophys **270**: 681-690

Huber SC, Huber JL (1991) Regulation of maize leaf sucrose-phosphate synthase by protein phosphorylation. Plant Cell Physiol **32**: 319-326

Huber SC, Israel DW (1982) Biochemical basis for partitioning of photosynthetically fixed carbon between starch and sucrose in soybean (*Glycine max* Merr.) leaves. Plant Physiol **69**: 691-696

Makino A (1994) Biochemistry of C_3-photosynthesis in high CO_2. J Plant Res **107**: 79-84

Pollock CJ, Chatterton NJ (1988) Fructans. *In* J Preiss, ed, The Biochemistry of Plants, Vol 14, Carbohydrates. Academic Press, San Diego, London, pp 109-140

Quilleré I, Dufossé C, Roux Y, Foyer CH, Caboche M, Morot-Gaudry JF (1994) The effects of deregulation of NR gene expression on growth and nitrogen metabolism of *Nicotiana plumbaginifolia* plant. J Exp Bot **45**: 1205-1211

Rocher JP (1988) Comparison of carbohydrate compartmentation in relation to photosynthesis assimilate export and growth in a range of maize genotypes. Aust J Plant Physiol **15**: 677-685

Rufty TW Jr, Huber SC (1983) Changes in starch formation and activities of sucrose-phosphate synthase and cytoplasmic fructose-1,6-bisphosphatase in response to source-sink alterations. Plant Physiol **72**: 474-480

Servaites JC, Fondy BR, Li B, Geiger DR (1989*a*) Sources of carbon for export from spinach leaves throughout the day. Plant Physiol **90**: 1168-1174

Servaites JC, Geiger DS, Tucci MA, Fondy BR (1989*b*) Leaf carbon metabolism and metabolite levels during a period of sinusoidal light. Plant Physiol **89**: 403-408

Sicher RC, Kremer DF (1984) Changes in sucrose-phosphate synthase activity in barley primary leaves during light-dark transitions. Plant Physiol **76**: 910-912

Stitt M (1991) Rising CO_2 levels and their potential significance for carbon flow in photosynthetic cells. Plant Cell Environ **14**: 741-762

Stitt M, Huber S, Kerr P (1987) Control of photosynthetic sucrose formation. *In* MD Hatch, NK Boardman, eds, The Biochemistry of Plants, Vol 10, Photosynthesis. Academic Press, New York, pp 327-409

Stitt M, Quick P (1989) Photosynthetic carbon partitioning: its regulation and possibilities for manipulation. Physiol Plant **77**: 633-641

Vincentz M, Caboche M (1991) Constitutive expression of nitrate reductase allows normal growth and development of *Nicotiana plumbaginifolia* plants. EMBO J **10**: 1027-1035

Williamson JD, Hirsch-Wyncott ME, Larkins BA, Gelvin SB (1989) Differential accumulation of a transcript driven by the CaMV 35S promoter in transgenic tobacco. Plant Physiol **90**: 1570-1576

Worrell AC, Bruneau JM, Summerfelt K, Boersig M, Voelker TA (1991) Expression of a maize sucrose-phosphate synthase in tomato alters leaf carbohydrate partitioning. Plant Cell **3**: 1121-1130

Yelle S, Beeson RC, Trudel Jr MJ, Gosselin A (1989) Acclimation of two tomato species to high atmospheric CO_2. II Ribulose-1,5-bisphosphate carboxylase/oxygenase and phospho*enol*pyruvate carboxylase. Plant Physiol **90**: 1473-1477

Stomata and Sucrose: A Full Circle

William H. Outlaw, Jr.

Department of Biological Science, Florida State University, Tallahassee, FL 32306-3050, USA

Osmotic water influx into the pair of guard cells that surrounds a stoma causes a widening of the aperture. Similarly, stomatal closure is brought about by osmotic water efflux.   These long-standing biophysical observations (Raschke, 1979) have been explained as resulting from large fluctuations in the concentration of potassium salts (Outlaw, 1983; Zeiger, 1983). More specifically, the increase in volume upon water influx causes cell enlargement; each of the two guard cells that lie parallel bows outward because of cell-wall asymmetry and the radial orientation of the cellulose microfibrils in the wall. Stomata—through which most gas exchange between the plant and the atmosphere occurs—are nonselective, admitting CO_2, which is required for photosynthesis, and permitting the escape of H_2O, which is usually the most limiting resource for a terrestrial plant. In fact, the rate of water-vapor efflux often exceeds that of carbon-dioxide influx by nominally 100 times because of differences in molecular velocities and driving forces of these gases. Guard cells integrate a number of environmental stimuli (Assmann, 1993), such as light and $[CO_2]$, and physiological parameters (Davies and Jones, 1991), such as water deficit, in this crucial regulation of gas exchange.

Since the late 1960s, the $\Delta\Psi_s$ that drives stomatal movements has, as previously mentioned, been explained as $\Delta[K+]$ together with changes in the concentration of balancing anions. By 1983 (Outlaw, 1983), the basic physiological parameters in many taxa and different photosynthetic modes and in response to myriad stimuli had been established. Research in the following decade (Tallman, 1992; Schroeder *et al.*, 1994; Outlaw *et al.*, 1995) focused on obtaining a mechanistic explanation (e.g. Schroeder *et al.*, 1984) of potassium permeation of guard-cell membranes and of requisite regulatory mechanisms. As research in guard-cell ion transport intensified, interest in the unique carbon metabolism of these cells (Outlaw, 1982, 1987; Robinson and Preiss, 1985) waned except that in the contentious question of whether guard cells have the ability to reduce a biologically relevant amount of CO_2 photosynthetically (Outlaw, 1989). During this era, progress was made in explaining the physiological implications of the kinetic properties of guard-cell phospho*enol*pyruvate carboxylase (Outlaw, 1990; Denecke *et al.*, 1993; Wang *et al.* 1994; Zhang *et al.*, 1994) in the context of plant-cytosolic-malate levels (Bodson *et al.*, 1991, and references therein). Progress was also made in characterizing the phosphate translocator of guard-cell chloroplasts (Overlach *et al.*, 1993), which is reminiscent of that of amyloplasts, and in other areas too numerous to list here. A most unanticipated discovery (Poffenroth *et al.*, 1992; Hite *et al.*, 1993; Talbott and Zeiger, 1993) was that sucrose has a central role in guard cells. A discussion of this role is the central point of this brief review.

MULTIPLE FOLIAR POOLS EXCHANGE SUCROSE

The first detailed studies of foliar sucrose compartmentation (Outlaw and Fisher, 1975; Outlaw *et al.*, 1975) clearly demonstrated the existence of separate sucrose pools in the mesomorphic dicotyledon *Vicia faba* (Fig. 1). In *Vicia*, the transport carbohydrate is sucrose. Thus, the specific activity of bulk-leaf sucrose increased to a maximum 15 min following a pulse of $^{14}CO_2$. The kinetics of sucrose-specific activity in rinsed abaxial epidermal peels, in contrast, did not reach a maximum until 40 min after the pulse. (This crisp time resolution probably resulted from the fact that 80% of epidermal cells, per se, which are in direct contact with the mesophyll, were ruptured during peeling. These epidermal cells are the pathway for photosynthate movement into guard cells, which are not in contact with the mesophyll.) These data, along with knowledge of the tissue organization and inferences regarding photosynthetic capacity (references in Nishio *et al.*, 1993), indicate that sucrose produced photosynthetically in the mesophyll is in relatively slow exchange with sucrose in the epidermis. A model (Fig. 2) was developed to describe sucrose redistribution throughout the leaf and export from it. Two assumptions—that the vacuolar ("nonmobile") pool was only in slow exchange with the cytosolic pool (Fisher and Outlaw, 1979) and that sucrose was excluded from the chloroplasts (Fry and Bidwell, 1977, and subsequent literature)—have been verified by additional experiments and modeling. Our model, which simulated well the observed kinetics of ^{14}C-sucrose-specific activities in lower epidermis, palisade mesophyll, lower spongy mesophyll, and vascular strands, was based on the assumption that the *concentrations* of sucrose in the cytosol and vacuole were equal and, therefore, that the pool-size ratio did not change. I cannot generalize on this point, however, as the ratio does change in spinach leaf (Gerhardt *et al.*, 1987), but does not change in barley leaf (Farrar and Farrar, 1986). Our value (Fig. 2) for the total abaxial

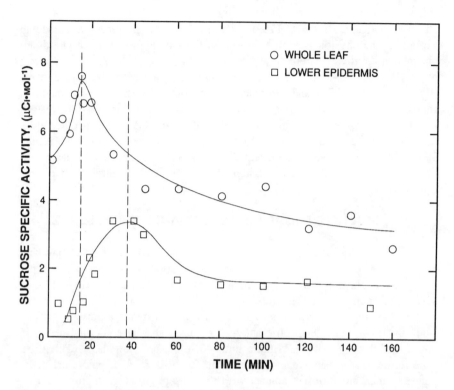

Figure 1. The time course for ^{14}C-sucrose specific activity in extracts of leaf and of rinsed abaxial epidermal peels of *Vicia faba*. The leaflets were pulse-labeled with $^{14}CO_2$ before the $^{12}CO_2$-chase period displayed. (Adapted from Outlaw and Fisher, 1975).

epidermal-sucrose content for photosynthesizing *Vicia* leaflet was 39 nmol· cm^{-2}, a point to which I will return.

GUARD CELLS HAVE A UNIQUE FOLIAR COMPLEMENT OF SUCROSE-METABOLIZING ENZYMES

Sucrose-exporting organs typically have high levels of the synthetic enzyme sucrose phosphate synthase (SPS; ref. in Worrell *et al.*, 1991) because this enzyme favors carbon partitioning from starch to sucrose (Worrell *et al.*, 1991; Galtier *et al.*, 1993). Sucrose sinks typically have high levels of the degradative enzyme sucrose synthase (SS; ref. in Dali *et al.*, 1992; Wang *et al.*, 1993). Many organs that carry out only modest photosynthesis also have high levels of SPS during a sucrose-accumulating phase (Hubbard *et al.*, 1991), regardless of the source of sucrose (conversion from starch, import as

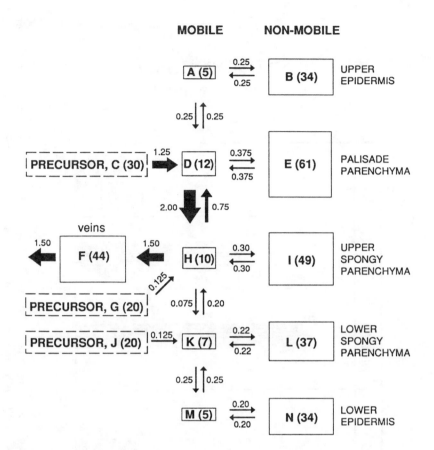

Figure 2. Compartmental analysis of sucrose in a *Vicia* leaflet. The numbers in each pool are nMol·cm^{-2}. The numbers over the arrows indicate the relative rates of exchange of sucrose between the compartments. (Adapted from Outlaw *et al.*, 1975).

sucrose or other carbohydrate). Thus, the levels of these two enzymes can be used to assess the biochemical functioning of an organ, or as attempted by Hite *et al.* (1993), the functioning of a particular kind of cell (Fig. 3). Photosynthetic mesophyll cells, net exporters, had a high ratio SPS:SS (36-48), whereas abaxial epidermal cells, which in *Vicia* have only few and rudimentary chloroplasts, had a low ratio SPS:SS (0.4). These ratios indicate that sink-source relationships may be discerned at the cellular level. Guard cells, surprisingly, had the highest specific activity (protein basis) of SPS of any leaf cell type, and they also had very high levels of SS. This anomalous pattern—consistent with that of a sucrose-accumulating sink—provided the impetus for further

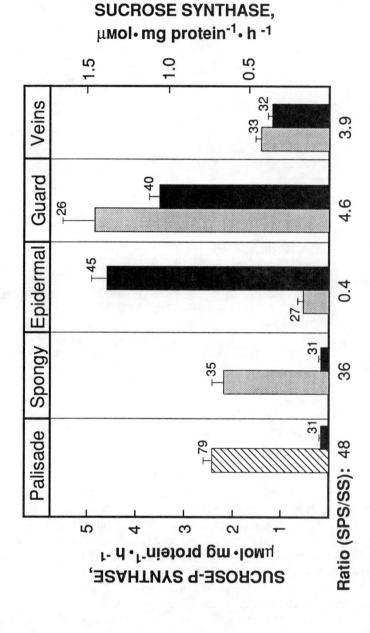

Figure 3. SPS (hatched columns) and SS (solid columns) in cells and tissues of *Vicia faba* leaflet. n is indicated adjacent to the SE bars. Reproduced from Hite *et al.* (1993) with permission from the American Society of Plant Physiologists.

study, because our previous determinations of guard-cell sucrose accumulation (Outlaw and Manchester, 1979) during stomatal opening had been carried out under conditions in which the leaf was not photosynthesizing.

GUARD CELLS ACCUMULATE SUCROSE DURING STOMATAL OPENING, BUT THE DETAILS REMAIN TO BE ELUCIDATED

Despite inconsistencies, earlier workers explained stomatal movements on the basis of (i) the accumulation of sugars (from starch, the abundance of which is remarkable in guard cells) during stomatal opening, and (ii) the dissipation of sugars (to reform starch) during stomatal closure. This so-called Classical Theory (e.g. Sayre, 1926) was rejected when the importance of potassium was recognized. Although potassium accumulation and dissipation, as the cardinal events that drive stomatal movements, have been studied intensively and under diverse conditions, studies generally were focused on "open" or "closed" stomata, were conducted on time courses of less than 2 h, or were nonquantitative. Pearson's (1973) work was atypical because he measured metabolite changes quantitatively over a long time course, and this work thus provides a reference for contemporary investigations. Pearson found that sucrose concentration fluctuated in the epidermis, and the concentration correlated strongly with time of day, but only weakly ($r^2 = 0.49$ for *Vicia*) with stomatal aperture. Similarly, the current research course has been set by longer time courses and, also, different stimuli for stomatal opening (Tallman and Zeiger, 1988). Over a 4-h time course in which stomata on sonicated epidermal strips were stimulated to open by weak red light, Poffenroth *et al.* (1992) reported changes of sucrose concentration *in* the guard cells of about 300 fMol·guard-cell pair^{-1}; under other stimulatory conditions, the changes that they reported were even larger. Subsequently, Talbott and Zeiger (1993), in experiments similar to those of Poffenroth *et al.* (1992), also found that guard-cell sucrose concentration increased, but the change was somewhat less (to a maximum value of about 165 fMol·guard-cell pair^{-1} after 2 h). Thus, the fact that sucrose concentration in guard cells increases along with stomatal aperture, which had previously been reported (Outlaw and Manchester, 1979) for individually assayed guard cells that were dissected from *Vicia* leaflets under nonphotosynthetic conditions, has led to exciting new developments. Talbott *et al.* (1994) followed the daily time course of guard-cell sucrose concentration, which was determined by assay of sonicated epidermal strips from plants that were maintained under growth conditions. In brief, they reported that sucrose replaces potassium as the main osmolyte in the afternoon. Our independent and parallel work (Fig. 4) was also aimed at measuring the guard-cell sucrose contents *in planta* over a daily time course. In addition to our measurements of conductance and apertures, two samples were harvested from plants: (i) an epidermal strip, which was rinsed to remove guard-cell apoplastic

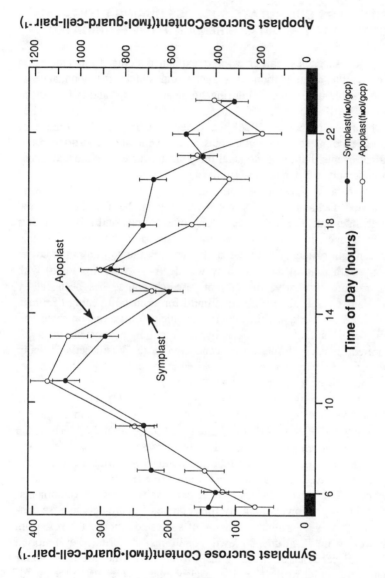

Figure 4. The time course of guard-cell sucrose content over a daily cycle. Individual guard cells were dissected from rinsed epidermis (symplast samples) or from leaf fragments (symplast + apoplast) and assayed for sucrose. A single experimental result is displayed, but a similar experiment with growth-cabinet-grown plants and one with greenhouse-grown plants were corroborative (P. Lu, S.Q. Zhang, and W.H. Outlaw, Jr., submitted).

solutes; and (*ii*) a leaflet fragment. Both samples were freeze-dried, and guard cells dissected from the samples were assayed for sucrose by quantitative histochemical procedures. Under physiological conditions of stomatal opening (P. Lu, S.Q. Zhang, and W.H. Outlaw, Jr, submitted), guard-cell-symplast sucrose concentration increased about three-fold to a maximum value of about 375 fMol·guard-cell pair[-1], whereas the guard-cell-apoplast sucrose concentration increased about five-fold to a maximum value of about 1250 fMol·guard-cell pair[-1]. Thus, at the maximum guard-cell-sucrose concentration, about 20% of total epidermal sucrose (cf. Fig. 2) is localized to guard cells. As the guard-cell values that include the apoplast are about twice as high as those obtained under nonphotosynthetic conditions by Outlaw and Manchester (1979), a component of the observed sucrose-concentration increase is time and photosynthesis dependent.

My view of guard-cell physiology does not incorporate a significant role for guard-cell photosynthetic CO_2 reduction, and my working hypothesis is that some sucrose may be formed from guard-cell starch degradation (cf. Outlaw and Manchester, 1979). The bulk of the increase of sucrose, I attribute most simply to peristomatal evapotranspiration. Although sucrose in the apoplast is present in only trace amounts (references in Correia and Pereira, 1994), except in specialized tissues (see Wang and Fisher, 1994), evaporation of water from the guard-cell wall would concentrate this metabolite, as we (M. Ewert, S.Q. Zhang, and W.H. Outlaw, Jr, unpubl. data) have demonstrated for ^{14}C-mannitol fed to the cut-off petiole of a *Vicia* leaflet. This mechanism would explain the delayed accumulation of sucrose in guard cells and diminution of accumulation in guard cells of a nontranspiring and nonphotosynthetic leaflet (Outlaw and Manchester, 1979). If the idea was correct, sucrose would link guard-cell physiological state to the photosynthetic activity of the leaf.

The accumulation of sucrose in the guard-cell apoplast (Fig. 4), as a result of evapotranspiration, can have several consequences that cannot be evaluated without a knowledge of its actual concentration there. Unfortunately, there are no good estimates, to my knowledge, of the *Vicia* guard-cell-wall aqueous volume. Thus, the following discussion must be qualified. *If* the apoplast is 10 pL·guard-cell pair[-1], i.e. equal to the symplast volume of "open" stomata, the minimum and maximum guard-cell-apoplast sucrose concentrations that we measured (Fig. 4) would be about 20 and 110 mM, respectively. At these external concentrations, guard cells can accumulate approximately 500 fmol·guard-cell pair[-1]·h[-1] (Fig. 5), which is in excess of any measured accumulation rate. Thus, whereas we have not "characterized" a guard-cell sucrose carrier, our data (S.A. Springer and W.H. Outlaw, Jr, unpubl. data) clearly demonstrate a high capacity for sucrose uptake, at least under the existing experimental conditions [the guard cells were dissected from freeze-dried epidermal strips that were floated in light or darkness over a linear time course in

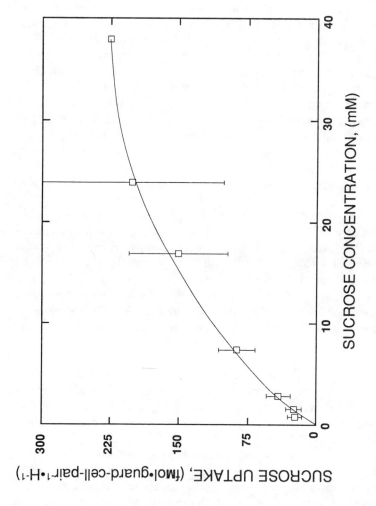

Figure 5. Uptake of ^{14}C-sucrose into guard cells as a function of sucrose concentration. The guard cells were dissected from epidermal peels that were incubated on ^{14}C-sucrose-containing medium (PO_4, pH 5.5, 1 mM $CaCl_2$). The displayed results are the average of three experiments. The large experimental errors indicate differences in rates among the three experiments, which individually yielded smooth kinetics (S.A. Springer and W.H. Outlaw, Jr., unpubl. data).

a ^{14}C-sucrose-containing artificial medium (pH 5.5, 1 mM $CaCl_2$, in 5 mM PO_4)]. This new information raises several questions, i.e. does carrier modulation or rate of leaf photosynthesis or rate of evapotranspiration influence stomatal aperture or choice of guard-cell osmolyte?

SUMMARY

The explanation of the involvement of sucrose in stomatal-aperture changes has come full circle. Earlier, putative changes in the concentration of sugars were used to describe the osmotic fluctuations that drive stomatal movements. These ideas were abandoned as the central role of potassium became recognized, notwithstanding occasional reports (references in Lu *et al.*, submitted) that potassium salts could not account for the observed Ψ_s changes. Recently, new roles—including that as a significant fluctuating osmolyte—for sucrose (see also Outlaw, 1983) in stomatal movements have been proposed. This new model and line of inquiry should lead to a fuller understanding of the regulation of gas exchange by plants.

LITERATURE CITED

Assmann SM (1993) Signal transduction in guard cells. Annu Rev Cell Biol **9**: 345-375

Bodson MJ, Outlaw WH Jr, Silvers SH (1991) Malate content of picoliter samples of *Raphanus sativus* cytoplasm. J Histochem Cytochem **39**: 435-440

Correia MJ, Pereira JS (1994) Abscisic acid in apoplastic sap can account for the restriction in leaf conductance of white lupins during moderate soil drying and after rewatering. Plant Cell Environ **17**: 845-852

Dali N, Michaud D, Yelle S (1992) Evidence for the involvement of sucrose-phosphate synthase in the pathway of sugar accumulation in sucrose accumulating tomato fruits. Plant Physiol **99**: 434-438

Davies WJ, Jones HG (eds) (1991) Abscisic Acid. Physiology and Biochemistry. Bios Scientific Publishers, Oxford, UK

Denecke M, Schulz M, Fischer C, Schnabl H (1993) Partial purification and characterization of stomatal phospho*eno*/pyruvate carboxylase from *Vicia faba*. Physiol Plant **87**: 96-102

Farrar SC, Farrar JF (1986) Compartmentation and fluxes of sucrose in intact leaf blades of barley. New Phytol **103**: 645-657

Fisher DB, Outlaw WH Jr (1979) Sucrose compartmentation in the palisade parenchyma of *Vicia faba* L. Plant Physiol **64**: 481-483

Fry SC, Bidwell RGS (1977) An investigation of photosynthetic sucrose production in bean leaves. Can J Bot **55**: 1457-1464

Galtier N, Foyer CH, Huber J, Voelker TA, Huber SC (1993) Effects of elevated sucrose-phosphate synthase activity on photosynthesis, assimilate partitioning, and growth in tomato (*Lycopersicon esculentum* var UC82B). Plant Physiol **101**: 535-543

Gerhardt R, Stitt M, Heldt HW (1987) Subcellular metabolite levels in spinach leaves. Regulation of sucrose synthesis during diurnal alterations in photosynthetic partitioning. Plant Physiol 83: 399-407

Hite DRC, Outlaw WH Jr, Tarczynski MC (1993) Elevated levels of both sucrose-phosphate synthase and sucrose synthase in *Vicia* guard cells indicate cell-specific carbohydrate interconversions. Plant Physiol 101: 1217-1221

Hubbard NL, Pharr MD, Huber SC (1991) Sucrose phosphate synthase and other sucrose metabolizing enzymes in fruits of various species. Physiol Plant 82: 191-196

Nishio JN, Sun J, Vogelmann TC (1993) Carbon fixation gradients across spinach leaves do not follow internal light gradients. Plant Cell 5: 953-961

Outlaw WH Jr (1982) Carbon metabolism in guard cells. Rec Adv Phytochem 16: 185-222

Outlaw WH Jr (1983) Current concepts on the role of potassium in stomatal movements. Physiol Plant 59: 302-311

Outlaw WH Jr (1987) A minireview: Comparative biochemistry of photosynthesis in palisade cells, spongy cells, and guard cells of C3 leaves. *In* J Biggins, ed, Progress in Photosynthesis Research, Vol IV.5. Martinus Nijhoff Publ, Dordrecht, The Netherlands, pp 265-272

Outlaw WH Jr (1989) Critical examination of the quantitative evidence for and against photosynthetic CO_2 fixation by guard cells. Physiol Plant 77: 275-281

Outlaw WH Jr (1990) Kinetic properties of guard-cell phospho*enol*pyruvate carboxylase. Biochem Physiol Pflanzen 186: 317-325

Outlaw WH Jr, Fisher DB (1975) Compartmentation in *Vicia faba* leaves. I. Kinetics of ^{14}C in the tissues following pulse labeling. Plant Physiol 55: 699-703

Outlaw WH Jr, Fisher DB, Christy AL (1975) Compartmentation in *Vicia faba* leaves. II. Kinetics of ^{14}C-sucrose redistribution among individual tissues following pulse labeling. Plant Physiol 55: 704-711

Outlaw WH Jr, Manchester J (1979) Guard cell starch concentration quantitatively related to stomatal aperture. Plant Physiol 64: 79-82

Outlaw WH Jr, Zhang SQ, Hite DRC, Thistle AB (1995) Stomata: biophysical and biochemical aspects *In* NR Baker, ed, Photosynthesis and the Environment. Kluwer Academic Publ, Dordrecht, The Netherlands (in press)

Overlach S, Diekmann W, Raschke K (1993) Phosphate translocator of isolated guard-cell chloroplasts from *Pisum sativum* L. transports glucose-6-phosphate. Plant Physiol 101: 1201-1207

Pearson CJ (1973) Daily changes in stomatal aperture and in carbohydrates and malate within epidermis and mesophyll of leaves of *Commelina cyanea* and *Vicia faba*. Aust J Biol Sci 26: 1035-1044

Poffenroth M, Green DB, Tallman G (1992) Sugar concentrations in guard cells of *Vicia faba* illuminated with red or blue light. Analysis by high performance liquid chromatography. Plant Physiol 98: 1460-1471

Raschke K (1979) Movements of stomata. *In* W Haupt, ME Feinleib, eds, Physiology of Movements. Encyclopedia of Plant Physiology, New Series, Vol 7. Springer-Verlag, Berlin, pp 383-441

Robinson N, Preiss J (1985) Biochemical phenomena associated with stomatal function. Physiol Plant **64:** 141-146

Sayre JD (1926) Physiology of stomata of *Rumex patientia*. Ohio J Sci **26:** 233-266

Schroeder JI, Hedrich R, Fernandez JM (1984) Potassium-selective single channels in guard cell protoplasts of *Vicia faba*. Nature **312:** 361-362

Schroeder JI, Ward JM, Gassmann W (1994) Perspectives on the physiology and structure of inward rectifying K+ channels in higher plants-biophysical implications for K + uptake. Annu Rev Biophys Biomol Struc **23:** 441-471

Talbott LD, Haung C, Zeiger E (1994) Guard cells of intact *Vicia* leaves can use K+ and sucrose as their main osmotica. Plant Physiol **105s:** 527

Talbott LD, Zeiger E (1993) Sugar and organic acid accumulation in guard cells of *Vicia faba* in response to red and blue light. Plant Physiol **102:** 1163-1169

Tallman G (1992) The chemiosmotic model of stomatal opening revisited. Crit Rev Plant Sci **11:** 35-57

Tallman G, Zeiger E (1988) Light quality and osmoregulation in *Vicia* guard cells: evidence for the involvement of three metabolic pathways. Plant Physiol **88:** 887-895

Wang F, Sanz A, Brenner ML, Smith A (1993) Sucrose synthase, starch accumulation, and tomato fruit sink strength. Plant Physiol **101:** 321-327

Wang N, Fisher DB (1994) Monitoring phloem unloading and post-phloem transport by microperfusion of attached wheat grains. Plant Physiol **104:** 7-16

Wang XC, Outlaw WH Jr, De Bedout JA, Du Z (1994) Kinetic characterization of phospho*enol*pyruvate carboxylase extracted from whole leaf and from guard-cell protoplasts of *Vicia faba* L. (C $_3$ plant) with respect to tissue pre-illumination. Histochem J **26:** 152-160

Worrell AC, Bruneau JM, Summerfelt K, Boersig M, Voelker TA (1991) Expression of a maize sucrose phosphate synthase in tomato alters leaf carbohydrate partitioning. Plant Cell **3:** 1121-1130

Zeiger E (1983) The biology of stomatal guard cells. Annu Rev Plant Physiol **34:** 441-475

Zhang SQ, Outlaw WH Jr, Chollet R (1994) Lessened malate inhibition of guard-cell phospho*enol*pyruvate carboxylase during stomatal opening. FEBS Lett **352:** 45-48

Carbon Partitioning and Source-Sink Interactions in Plants, *Monica A. Madore* and *William J. Lucas*, eds, Copyright 1995, published by The American Society of Plant Physiologists

Do Carbohydrates Regulate Photosynthesis and Allocation by Altering Gene Expression?

**Mark Stitt, Anne Krapp, Diana Klein,
Ursula Röper-Schwarz, and Matthew Paul**

*Botanisches Institut, Im Neuenheimer Feld 360,
69120 Heidelberg, Germany*

*Present addresses: INRA, Versailles, France (A.K.); and Rothamsted
Experimental Station, Harpenden, England (M.P.)*

Considerable advances have been made in understanding the short-term regulation of photosynthetic carbon metabolism. The growth and performance of higher organisms also depends on their ability to coordinate developmental processes and to sense and respond to long-term changes in their environment. The ability of plants to modulate gene expression and development in response to external signals like light has long been recognized, and the signaling pathways are being intensively researched (Bowler and Chua, 1994; Deng, 1994). Plant gene expression and development may also be regulated and coordinated by signals originating from within the plant's metabolic processes. Internal signals provide information about the physiological status of the cell, and could act to modulate development, or initiate new developmental sequences in response to a perceived resource (im)balance.

One potential source for internal signals is carbohydrate availability. High levels of carbohydrate inhibit expression of genes encoding proteins involved in photosynthesis (Sheen, 1990; Van Oosten and Besford, 1994) and gluconeogenesis (Graham *et al.*, 1994); increase expression of genes involved in nitrate assimilation; and modulate expression of genes involved in growth, storage (see Grierson *et al.*, 1994, for references), and starch remobilization during germination (Thomas and Rodriguez, 1994). When the availability or use of carbohydrate is changed, there are far-reaching changes in carbon metabolism, nitrogen metabolism, and whole plant growth and allocation (Müller-Röber *et al.*, 1992; Stitt and Schulze, 1994). The following chapter summarizes our investigations into the way in which carbohydrate status modulates gene expression, photosynthesis, and allocation.

ACCUMULATION OF CARBOHYDRATE IN LEAVES LEADS
TO RAPID, REVERSIBLE, AND SPECIFIC CHANGES
IN GENE EXPRESSION

We have used four model systems to investigate whether carbohydrates regulate gene expression in leaves. (*i*) Invertase from yeast was expressed in the apoplasm of tobacco leaves to inhibit apoplasmic phloem loading (Von Schaewen *et al.*, 1990). The accumulation of carbohydrate in the source leaves was accompanied by a decrease of *rbc*S transcript (encoding the small nuclear-encoded subunit of Rubisco) (Krapp *et al.*, 1993). Identical changes of *rbc*S and transcripts encoding other proteins needed for photosynthesis (*cab*, *atp*-D) occur when (*ii*) sucrose is supplied to detached leaves via the petiole (Krapp *et al.*, 1991, 1993); (*iii*) glucose is added to autotrophic cell suspension cultures of *Chenopodium rubrum* (Krapp *et al.*, 1993); and (*iv*) export from tobacco, potato or spinach leaves is inhibited on intact plants by cooling their petiole (Krapp *et al.*, 1993; Krapp and Stitt, 1994*b*).

The decrease in these mRNA levels is due to a lower rate of transcription. Run-on transcription experiments with isolated nuclei revealed a 6- to 20-fold and 3- to 4-fold inhibition of *rbc*S and *cab* transcription, respectively, after adding glucose to *Chenopodium* cells (Krapp *et al.*, 1993). ^{35}S-Methionine-labeling experiments and immunoprecipitation revealed 3- to 4-fold inhibition of the *de novo* synthesis of the small subunit of Rubisco (Krapp *et al.*, 1993) after adding glucose to *Chenopodium* cells. The changes are rapid, in that transcripts for *rbc*S and other proteins began to decrease within 3 to 7 h of adding glucose to *Chenopodium* cells or cooling the petiole of tobacco, potato (Krapp *et al.*, 1993), and spinach (Krapp and Stitt, 1994*b*).

Changes of protein amount and enzyme activity were slower in response to the applied treatments. After 3 to 4 d, Rubisco protein and activity were halved in *Chenopodium* cells, potato, tobacco (Krapp *et al.*, 1993), and spinach (Krapp and Stitt, 1994b) leaves. Calvin cycle enzymes and chlorophyll decreased at a similar or slightly slower rate (Schäfer *et al.*, 1992; Krapp *et al.*, 1991, 1993; Krapp and Stitt, 1994*b*). The delay presumably reflects the time needed for turnover of Rubisco and other proteins.

The experimentally induced changes of transcripts and enzyme activity are reversible. When *Chenopodium* cells were given a short pulse of glucose (Krapp *et al.*, 1993) or the petiole of cold-girdled spinach leaves was rewarmed (Krapp and Stitt, 1994*b*), *rbc*S recovered to the control value within 48 h, and Rubisco protein began to increase back to the original level.

The decrease of transcripts and/or enzyme activity was restricted to proteins which are unique for photosynthesis. There was no change in the activity of the plastid isoforms of aldolase, triose-phosphate isomerase or phosphoglucose isomerase, which are required for respiratory metabolism as well as photosynthetic metabolism (Krapp and Stitt, 1994*a*). The activities of many glycolytic enzymes remained unaltered or even increased (Stitt et al., 1991; Krapp and Stitt, 1994a). Transcripts for enzymes involved in nitrate assimilation and starch synthesis also increased (see below).

CHANGED GENE EXPRESSION LEADS TO A DELAYED INHIBITION OF PHOTOSYNTHESIS

The decrease of Rubisco and other enzymes leads to an inhibition of photosynthesis (Stitt et al., 1991) which also develops after 3 to 4 d (Krapp et al., 1991; Schäfer et al., 1992; Krapp and Stitt, 1994b). The inhibition of photosynthesis was always accompanied by an increase of ribulose-1,5-bisphosphate (Ru1,5bisP), a decrease of glycerate-3-phosphate (3PGA), increased activation of Rubisco, and in leaves, an increase of the CO_2 concentration in the leaf (Stitt et al., 1991; Krapp et al., 1991, 1993; Krapp and Stitt, 1994b), showing that decreased expression of Rubisco contributes to the inhibition of photosynthesis. Other metabolites including triose-phosphates and Fru-1,6-bisP also rise slightly, indicating that decreased expression of the other Calvin cycle enzymes is simultaneously restricting Ru1,5bisP regeneration (Krapp et al., 1991; Krapp and Stitt, 1994b). The increase of the 3PGA/trioseP ratio (Stitt et al., 1991; Krapp et al., 1991; Krapp and Stitt, 1994b), the increased ATP/ADP ratio and activation of NADP-malate dehydrogenase (an indicator for the stromal NADPH/NADP ratio), and the lack of inhibition of photosynthesis in low irradiance (Krapp et al., 1991) indicate that light-harvesting and electron transport are not inhibited as strongly as the "dark" reactions. There was no evidence in any of these model systems for a limitation of photosynthesis by Pi (see Krapp and Stitt, 1994b, for discussion).

CARBOHYDRATE MODULATES GENES INVOLVED IN ALLOCATION TO NITROGEN AND STARCH METABOLISM

Within 3 to 7 d of adding glucose to Chenopodium cells (Krapp et al., 1993) or cooling the petiole of spinach leaves (Krapp and Stitt, 1994b), there is a 2- to 3-fold increase in the level of transcript for nitrate reductase (nra). Nitrate reductase activity increased 2.5-fold in Chenopodium cells (Krapp and Stitt, 1994a). Altered gene expression could be involved in increasing allocation to nitrogen metabolism when carbohydrate accumulates.

There is also a rapid increase of agp-S transcript (encoding the regulatory subunit of ADPglucose pyrophosphorylase, AGPase) when glucose is added to Chenopodium cells or spinach leaves are girdled (Krapp et al., 1993; Stitt and Krapp, 1994b). The significance of this increase is not clear, because overall AGPase activity does not increase (Krapp and Stitt, 1994a). This could be because AGPase levels are relatively insensitive to transcript level (see also Müller-Röber et al., 1992), or because the changed expression of this regulatory subunit leads to a subtle change in activity or properties. Carbohydrate might also modulate starch accumulation via changes in degradation. There is a decrease of the activity of the plastidic (but not the cytosolic) isoform of starch phosphorylase when glucose is supplied to *Chenopodium* cells, or carbohydrates accumulate in leaves (Krapp et al., 1994a). Altered expression may be important for regulating starch metabolism (see Krapp and Stitt, 1994b, for discussion), because it is not clear that allosteric regulation by 3PGA and Pi alone can explain the large stimulation of starch accumulation after adding glucose, or inhibiting export.

HOW IS CARBOHYDRATE STATUS SENSED?

In tobacco, petiole girdling leads to a faster decrease of *rbcS* transcript, and a larger change of hexose sugars and smaller increase of sucrose and starch than in potato or spinach (Krapp et al., 1993; Krapp and Stitt, 1994b). Jang and Sheen (1994) electroporated different sugars into protoplasts containing a *gus* reporter gene construct with a p*rbsS* or p*cab* promoter. Hexoses produced a larger inhibition of *gus* expression than sucrose. The extent of the inhibition of photosynthesis, after heat-girdling the petiole of a range of species, was correlated with the acid invertase activity in the leaf (Goldschmidt and Huber, 1992). Overexpression of yeast invertase in the vacuole of tobacco leads to a phenotype similar to that after blocking phloem transport (Sonnewald et al., 1991). These observations from several groups indicate that hexoses are involved in signaling, rather than sucrose or starch.

However, the overall content of glucose or fructose and the behavior of the transcripts are not always correlated. When a short pulse of glucose was supplied to *Chenopodium* cells (Krapp et al., 1993) or the petiole of spinach leaves was cooled and rewarmed (Krapp and Stitt, 1994b), the *rbcS* and *atp*-D transcript levels rose back to their control values within 1 to 2 d (and *nra* and *agp*-S transcripts started to fall) even though the leaves still contained large amounts of glucose, fructose, and sucrose. Removal of CO_2 from glucose-supplied *Chenopodium* cells led to a 4-fold increase of *rbcS*, even though glucose, fructose, and sucrose were as high as in the presence of CO_2 (Krapp et al., 1993).

Transport Across the Plasma Membrane Does Not Provide the Signal

The above-mentioned experiments indicate that the net balance of carbohydrate flux into and out of the cell, or leaf, is more important than the momentary content. Therefore, we investigated whether metabolic changes related to uptake or metabolization of hexoses act as a signal. Addition of transportable, but nonphosphorylatable, sugar analogs like 6-deoxyglucose and 3-O-methylglucose had no effect on the transcript level of *rbcS* (Krapp et al., 1993). In contrast, low concentrations of mannose (10 mM) and 2-deoxyglucose (0.2 mM) led to a rapid decrease of *rbc*S transcripts in *Chenopodium* cells, however, transcripts for *nra* were not decreased (D. Klein, unpubl. results). These analogs are rapidly phosphorylated by hexokinase, to mannose-6-P and 2-deoxyglucose-6-P, which then accumulate because they cannot be further metabolized at significant rates. Either (*i*) a system directly senses the rate at which hexoses are being phosphorylated or (*ii*) the analogs are inducing a change in metabolism which mimics a signal produced when glucose is metabolized.

One potential candidate would be a decrease of Pi. Addition of glucose leads to a decrease of cytoplasmic Pi, as the levels of phosphorylated metabolites rise. Cytosolic Pi will fall dramatically when the analogs are added, due to sequestration as mannose-6-P and 2-deoxyglucose-6-P. We therefore added 50 mM exogenous Pi to increase the internal Pi pool, or glycerol to decrease the cytosolic Pi (glycerol is phosphorylated to glycerol-3-P, allowing Pi to be sequestered independently of hexokinase, see Leegood *et al.*, 1988). Both treatments led to the expected changes in metabolite levels, but had no effect on *rbc*S or *nra* transcripts (A. Krapp, unpubl. data). Addition of Pi also had no effect on the response of the transcripts to added glucose (A. Krapp, unpubl. results). To check whether Pi-limitation in the plastid acts as a signal, we investigated antisense triose-phosphate translocator plants. These plants contain high levels of phosphorylated metabolites and low Pi in the plastid (Heineke *et al.*, 1994). Their *rbc*S transcript level was identical to wild-type plants (A. Krapp, unpubl. results). It therefore seems unlikely that changes in free Pi act as a signal to regulate the expression of genes for proteins involved in photosynthesis. This contrasts with studies by other groups on soybean glycoprotein phosphatases and chalcone synthase and potato proteinase inhibitor II and class I patatin. The sucrose-induction of these genes can be minimized by phosphate depletion, and counteracted by adding phosphate (Sadka *et al.*, 1994).

Carbohydrate status might be signaled via changes of Fru-2,6-bisP (Stitt, 1990). Fru-2,6-bisP levels were increased 2- to 3-fold by adding vanadate (to inhibit Fru-2,6-bisPase, Brauer and Stitt, 1990) or lanthanium (to inhibit the cytosolic Fru-1,6-bisPase, Brauer *et al.*, 1990). The potential contribution of Fru-2,6-bisP was also investigated by comparing wild-type tobacco plants and transformants with decreased expression of PPi-dependent phosphofructokinase (PFP) and 2-fold higher Fru2,6bisP (Paul *et al.*, in press). None of these treatments had any effect on *rbc*S transcript levels.

Addition of carbohydrate will alter the carbon-nitrogen balance, by increasing the supply of oxoglutarate to the GOGAT pathway. It is known that *nra* transcription is regulated by signals involving changes of glutamine (Vincentz *et al.*, 1992). We supplied glutamine or azaserine (an inhibitor of GOGAT) to *Chenopodium* cells (A. Krapp, unpubl. results). Glutamine led, as expected, to a 3-fold decrease in the level of *nra* transcript, but had no effect on the level of *rbc*S transcript present in these cells. Addition of 1 mM azaserine led to a 4-fold increase of the internal glutamine pool and a 4-fold decrease of *nra*, but this again had no effect on *rbc*S transcript levels. When glucose was added in the presence of azaserine, *rbc*S transcripts decreased 4-fold. This is identical to the change in the absence of azaserine. Clearly, (*i*) *rbc*S expression is not regulated via changes of glutamine, and (*ii*) the signal sequence from carbohydrates still operates even when the GOGAT pathway is inhibited. It should also be mentioned that glucose produced a 5-fold increase of *nra* transcript even when azaserine was present. This indicates that *nra* expression is regulated by a glutamine-related signal and by another signal related more directly to carbohydrate supply.

Summarizing, mannose and 2-deoxyglucose mimic the action of high carbohydrate on *rbc*S transcription. Transports of hexose analogs, and changes of Pi, phosphorylated metabolites, Fru2,6bisP, and nitrogen metabolites have no effect. Similar results for glucose analogs have been reported in two other experimental systems. Jang and Sheen (1994) reported that 2-deoxyglucose and mannose mimic the action of glucose on the expression of reporter genes in a maize bundle sheath protoplast transient expression system, whereas electroporation of Glu-6-P or Pi had no effect. Graham *et al.* (1994) have shown that mannose and 2-deoxyglucose mimic the repressing action of glucose on genes encoding enzymes of the glyoxylate pathway in cotyledons of germinating cucumber seedlings. Both groups have proposed that the rate of hexose phosphorylation via hexokinases provides a sensing system for carbohydrates. A similar system is postulated to operate in yeast (see Sheen, 1990, and the above references). This hypothesis is attractive, but the evidence is still indirect. It is possible that these sugar analogs (which are, strictly speaking, very slowly metabolized, rather than nonmetabolized) generate other unsuspected changes in metabolism, in addition to changes of phosphate. It is also possible that general toxic effects block the expression of highly regulated genes, but not of the housekeeping or heterolous constitutive genes used as controls.

OPERATION AND CONSEQUENCES IN THE WHOLE PLANT

Decreased expression of genes which encode proteins involved in photosynthesis not only leads to a decreased rate of photosynthesis, but could also allow reallocation of nitrogen and other resources. This represents an adaptive response to a sink-source imbalance (see Stitt, 1991). To investigate the manner in which high carbohydrate levels interact with gene expression, allocation, and growth in different conditions, we grew tobacco seedlings on nutrient agar in the presence or absence of hexogeous sucrose (Paul and Stitt, 1993). (*i*) When the seedlings were grown on full nutrient medium at 25°C and low light (200 μmol · m-2 · s-1), they responded to sucrose by increasing their root and shoot growth. Even though the leaves contained substantial amounts

(10-15 μmol · g fresh weight[-1]) of glucose, fructose, and sucrose, there was no decrease of *rbc*S transcript (A. Krapp, unpubl. results), Rubisco, chlorophyll, or leaf protein (Paul and Stitt, 1993). (*ii*) When the plantlets were grown on limiting (0.1 mM) NH_4NO_3, they could not respond to added sucrose by increasing whole plant growth. Addition of sucrose led to a 5-fold decreased expression of *rbc*S even though leaf glucose and fructose were only 25 to 30% higher than in plants on full medium plus sucrose (A. Krapp, unpubl. results). Rubisco, chlorophyll, and leaf protein decreased, and twice as much protein was allocated to the roots (Paul and Stitt, 1993). (*iii*) Growing the seedlings on low (0.3 μM) Pi also prevented a growth response to sucrose. Unexpectedly, in these plants there was no decrease in *rbc*S transcript (A. Krapp, unpubl. results) and no decrease of Rubisco, chlorophyll, and leaf protein when sucrose was added (Paul and Stitt, 1993). The different response in the nitrogen- and phosphate-limited plants occurred even though the leaves contained similar levels of reducing sugars and sucrose in both conditions (Paul and Stitt, 1993).

These results point to three interesting conclusions. Firstly, they show that decreased expression of proteins needed for photosynthesis allows redistribution of protein to sink organs. This has implications for the regulation of nitrogen-use efficiency in plants. Secondly, they show that high carbohydrate level does not always lead to repression of *rbc*S. This implies that the perception or the transduction of the high carbohydrate signal is modulated. Thirdly, Pi-deficiency typically leads to dark-green leaves. The activities of many enzymes of photosynthetic metabolism increase in Pi-deficient plants (Sicher and Kremer, 1988; Rao and Terry, 1989) even though carbohydrates also rise to high levels. It is intriguing that expression of *rbc*S is apparently insensitive to carbohydrate levels in Pi-limited seedlings. Further studies of this phenomenon could provide insights into sugar-sensing by plants, and into the molecular basis for the symptoms of Pi deficiency, and will also be important for interpreting results with enhanced CO_2 under different nutrient conditions.

ACKNOWLEDGMENTS

The work described in this review was supported by the Deutsche Forschungsgemeinschaft. We are grateful to A. van Schaewen, U. Sonnewald, L. Willmitzer, and C. Schäfer for their help in collaborative experiments.

LITERATURE CITED

Bowler C, Chua N-H (1994) Emerging themes of plant signal transduction. Plant Cell **6**: 1529-1541

Brauer M, Sanders D, Stitt M (1990) Regulation of photosynthetic sucrose synthesis. A role for calcium? Planta **182**: 226-243

Brauer M, Stitt M (1990) Vanadate inhibits fructose-2,6-bisphosphate and leads to an inhibition of sucrose synthesis in barley leaves. Physiol Plant 78: 568-573

Deng X-W (1994) Fresh view of light signal transduction. Cell 76: 423-426

Graham IA, Denby KJ, Leaver CJ (1994) Carbon catabolite repression regulates glyoxalate cycle gene expression in cucumber. Plant Cell 6: 761-777

Grieson C, Du J-S, de Torres Zabala M, Smith C, Holdsworth M, Bevan M (1994) Separate cis sequences and trans factors direct metabolic and developmental regulation of a potato tuber storage protein gene. Plant J 5: 815-826

Heineke D, Kruse A, Flügge U-I, Frommer UB, Riesmeier JW, Willmitzer L, Heldt HW (1994) Effect of antisense repression of the chloroplast triose phosphate translocator on photosynthesis metabolism in transgenic potato plants. Planta 193: 174-180

Jang J-C, Sheen J (1994) Sugar sensing in higher plants. Plant Cell 6: 1665-1679

Krapp A, Hofmann B, Schäfer C, Stitt M (1993) Regulation of the expression of rbcS and other photosynthetic genes by carbohydrates: a mechanism for the "sink" regulation of photosynthesis. Plant J 3: 817-828

Krapp A, Quick WP, Stitt M (1991) Ribulose-1,5-bisphosphate carboxylase/oxygenase, other photosynthetic enzymes and chlorophyll decrease when glucose is supplied to mature spinach leaves via the transpiration stream. Planta 186: 58-69

Krapp A, Stitt M (1994a) Influence of high carbohydrate content on the activity of plastids and cytosolic isoenzymes pairs in photosynthetic tissues. Plant Cell Environ 17: 861-866

Krapp A, Stitt M (1994b) An evaluation of direct and indirect mechanisms for the "sink-regulation" of photosynthesis in spinach: changes in gas exchange, carbohydrates, metabolites, enzyme activities and steady-state transcript levels after cold girdling source leaves. Planta (in press)

Leegood RC, Labate CA, Huber SC, Neuhaus HE, Stitt M (1988) Phosphate sequestration by glycerol and its effects on photosynthetic carbon assimilation in leaves. Planta 176: 117-126

Müller-Röber B, Koßmann J, Hannah CL, Willmitzer L, Sonnewald U (1990) One of the two ADP-glucose pyrophosphorylase genes from potato responds strongly to elevated levels of sucrose. Mol Gen Genet 224: 136-146

Müller-Röber B, Sonnewald U, Willmitzer L (1992) Inhibition of ADP-glucose pyrophosphorylase in transgenic potatoes leads to sugar-storing tubers and influences tuber formation and expression of tuber storage proteins. EMBO J 11: 1129-1238

Paul M, Sonnewald U, Hajirezaei M, Dennis D, Stitt M (1995) Transgenic tobacco plants strongly decreased expression of pyrophosphate:fructose-6-phosphate phosphotransferase do not differ significantly from the wild-type in photosynthate partitioning, plant growth or ability to cope with limiting phosphate, limiting nitrogen on suboptimal temperatures. Planta (in press)

Paul M, Stitt M (1993) Effects of nitrogen and phosphorus deficiencies on levels of carbohydrates, respiratory enzymes and metabolites in seedlings of tobacco and their response to exogenous sucrose. Plant Cell Environ 16: 1047-1057

Rao M, Terry N (1989) Leaf phosphate status, photosynthesis and carbon partitioning in sugar beet. I. Changes in growth, gas exchange and Calvin cycle enzymes. Plant Physiol 90: 814-819

Sadka A, Dewald DB, May GD, Park WD, Mullet JE (1994) Phosphate modulates transcription of soybean VspB and other sugar-inducible genes. Plant Cell 6: 737-749

Schäfer C, Simper H, Hofman B (1992) Glucose feeding results in coordinated changes of chlorophyll content, ribulose-1,5-bisphosphate carboxylase/oxygenase activity and photosynthetic potential in photoautotrophic suspension cultured cells of Chenopodium rubrum. Plant Cell Environ 15: 343-350

Sheen J (1990) Metabolic repression of transcription in higher plants. Plant Cell 2: 1027-1038

Sicher RC, Kremer DF (1988) Effects of phosphate deficiency on assimilate partitioning in barley seedlings. Plant Sci 57: 9-17

Sonnewald U, Brauer M, von Schaewen A, Stitt M, Willmitzer L (1991) Transgenic tobacco plants expressing yeast derived invertase in either the cytosol, the vacuole or the apoplast; a powerful tool to study sucrose metabolism and sink-source interactions. Plant J 1: 95-106

Stitt M (1990) Fructose-2,6-bisphosphate as a regulatory molecule in plants. Annu Rev Plant Physiol Mol Biol 41: 153-185

Stitt M (1991) Rising CO_2 levels and their potential significance for carbon flow in photosynthetic cells. Plant Cell Environ 14: 741-762

Stitt M, Schulze E-D (1994) Does Rubisco control the rate of photosynthesis and plant growth? An exercise in molecular ecophysiology. Plant Cell Environ 17: 465-467

Stitt M, Von Schaewen A, Willmitzer L (1991) "Sink-regulation" of photosynthetic metabolism in transgenic tobacco plants expressing yeast invertase in their cell wall involves a decrease of the Calvin cycle enzymes and an increase of glycolytic enzymes. Planta 183: 40-50

Thomas BR, Rodriguez RL (1994) Metabolite signals regulate gene expression and source/sink relations in cereal seedlings. Plant Physiol 106: 1235-1239

Van Oosten JJ, Besford RT (1994) Sugar feeding mimics effects of acclimation to high CO_2-rapid down regulation of Rubisco small subunit transcripts but not of the large subunit transcripts. J Plant Physiol 143: 306-312

Vincentz M, Maireaux T, Leydecker M-T, Vaucheret H, Caboche M (1992) Regulation of nitrate and nitrite reductase expression in Nicotiana plumbaginifolia leaves by nitrogen and carbon metabolites. Plant J 3: 315-324

Von Schaewen A, Stitt M, Schmidt R, Sonnewald U, Willmitzer L (1990) Expression of yeast-derived invertase in the cell wall of tobacco and Arabidopsis leads to inhibition of sucrose export, accumulation of carbohydrate, and inhibition of photosynthesis, and strongly influences the growth and habits of transgenic tobacco. EMBO J 9: 3033-3044

Metabolic Regulation of Source-Sink Relations in Cereal Seedlings

Bruce R. Thomas, Masaaki Terashima, Shigeo Katoh, Tod Stoltz, and Raymond L. Rodriguez

Section of Molecular and Cellular Biology, University of California, Davis, CA 95616, USA (B.R.T.; T.S.; R.L.R.); and Department of Synthetic Chemistry and Biological Chemistry, Kyoto University, Kyoto, Japan (M.T.; S.K.)

Metabolic regulation controls expression of a number of genes at various stages of plant development. This provides a new perspective on cereal seedling development, which has previously been studied primarily in terms of phytohormone regulation. It is very likely that metabolite signals and phytohormone signals both participate in the regulation of source-sink relations in cereal seedlings.

METABOLIC REGULATION OF GENE EXPRESSION

Expression of many plant genes is regulated in response to various metabolites or inorganic nutrients (Table I) (Farrar, 1991; Sheen, 1994). This type of regulation has long been known in procaryotic and eucaryotic microorganisms (Saier, 1991; Sheen, 1994) and in animals (Vaulont and Kahn, 1994). In plants, when the sinks cannot absorb photosynthate as fast as it is produced, the accumulation of sugars in the source may cause feedback inhibition of photosynthesis-related gene expression and thereby regulate source strength (Sheen, 1994; Stitt *et al.*, 1995). Genes expressed in sink tissues are also regulated in response to sugar concentrations, so sucrose transport from source to sink may serve as a regulatory signal to control metabolism and growth in sink tissues (Farrar, 1991). Many genes of nitrogen metabolism are regulated by nitrogen compounds such as nitrate, ammonia, or amino acids. A secreted ribonuclease is induced during phosphate starvation (Glund and Goldstein, 1993). Thus, many genes are regulated by metabolites from the pathways in which the genes function.

Table I. Metabolite-Regulated Genes in Plants

Expression of these genes is regulated in response to the concentration of certain effectors, such as metabolites and inorganic nutrients. Separate classifications are reserved for genes regulated by metabolites such as phytohormones or stress metabolites. Compounds tested as effectors may require metabolism in order to be converted into the substances which are the direct effectors of gene expression. Until more is known about the precise mechanisms that regulate these genes, general terms like metabolite-regulated gene or sugar-regulated gene will be used.

Metabolite-repressed	Effector	Reference
Amy3D,Amy3E α-amylase	Suc, Glc, Fru maltose	(Huang *et al.*, 1993)
asparagine synthetase	Suc	(Lam *et al.*, 1994)
atp-δ thylakoid ATPase	Glc	(Krapp *et al.*, 1993)
chalcone synthase	phosphate	(Sadka *et al.*, 1994)
chlorophyll a/b-binding protein	Suc, Glc, acetate	(Sheen, 1994)
isocitrate lyase	Suc, Glc, Fru	(Graham *et al.*, 1994)
Ivr1 acid invertase	Glc	(Koch and Nolte, 1995)
lipoxygenase	phosphate	(Sadka *et al.*, 1994)
malate synthase	Suc, Glc, Fru	(Graham *et al.*, 1994)
malic enzyme, C4	Suc, Glc, acetate	(Sheen, 1994)
nitrate reductase	Glu, Gln	(Vincentz *et al.*, 1993)
patatin	phosphate	(Sadka *et al.*, 1994)
PEP carboxylase, C4	Suc, Glc, acetate	(Sheen, 1994)
phosphate translocator	Suc	(Knight and Gray, 1994)
proteinase inhibitor II	phosphate	(Sadka *et al.*, 1994)
pyruvate phosphodikinase, C4	Suc, Glc, Fru acetate, glycerol	(Sheen, 1994)
pyruvate phosphodikinase, cytosolic	Suc, Glc	(Sheen, 1994)
RNS1 ribonuclease	phosphate	(Bariola *et al.*, 1994)
RUBP carboxylase small subunit	Suc, Glc, acetate	(Sheen, 1994)
Sus2 Suc synthase	Suc	(Koch and Nolte, 1995)
vegetative storage protein	phosphate	(Sadka *et al.*, 1994)

cont...

Table I. (cont.)

Metabolite-induced	Effector	Reference
ADPG pyrophosphorylase	Suc	(Müller-Röber et al., 1990)
asparagine synthetase	Asn, Gln, Glu	(Lam et al., 1994)
β-amylase and sporamin	Suc	(Nakamura et al., 1991)
β-isopropylmalate dehydrogenase	Suc, Leu, Thr	(Jackson et al., 1993)
chalcone synthase	Suc, Glc, Fru	(Tsukaya et al., 1991)
	p-coumaric acid	(Loake et al., 1991)
chaperonin 60β	Suc	(Zabaleta et al., 1992)
cytosolic GPDH	Suc	(Yang et al., 1993)
glutamate synthase (Fd-GOGAT)	nitrate	(Redinbaugh and Campbell, 1993)
glutamine synthetase	nitrate, ammonia	(Kozaki et al., 1992)
Ivr2 acid invertase	Glc	(Koch and Nolte, 1995)
lipoxygenase	Suc	(Sadka et al., 1994)
	maltose	
Mn-superoxide dismutase	Suc	(Miao and Gaynor, 1993)
nitrate reductase	nitrate	(Redinbaugh and Campbell, 1993)
	Suc	(Cheng et al., 1992)
nitrate transporter	nitrate	(Tsay et al., 1993)
nitrite reductase	nitrate	(Rastogi et al., 1993)
patatin	Suc	(Rocha-Sosa et al., 1989)
		(Grierson et al., 1994)
PEP carboxylase	Gln	(Manh et al., 1993)
proteinase inhibitor II	Suc, Glc, Fru	(Johnson and Ryan, 1990)
rolC gene of Ri plasmid	Suc	(Yokoyama et al., 1994)
starch phosphorylase	Suc	(St-Pierre and Brisson, 1995)
starch synthase & branching enzyme	Suc, Glc, Fru	(Koßmann et al., 1991)
Sus1 Suc synthase	Suc, Glc, Fru	(Koch and Nolte, 1995)
UDPG pyrophosphorylase	Suc	(Spychalla et al., 1994)
vegetative storage protein	Suc, Glc, Fru	(Mason et al., 1992)

Metabolic regulation may also function to coordinate the regulation of diverse metabolic pathways (Table I). Amino acid effectors require both nitrogen and carbon metabolism for their biosynthesis. Some genes are regulated by more than one class of effectors, some of which are not metabolically related to the genes that they regulate. For example, a number of genes are regulated both by sugars and by amino acid effectors, while others are regulated by sugars and by phosphate.

SUGAR-REGULATED GENE EXPRESSION IN CEREAL SEEDLINGS

During cereal seedling development, α-amylase and other enzymes secreted from the aleurone and scutellum hydrolyze the starch and other materials stored in the endosperm. α-Amylase genes have been cloned and characterized in rice (Goldman *et al.*, 1994; Itoh *et al.*, 1995; Mitsunaga *et al.*, 1994; Sheu *et al.*, 1994; Tanida *et al.*, 1994), barley (Rogers *et al.*, 1994), maize (Young *et al.*, 1994) and wheat (Lenton *et al.*, 1994). During rice seedling development, the α-amylase gene *Amy3D* is expressed at low levels through day 2 in the scutellum. High levels of *Amy1A* and moderate levels of *Amy3B, Amy3C*, and *Amy3E* are expressed in aleurone from day 2 to day 6. The phytohormone GA_3 stimulates expression of certain α-amylase genes, such as *Amy1A,* and many other genes encoding hydrolytic enzymes. Thus, the GA_3 signal functions to stimulate source metabolism, increasing the mobilization of the nutrients stored in the endosperm (Thomas and Rodriguez, 1994).

In contrast to the GA_3-regulated α-amylase genes, expression of α-amylase in rice-cultured cells is GA_3-independent, occurring after the sugar has been depleted from the culture medium. α-Amylase gene expression is repressed by either sucrose, glucose, or fructose. Equimolar concentrations of mannitol do not repress α-amylase gene expression, indicating that the sugar-repression of gene expression is not a general osmotic response (Yu *et al.*, 1991). *Amy3D* and *Amy3E* are the predominant α-amylase genes expressed in cultured cells, and expression of both genes is repressed in the presence of sugar (Huang *et al.*, 1993; Thomas *et al.*, 1994; Thomas and Rodriguez, 1994).

Sugar-regulation of the *Amy3D*, sucrose synthase (*Sus*), and acid invertase (*Ivr*) genes also occurs in the developing seedling. *Amy3D* expression is sugar-repressed in isolated rice embryos cultured in a range of sugar concentrations. In the intact rice seed, with sugar supplied from starch breakdown in the endosperm, the *Amy3D* gene is repressed to a low level of expression (Karrer and Rodriguez, 1992). In rice, the *Sus1* gene is sugar-induced in germinating embryos (Karrer and Rodriguez, 1992). In maize seedling root tips, expression of the *Sus1* and *Ivr2* genes are sugar-induced, while the *Sus2* (=*Sh1*) and *Ivr1* genes have sugar-repressed expression (Chourey and Taliercio, 1994; Chourey *et al.*, 1995; Koch and Nolte, 1995).

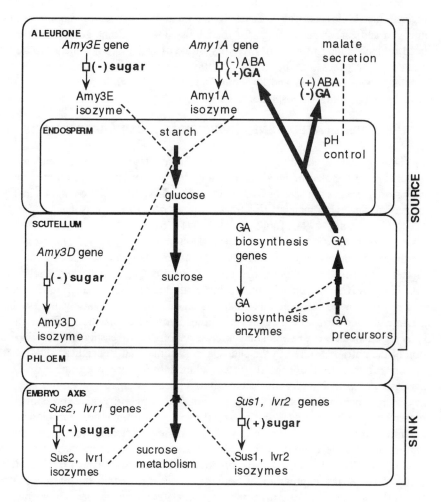

Figure 1. Sugar signals and GA_3 signals regulate gene expressoin in cereal seedlings.

CARBON METABOLITE SIGNAL HYPOTHESIS

The Carbon Metabolite Signal Hypothesis describes how sugar signals and sugar-regulated genes may participate in regulation of source-sink relations in cereal seedlings (Fig. 1) (Thomas and Rodriguez, 1994). Sugar-induced and sugar-repressed genes are expressed in a wide range of tissues (aleurone, scutellum, and root tip), each responding to the metabolite pool(s) at the site where each gene is expressed. Thus, there may be multiple metabolite signals regulating the expression of these genes within the developing cereal seedling. The sucrose synthase and invertase activities in the sink initiate the metabolism of the incoming sucrose and may be important for control of growth in the embryo axis. Transport of sugar to the sink may thus provide a signal that source metabolism is functioning and that sink metabolism in the quiescent embryo axis should begin. Rice seedlings of cv M202 germinate approximately 24 h after imbibition, while production of the GA_3-induced hydrolases does not begin until 48 h (Karrer et al., 1991). Thus, the role of GA_3 in the timing of the seedling germination event is open to question. The sugar-regulated genes that are expressed during the 0- to 48-h period may have a more significant role in the timing of this important developmental transition. Many of the genes listed in Table I have not yet been studied in the cereal seedling system, so many more metabolite-regulated genes acting during seedling development may be identified as this work proceeds.

Sugar-repression of the *Amy3D* and *Amy3E* genes may participate in regulating source strength in the seedling, just as described above for photosynthetic genes expressed in the leaf. Although α-amylase protein is highly abundant in cereal seedlings, with production peaking at 30% of the total protein synthesis (Khursheed and Rogers, 1988), three lines of evidence suggest that α-amylase may have a high flux-control coefficient for starch breakdown. First, in rice seedlings the abundant expression of α-amylase does not begin until day 2, so the small amount of α-amylase expression in the time period from imbibition until day 2 may be a rate-limiting factor. Second, starch breakdown intermediates are found at very low concentrations throughout seedling development (Murata et al., 1968), suggesting that the initial attack on the starch granule is the slowest step. This reaction is catalyzed primarily by α-amylase, possibly with some participation by α-glucosidase (Sun and Henson, 1990). The other enzymes of starch breakdown appear to be present in excess and convert their substrates to glucose without delay. Third, *in vitro* assays of total α-amylase activity may not accurately reflect the rate at which starch is broken down *in planta*. Changes in the endosperm pH of developing seedlings (Fig. 2) (Terashima et al., 1995) are regulated in response to phytohormones (Heimovaara-Dijkstra et al., 1994). These pH changes then affect the catalytic activity of the α-amylase isozymes. The Amy1A and Amy3D isozymes have distinct pH optima (Fig. 2) (Terashima et al., 1995), so the relative catalytic efficiencies of these two isozymes will change over time as the endosperm pH changes. Thus, *in vitro* assays of α-amylase activity must be conducted at the pH found in the endosperm in order to predict the rate of α-amylase function *in planta*. α-Amylase hydrolyzes the following series of distinct substrates: native starch granules, soluble starch polymers, and oligosaccharides. The Amy1A isozyme functions 3-fold more rapidly than the Amy3D isozyme for hydrolysis of native starch granules, whereas with starch oligosac

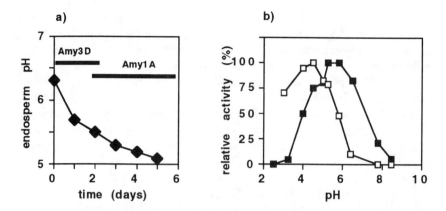

Figure 2. Endosperm pH vs pH optimum of α-amylase isozymes. a, The pH of rice seedling endosperm was measured in homogenates prepared after removal of the embryo (◆ pH). The bars indicate the time in seedling development when each isozyme is produced. b, α-Amylase isozymes were purified from transgenic yeast cell lines expressing rice a-amylase cDNA clones. Activity of rice a-amylase isozymes as a function of pH (□, Amy1A; ■, Amy3D).

charides as the substrate, Amy3D is 10-fold more reactive than the Amy1A isozyme (Terashima *et al.*, 1995). Thus, depending on the endosperm pH and the mixture of isozymes present at a given time in seedling development, even when total α-amylase activity is high, it is possible that not all of the α-amylase substrates are being hydrolyzed efficiently.

Considering the roles of sugar in gene regulation, plant nutrition, and water relations, if α-amylase controls sugar production and source strength, then a role for α-amylase in control of seedling growth is also plausible. α-Amylase activity is correlated with seedling vigor in several varieties of rice (Karrer *et al.*, 1993; Sasahara *et al.*, 1986; Williams and Peterson, 1973) and barley (Karrer *et al.*, 1991). α-Amylase activity is also inherited together with seedling vigor in rice (Lee *et al.*, 1986). Thirteen quantitative trait loci (QTL) for seedling vigor have been identified in rice. Two of these seedling vigor QTLs are linked to α-amylase gene loci on the molecular map of the rice genome (Redoña and Mackill, 1994) (D.J. Mackill, pers. commun.). Thus, some of the QTLs for seedling vigor in rice may represent genes of the α-amylase gene family or regulatory loci that control α-amylase gene expression.

In eucaryotic organisms, signal transduction pathways are frequently used to connect regulatory signals to the changes in gene expression and enzyme activity that result. Regulatory mechanisms are being defined for α-amylase (Allan and Trewavas, 1994; Goldman *et al.*, 1994; Lue and Lee, 1994; Sutliff *et al.*, 1993), a number of genes of photosynthesis (Jang and Sheen, 1994; Stitt *et al.*, 1995), sucrose synthase (Lugert and Werr, 1994) and β-amylase (Ishiguro and Nakamura, 1994). Changes in pH have been implicated as second messengers in some signal transduction pathways in plants (Guern *et al.*, 1992), including the induction of α-amylase by GA_3 in the cereal seed aleurone (Hamabata *et al.*, 1994). Crosstalk, regulatory interactions between signal transduction pathways, has been identified for regulation of sugar metabolism in humans (Caro *et al.*, 1994). Crosstalk between sugar regulation and GA_3 regulation may provide some of the regulatory complexity needed to control source-sink relations in cereal seedlings.

ACKNOWLEDGMENTS

We thank Prem Chourey, Wolf Frommer, Karen Koch, and Mark Stitt for stimulating discussions, critical review of the manuscript, and sharing of manuscripts prior to publication.

LITERATURE CITED

Allan AC, Trewavas AJ (1994) Abscisic acid and gibberellin perception: inside or out? Plant Physiol **104**: 1107-1108

Bariola P, Howard CJ, Taylor CB, Verburg MY, Jagian VD, Green PJ (1994) The *Arabidopsis* ribonuclease gene *RNS1* is tightly controlled in response to phosphate limitation. Plant J **6**: 673-685

Caro JF, Raju MS, Caro M, Lynch CJ, Poulos J, Exton JH, Thakkar JK (1994) Guanine nucleotide binding regulatory proteins in liver from obese humans with and without type II diabetes: evidence for altered "crosstalk" between the insulin receptor and GI-proteins. J Cell Biochem **54**: 309-319

Cheng C-L, Acedo GN, Christinsin M, Conkling MA (1992) Sucrose mimics the light induction of *Arabidopsis* nitrate reductase gene transcription. Proc Natl Acad Sci USA **89**: 1861-1864

Chourey PS, Cheng W-H, Taliercio EW, Im KH (1995) Genetic aspects of sucrose-metabolizing enzymes in developing maize seed. *In* MA Madore, WJ Lucas, eds, Carbon Partitioning and Source/Sink Interactions in Plants. American Society of Plant Physiologists, Rockville, MD, this volume

Chourey PS, Taliercio EW (1994) Epistatic interaction and functional compensation between the two tissue- and cell-specific sucrose synthase genes in maize. Proc Natl Acad Sci USA **91**: 7917-7921

Farrar JF (1991) Starch turnover: its role in source-sink relations and a comparison with the role of sucrose. *In* JL Bonnemain, S Delrot, WJ Lucas, J Dainty, eds, Recent Advances in Phloem Transport and Assimilate Compartmentation. Presses Academiques, Nantes, pp 213-223

Glund K, Goldstein AH (1993) Regulation, synthesis and excretion of a phosphate starvation inducible RNase by plant cells. *In* DPS Verma, ed, Control of Plant Gene Expression. CRC Press, Boca Raton, FL, pp 311-323

Goldman S, Mawal Y, Tanida I, Wu R (1994) Studies of a gibberellin-dependent DNA-binding protein related to the expression of a rice α-amylase gene. Plant Sci **99**: 75-88

Graham IA, Denby KJ, Leaver CJ (1994) Carbon catabolite repression regulates glyoxylate cycle gene expression in cucumber. Plant Cell **6**: 761-772

Grierson C, Du J-S, Zabala MT, Beggs K, Smith C, Holdsworth M, Bevan M (1994) Separate *cis* sequences and *trans* factors direct metabolic and developmental regulation of a potato tuber storage protein gene. Plant J **5**: 815-826

Guern J, Mathieu Y, Thomine S, Jouanneau J-P, Beloeil J-C (1992) Plant cells counteract cytoplasmic pH changes but likely use these pH changes as secondary messages in signal perception. Curr Topics Plant Biochem Physiol **11**: 249-269

Hamabata A, Rodriguez E, Garcia-Maya M, Bernal-Lugo I (1994) Effect of pH on the GA_3 induced α-amylase synthesis. J Plant Physiol **143**: 349-352

Heimovaara-Dijkstra S, Heistek JC, Wang M (1994) Counteractive effects of ABA and GA_3 on extracellular and intracellular pH and malate in barley aleurone. Plant Physiol **106**: 359-365

Huang N, Chandler J, Thomas BR, Rodriguez RL (1993) Metabolic regulation of α-amylase gene expression in rice cell cultures. Plant Mol Biol **23**: 737-747

Ishiguro S, Nakamura K (1994) Characterization of a cDNA encoding a novel DNA binding protein, SPF1, that recognizes SP8 sequences in the 5′ upstream regions of genes coding for sporamin and beta-amylase from sweet potato. Mol Gen Genet **244**: 563-571

Itoh K, Yamaguchi J, Huang N, Rodriguez RL, Akazawa T, Shimamoto K (1995) Developmental and hormonal regulation of rice α-amylase *(RAmy1A)-gusA* fusion genes in transgenic rice seeds. Plant Physiol **107**: 25-31

Jackson SD, Sonnewald U, Willmitzer L (1993) Cloning and expression analysis of β-isopropylmalate dehydrogenase from potato. Mol Gen Genet **236**: 309-314

Jang J-C, Sheen J (1994) Sugar sensing in higher plants. Plant Cell **6**: 1665-1679

Johnson R, Ryan CA (1990) Wound-inducible potato inhibitor II genes: enhancement of expression by sucrose. Plant Mol Biol **14**: 527-536

Karrer EE, Chandler JM, Foolad MR, Rodriguez RL (1993) Correlation between α-amylase gene expression and seedling vigor in rice. Euphytica **66**: 163-169

Karrer EE, Litts JC, Rodriguez RL (1991) Differential expression of α-amylase genes in germinating rice and barley seeds. Plant Mol Biol **16**: 797-805

Karrer EE, Rodriguez RL (1992) Metabolic regulation of rice α-amylase and sucrose synthase genes *in planta*. Plant J **2**: 517-523

Khursheed B, Rogers JC (1988) Barley α-amylase genes. Quantitative comparison of steady-state mRNA levels from individual members of the two different families expressed in aleurone cells. J Biol Chem **263**: 18953-18960

Knight JS, Gray JC (1994) Expression of genes encoding the tobacco chloroplast phosphate translocator is not light-regulated and is repressed by sucrose. Mol Gen Genet **242**: 586-594

Koßmann J, Visser RGF, Müller-Röber B, Willmitzer L, Sonnewald U (1991) Cloning and expression analysis of a potato cDNA that encodes branching enzyme: evidence for co-expression of starch biosynthetic genes. Mol Gen Genet **230**: 39-44

Koch K, Nolte KD (1995) Sugar modulated expression of genes for sucrose metabolism and their relationship to transport pathways. In MA Madore, WJ Lucas, eds, Carbon Partitioning and Source/Sink Interactions in Plants. American Society of Plant Physiologists, Rockville, MD, this volume

Kozaki A, Sakamoto A, Takeba G (1992) The promoter of the gene for plastidic glutamine synthetase (GS2) from rice is developmentally regulated and exhibits substrate-induced expression in transgenic tobacco plants. Plant Cell Physiol **33**: 233-238

Krapp A, Hofmann B, Schäfer C, Stitt M (1993) Regulation of the expression of rbcS and other photosynthetic genes by carbohydrates: a mechanism for the 'sink regulation' of photosynthesis. Plant J **3**: 817-828

Lam H-M, Peng SS-Y, Coruzzi GM (1994) Metabolic regulation of the gene encoding glutamine-dependent asparagine synthetase in *Arabidopsis thaliana*. Plant Physiol **106**: 1347-1357

Lee CC, Li CC, Sung FJM (1986) Physiological and genetic studies on seedling vigor in rice (*Oryza sativa* L.) II. Inheritances of alpha-amylase activity and seedling vigor in rice. J Agric Assoc China **135**: 17-24

Lenton JR, Appleford NEJ, Croker SJ (1994) Gibberellins and α-amylase gene expression in germinating wheat grains. Plant Growth Reg **15**: 261-270

Loake GJ, Choudhary AD, Harrison MJ, Mavandad M, Lamb CJ, Dixon RA (1991) Phenylpropanoid pathway intermediates regulate transient expression of a chalcone synthase gene promoter. Plant Cell **3**: 829-840

Lue M-Y, Lee H-T (1994) Protein phosphatase inhibitors enhance the expression of an α-amylase gene, aAmy3, in cultured rice cells. Biochem Biophys Res Commun **205**: 807-816

Lugert T, Werr W (1994) A novel DNA-binding domain in the *Shrunken* initiator-binding protein (IBP1). Plant Mol Biol **25**: 493-506

Manh CT, Bismuth E, Boutin J-P, Provot M, Champigny M-L (1993) Metabolite effectors for short-term nitrogen-dependent enhancement of phosphoenolpyruvate carboxylase activity and decrease of net sucrose synthesis in wheat leaves. Physiol Plant **89**: 460-466

Mason HS, DeWald DB, Creelman RA, Mullet JA (1992) Coregulation of soybean vegetative storage protein gene expression by methyl jasmonate and soluble sugars. Plant Physiol **98**: 859-867

Miao Z, Gaynor JJ (1993) Molecular cloning, characterization and expression of Mn-superoxide dismutase from the rubber tree (*Hevea brasiliensis*). Plant Mol Biol **23**: 267-277

Mitsunaga S, Rodriguez RL, Yamaguchi J (1994) Sequence-specific interactions of a nuclear protein factor with the promoter region of a rice gene for alpha-amylase, *RAmy3D*. Nucl Acids Res **22**: 1948-1953

Müller-Röber BT, Koßmann J, Hannah LC, Willmitzer L, Sonnewald U (1990) One of two different ADP-glucose pyrophosphorylase genes from potato responds strongly to elevated levels of sucrose. Mol Gen Genet **224**: 136-146

Murata T, Akazawa T, Fukuchi S (1968) Enzymic mechanism of starch breakdown in germinating rice seeds. I. An analytical study. Plant Physiol **43**: 1899-1905

Nakamura K, Ohto M, Yoshida N, Nakamura K (1991) Sucrose-induced accumulation of β-amylase occurs concomitant with the accumulation of starch and sporamin in leaf-petiole cuttings of sweet potato. Plant Physiol **96**: 902-909

Rastogi R, Back E, Schneiderbauer A, Bowsher CG, Moffatt B, Rothstein SJ (1993) A 330 bp region of the spinach nitrite reductase gene promoter directs nitrate-inducible tissue-specific expression in transgenic tobacco. Plant J **4**: 317-326

Redinbaugh MG, Campbell WH (1993) Glutamine synthetase and ferredoxin-dependent glutamate synthase expression in the maize (*Zea mays*) root primary response to nitrate. Plant Physiol **101**: 1249-1255

Redoña ED, Mackill DJ (1994) Mapping quantitative trait loci for seedling vigor-related traits in rice. Agron Abstr, pp. 211

Rocha-Sosa M, Sonnewald U, Frommer W, Stratmann M, Schell J, Willmitzer L (1989) Both developmental and metabolic signals activate the promoter of a class I patatin gene. EMBO J **8**: 23-29

Rogers JC, Lanahan MB, Rogers SW (1994) The *cis*-acting gibberellin response complex in high-pI α-amylase gene promoters. Requirement of a coupling element for high-level transcription. Plant Physiol **105**: 151-158

Sadka A, Dewald DB, May GD, Park WD, Mullet JE (1994) Phosphate modulates transcription of soybean *VspB* and other sugar-inducible genes. Plant Cell **6**: 737-749

Saier MH (1991) A multiplicity of potential carbon catabolite repression mechanisms in prokaryotic and eukaryotic microorganisms. New Biol **3**: 1137-1147

Sasahara T, Ikarashi H, Tsuroka M (1986) Genetic variations in embryo and endosperm weights, seedling growth parameters and α-amylase activity of the germinated grains in rice (*O. sativa* L.). Japan J Breed **36**: 248-261

Sheen J (1994) Feedback control of gene expression. Photosyn Res **39**: 427-438

Sheu J-J, Jan S-P, Lee H-T, Yu S-M (1994) Control of transcription and mRNA turnover as mechanisms of metabolic repression of α-amylase gene expression. Plant J **5**: 655-664

Spychalla JP, Scheffler BE, Sowokinos JR, Bevan MW (1994) Cloning, antisense RNA inhibition, and the coordinated expression of UDP-glucose pyrophosphorylase with starch biosynthetic genes in potato tubers. J Plant Physiol **144**: 444-453

St-Pierre B, Brisson N (1995) Induction of the plastidic starch-phosphorylase gene in potato storage sink tissue - effect of sucrose and evidence for coordinated regulation of phosphorylase and starch biosynthetic genes. Planta **195**: 339-344

Stitt M, Krapp A, Klein D, Roper-Schwarz U, Paul M (1995) Do carbohydrates regulate photosynthesis and allocation by altering gene expression? *In* MA Madore, WJ Lucas, eds, Carbon Partitioning and Source/Sink Interactions in Plants. American Society of Plant Physiologists, Rockville, MD, this volume

Sun Z, Henson CA (1990) Degradation of native starch granules by barley α-glucosidases. Plant Physiol **94**: 320-327

Sutliff TD, Lanahan MB, Ho T-HD (1993) Gibberellin treatment stimulates nuclear factor binding to the gibberellin response complex in a barley α-amylase promoter. Plant Cell **5**: 1681-1692

Tanida I, Kim JK, Wu R (1994) Functional dissection of a rice high-pI alpha-amylase gene promoter. Mol Gen Genet **244**: 127-134

Terashima M, Katoh S, Thomas BR, Rodriguez RL (1995) Characterization of rice α-amylase isozymes expressed by *Saccharomyces cerevisiae*. Appl Microbiol Biotechnol (in press)

Thomas BR, Chandler J, Simmons CR, Huang N, Karrer E, Rodriguez RL (1994) Gene regulation and protein secretion from plant cell cultures: the rice α-amylase system. *In* DDY Ryu, S Furusaki, eds, Advances in Plant Biotechnology. Elsevier, Amsterdam, pp 37-55

Thomas BR, Rodriguez RL (1994) Metabolite signals regulate gene expression and source/sink relations in cereal seedlings. Plant Physiol **106**: 1235-1239

Tsay Y-F, Schroeder JI, Feldmann KA, Crawford NM (1993) The herbicide sensitivity gene *CHL1* of Arabidopsis encodes a nitrate-inducible nitrate transporter. Cell **72**: 705-713

Tsukaya H, Oshima T, Naito S, Chino M, Komeda Y (1991) Sugar-dependent expression of the *CHS-A* gene for chalcone synthase from petunia in transgenic *Arabidopsis*. Plant Physiol **97**: 1414-1421

Vaulont S, Kahn A (1994) Transcriptional control of metabolic regulation genes by carbohydrates. FASEB J **8**: 28-35

Vincentz M, Moureaux T, Leydecker M-T, Vaucheret H, Caboche M (1993) Regulation of nitrate and nitrite reductase expression in *Nicotiana plumbaginifolia* leaves by nitrogen and carbon metabolites. Plant J **3**: 315-324

Williams JF, Peterson ML (1973) Relations between alpha-amylase activity and growth of rice seedlings. Crop Sci **13**: 612-615

Yang Y, Kwon H-B, Peng H-P, Shih M-C (1993) Stress responses and metabolic regulation of glyceraldehyde-3-phosphate dehydrogenase genes in *Arabidopsis*. Plant Physiol **101**: 209-216

Yokoyama R, Hirose T, Fujii N, Aspuria ET, Kato A, Uchimiya H (1994) The *rolC* promoter of *Agrobacterium rhizogenes* Ri plasmid is activated by sucrose in transgenic tobacco plants. Mol Gen Genet **244**: 15-22

Young TE, DeMason DA, Close TJ (1994) Cloning of an α-amylase cDNA from aleurone tissue of germinating maize seed. Plant Physiol **105**: 759-760

Yu S-M, Kuo Y-H, Sheu G, Sheu Y-J, Liu L-F (1991) Metabolic derepression of α-amylase gene expression in suspension cultured cells of rice. J Biol Chem **266**: 21131-21137

Zabaleta E, Oropeza A, Jiménez B, Salerno G, Crespi M, Herrera-Estrella L (1992) Isolation and characterization of genes encoding chaperonin 60β from *Arabidopsis thaliana*. Gene **111**: 175-181

Carbon Partitioning and Source-Sink Interactions in Plants, *Monica A. Madore* and *William J. Lucas*, eds, Copyright 1995, published by The American Society of Plant Physiologists

Studies on the Starch Biosynthetic Enzymes for Manipulation of Starch Content and Quality

Jack Preiss, Miguel A. Ballicora, Mary J. Laughlin, Ying-bin Fu, Thomas W. Okita, Gerard F. Barry, Hanping Guan, and Mirta N. Sivak

Department of Biochemistry, Michigan State University, East Lansing, MI 48824 (J.P.; M.A.B.; Y-b.F.; H.G.; M.N.S.); Institute of Biological Chemistry, Washington State University, Pullman, WA 99164 (M.J.L.; T.W.O.); Plant Science Technology, The Agricultural Group, The Monsanto Company, St. Louis, MO 63198 (G.F.B.)

Present address: ExSeed Genetics LLC, 1568 Food Science Building, Iowa State University, Ames, IA 50011, USA (H.G.)

The key enzymes of starch biosynthesis are: (*i*) ADP-glucose pyrophosphorylase [(ADP-Glc PPase); EC 2.7.7.27], which catalyzes synthesis of ADP-Glc, the glucosyl donor for (*ii*), starch synthase (EC 2.4.1.21), which transfers the glucosyl unit of ADP-Glc to the nonreducing end of an α-1,4-glucan primer, and (*iii*), the branching enzyme (EC 2.4.1.18), which forms the α-1,6-linkage found in amylopectin [for reviews, see Preiss (1991), Sivak and Preiss (1995), and Preiss and Sivak (1995)].

1) $\text{ATP} + \text{Glc-1-P} <========> \text{ADP-Glc} + \text{PPi}$
2) $\text{ADP-Glc} + (\text{glucosyl})_n --------> \text{ADP} + (\text{glucosyl})_{n+1}$
3) Linear glucosyl chain of α-glucan ------> Branched chain of α-glucan with α-1->6 linkage branch point

Data obtained from a number of biochemical and genetic studies support the view that the ADP-Glc pathway, comprising the three reactions indicated above, is the dominant, or only route, leading to starch synthesis. Studies show that isolated mutants of maize endosperm (Tsai and Nelson, 1966; Dickinson and Preiss, 1969) deficient in ADP-Glc PPase activity are also deficient in starch. A pea line having recessive *rb* genes contained 3 to 5% of the ADP-Glc PPase activity and only 38 to 72% of the starch found in the pea line having the normal gene (Smith *et al.*, 1989). Müller-Röber *et al.* (1992) expressed in potato tuber a chimeric gene encoding antisense RNA for the ADP-Glc PPase that caused a reduction in enzymatic activity to 2 to 5% of the wild-type levels. This resulted in a reduction of starch content and confirmed the above results obtained with ADP-Glc PPase-deficient mutants. Another significant demonstration of the role of ADP-Glc PPase in starch synthesis was provided by Stark *et al.* (1992). Starch content of potato tubers was increased 30 to 60% by increasing ADP-Glc PPase activity. This was achieved by transformation of the potato plant with a mutant *Escherichia coli* ADP-Glc PPase gene insensitive to the allosteric regulators affecting the plant enzyme. Other data demonstrating a direct relationship between activity of the ADP-Glc PPase and starch accumulation in several plant species have been cited in previous reviews (Preiss and Levi, 1980; Preiss, 1988, 1991; Okita, 1992; Sivak and Preiss, 1995) and support the hypothesis that the ADP-Glc PPase is the major regulatory step in starch synthesis.

These results indicate that the bacterial enzyme can be expressed in plant tissues and stimulate starch production, and also strongly suggest that the ADP-Glc PPase is a rate-limiting enzyme for starch synthesis even in nonphotosynthetic plant tissues. The data obtained by the Monsanto group also demonstrate that transfection of a plant with a bacterial ADP-Glc PPase increases the level of starch in an important crop product.

It is conceivable, therefore, that similar methods can be used to change, in addition to quantity, starch quality via expression/transformation of the isoforms of starch synthase and branching enzymes (BE) in plants. These "new starches" may have more wide-spread utilization in food and industrial processes. The production of modified "specialty" starches via molecular biology techniques is promising, and perhaps more beneficial and more economical than the chemical production of modified starch.

Since there has been an increased demand for starch in the past decade (Katz, 1991) for both specialized industrial and food uses, the simple study of basic questions on the structure-function relationships of the allosteric regulation of an enzyme involved in sugar nucleotide synthesis now appears to possibly have great impact on both agriculture and industry. Moreover, a detailed study of the starch branching enzymes and starch synthases is warranted in their detailed and specific roles in synthesizing starch. The starch structure from various plants are different and these variances must be attributed, in great part, to the specific properties of the starch biosynthetic enzymes of the plant. In this report, we describe some of our current studies which strongly suggest different roles for the two heterologous subunits of the plant ADP-Glc PPase and describe possible roles of the maize endosperm-branching enzyme and starch synthase isozymes.

RESULTS

A Study of the Potato Tuber ADP-Glc Pyrophosphorylase Expressed in *E. coli*

Two cDNAs encoding the mature large subunit and small subunits of the potato tuber (*Solanum tuberosum* L.) ADP-Glc pyrophosphorylase (ADP-Glc PPase) have been expressed in *E. coli* (Iglesias *et al.*, 1993). Although the properties of the recombinant enzyme were very similar to the native potato tuber enzyme, there were some notable differences in properties. The transgenic enzyme was heat labile, in contrast to the tuber enzyme which was stable to temperatures of 65°C. Moreover, the transgenic enzyme was less sensitive than the tuber enzyme to inhibition by the allosteric effector, Pi. Some explanations of these differences were presented (Iglesias *et al.*, 1993), and one suggestion was that the small subunit cDNA was truncated in such a way that 10 amino acids at the N-terminus were missing. In comparing the deduced N-terminus amino acid sequence of the potato tuber enzyme (Table I) with the spinach leaf N-terminus obtained via protein sequencing (Morell *et al.*, 1987), there is almost complete identity of the sequences. Since the N-terminal sequence of the mature spinach leaf subunit is known and is almost completely identical to the potato tuber small subunit N-terminus, it was thought that the possible differences in the allosteric kinetics and heat stability between the transgenic and native potato tuber enzymes may be due to the small subunit, used by Iglesias *et al.* (1993), having been designed with a shortened N-terminal. In other words, the native potato tuber enzyme small subunit's N-terminal sequence may be very similar to the spinach leaf ADP-Glc PPase small subunit.

Table I. *N-terminal Amino Acid Sequences of the Small Subunit ADP-Glc PPases of Potato Tuber and Spinach Leaf*

66 indicates the residue number of Met in the small subunit sequence shown by Nakata *et al.* (1991). The references provide the descriptions of the plasmids and the methods of sequencing. The pMLaugh10 plasmid is described in the text, and the double underline indicates the identities between the potato tuber and spinach leaf subunit sequences and the 10 amino acids added to pMLaugh10.

Source of Small Subunit	Amino Acid Sequence	cDNA Clone	Reference
Potato tuber	66MIVSPKAVSDSQNSQTCLDPDA...	-------	Nakata *et al.* (1991)
Potato tuber	MALDPDA...	pMON17335	Iglesias *et al.* (1993)
Potato tuber	MAVSDSQNSQTCLDPDA...	pMLaugh10	This study
Spinach leaf	VSDSQNSQTCLDPEA...	-------	Morell *et al.* (1987)

93

Thus, a new plasmid, pMLaugh10, was constructed containing a cDNA encoding the 10 extra amino acids at the N-terminal, as shown in Table I, taking into account what is known about the spinach leaf N-terminal. The new plasmid was a derivative from pMON17335, where a Met residue was engineered at position 71 [sequence position as indicated by Nakata *et al.* (1991)] introducing a NcoI restriction site. The PCR-amplified, full-length NcoI/KpnI fragment of the small subunit was then ligated to pMON17335 cut with NcoI and KpnI.

Table II shows the expression of the recombinant enzyme in *E. coli* when the cDNA of the large subunit pMON17336 was expressed together with either pMON17335 or with pMLaugh10, the plasmids containing the cDNAs encoding the small subunit. In both cases, high ADP-Glc PPase activity was expressed.

When pMON17336 was expressed alone, very little activity was expressed. Thus, both the small and large subunits must be expressed together to obtain optimal activity. Of interest, is that the small subunit encoded in pMlaugh10 (small subunit increased at the N-terminus by 10 amino acids), when expressed alone, had significant ADP-Glc PPase activity. This activity accounted for approximately 10% of that observed when the large and small subunit were expressed together. The activity seen with the small subunit expressed alone is significant and will be discussed later.

The properties of the recombinant potato tuber enzyme in *E. coli*, with the large subunit and small subunit having the 10 extra amino acids at the N-terminal, does have regulatory properties more similar to the native potato tuber

---

Table II. *Expression of the Potato Tuber ADP-Glc PPase Subunits in E. coli*

ADP-Glc deficient mutant, AC70R1. The plasmids containing the cDNAs encoding the small and large subunits and the procedures used for expression have been described (Iglesias *et al.*, 1993). The plasmid pMLaugh10, encoding the ADP-Glc PPase small subunit extended by added 10 amino acids at the N-terminal is described in the text.

Plasmids Expressed	Subunits	Enzyme Activity
		$\mu mol \cdot min^{-1} \cdot mg^{-1}$
None	None	<0.0003
pMON17335 + pMON17336	Small + Large	0.86
pMLaugh10 + pMON17336	Small + Large	1.8
pMON17335	Small	0.10
pMLaugh10	Small	0.17
pMON17336	Large	0.002

enzyme and is also stable to heat treatment at temperatures of 65 °C (Table III). The recombinant enzyme has an $A_{0.5}$ for the activator, 3-phosphoglycerate (3PGA), more similar to that of the native potato enzyme than what was observed for the expressed enzyme having the shorter small subunit. In addition, the expressed enzyme with the small subunit extended by 10 amino acids is as sensitive as the native potato enzyme to Pi inhibition. These results suggest that the N-terminal of the small subunit is important in maintaining the protein structure with respect to the enzyme's heat stability and its allosteric properties. It also suggests that the mature, small subunit of the potato tuber enzyme is closer in size to the subunit having the 10 extra amino acids at the N-terminal. This suggestion is also supported by the very close identity of the N-terminal sequences of the mature spinach leaf ADP-Glc PPase with the potato tuber small subunit expressed by pMLaugh10.

Of significance is the substantial activity when pMLaugh10 was expressed alone (Table II). The activity of this enzyme has been purified to about 50% purity with a specific activity of 22 μmol·min^{-1}·mg^{-1} in the presence of 4 mM 3PGA. The recombinant enzyme 70% purified, having both the large and small subunits, has a specific activity of 52 μmol·min^{-1}·mg^{-1} in the presence

---

Table III. *Comparison of the Properties of the Transgenic ADP-Glc PPases with the Native Potato Tuber Enzyme*

The ADP-Glc synthesis assay has been described by Iglesias *et al.* (1993). The kinetic constants of the recombinant enzyme purified from *E. coli* were repeated and agreed with the data of Iglesias *et al.* (1993), and the data for the native potato tuber enzyme is from Sowokinos and Preiss (1982). $A_{0.5}$ and $I_{0.5}$ are concentrations of activator needed for 50% of maximal activation and concentrations of inhibitor giving 50% inhibition, respectively.

Enzyme from:	$A_{0.5}$	$I_{0.5}$ at:		Heat stability at:	
		0.25 mM 3PGA	3.0mM 3PGA	60 °C	65 °C
	mM	*mM*		%	
pMON17335 + pMON17336 (large and small subunits)	0.057	0.68	----	24	1.4
pMLaugh10 + pMON17336 (large and small subunits)	0.16	0.07	0.63	89	83
Potato tuber	0.40	0.12	0.33	90	95
pMLaugh10	2.4	----	0.08	100	102

of 3 mM 3PGA. As shown in Table III, the small subunit activity has a lower apparent affinity ($A_{0.5}$ = 2.4 mM) for the activator, 3PGA, than the enzyme having both the large and small subunits. The enzyme with only the small subunit is also more sensitive to Pi inhibition ($I_{0.5}$ of 0.08 mM in the presence of 3 mM 3PGA) as compared to the heteromeric enzyme ($I_{0.5}$ value of O.63 mM). The K_m values for the substrates and Mg^{+2} are essentially the same whether the enzyme is composed of only one subunit, the small subunit, or two subunits, the small and large (Ballicora et al., 1995). In both cases, the native enzyme is a tetramer, a homotetramer in the case of the small subunit, and a heterotetramer in the case of the large and small subunits (Ballicora et al., 1995).

On the basis of these data, we suggest that the small subunit is primarily involved in catalysis. It appears to have substantial activity in the absence of the large subunit if the concentration of 3PGA, the activator, is high. On the other hand, the large subunit, when expressed alone, has very little activity, but when expressed with the small subunit, the resulting enzyme has similar regulatory kinetic constants as seen for the native potato enzyme. This suggests that the prime function of the large subunit is to modify the action, i.e. regulate the small subunit. It increases the apparent affinity for the activator and can decrease the inhibition due to Pi. These results are consistent with the report of Li and Preiss (1992) which showed that an *Arabidopsis* mutant ADP-Glc PPase lacking the large subunit still had activity, except it had lower affinity for the activator, 3PGA, and higher affinity for Pi than the wild-type heterotetrameric enzyme.

As indicated by Smith-White and Preiss (1992), the small subunit of the higher plant ADP-Glc PPases is highly conserved (85-95% identity), while the large subunit is less conserved (50-60% identity). It is quite possible that the differences seen in the large subunit confer differences in modulating sensitivity of the small subunit to allosteric activation and inhibition. Expression of various large subunits could differ during development or in their occurrences in different plants and tissues (e.g. leaf, stem, guard cells, tuber, endosperm, root, embryo) and provide ADP-Glc PPases with differing sensitivities to regulation. The availability of the current system of small and large subunits and their expression in *E. coli* will enable us to study the various amino acid residues and domains involved in catalysis and regulation both at the biochemical and molecular biological level.

In Vivo Function of the Maize Endosperm Branching Isoenzymes and a Hypothesis of the Specific Roles of the Starch Synthase and Branching Isozymes in Synthesizing Amylopectin

The structure of amylopectin, as postulated by Hizukuri (1986), is generally accepted and is known as the cluster model due to the clustering of the α-1,6 linkage branch points in certain regions of the amylopectin. However, the question that remains to be answered is, "What are the specific roles of the starch synthase (SS) and branching enzyme (BE) isozymes in forming the starch and amylopectin structures?" Many details are still missing from the general picture that it is not possible to give a precise description of how the synthesis of the starch granule starts, how amylopectin and amylose are made, or why starch granules from different species differ in their size, number per cell, and composition. Some progress has been made with the maize endosperm BEI and BEII isozymes with respect to their mode of chain transfer, their substrate specificity and possible roles in the synthesis of amylopectin (Guan and Preiss, 1993; Takeda *et al.*, 1993; Guan *et al.*, 1995). BEI can transfer long branch chains (DP 40 to >100), while BEII transfers shorter branch chains (DP 6 to 14). Moreover, the preferred substrate for BEI is amylose, while the preferred substrate for BEII is amylopectin. It was postulated that BEI was more involved in synthesis of the interior B chains, while BEII was involved in the synthesis exterior A and shorter B chains. The activities of BEI and BEII have also been shown to differ *in vivo* (Guan *et al.*, 1995). In this study, the maize endosperm cDNAs encoding BEI and BEII were expressed in an *E. coli* mutant deficient in BE activity, and the glucans formed were analyzed. The results indicated that *in vivo*, BE I transferred longer chains than BEII, while BEII preferably transferred shorter chains.

In order to understand the various functions of the different starch synthases, Ball and associates isolated various mutants of *Chlamydomonas* deficient in starch synthase activities. They were successful in isolating a soluble starch synthase II (SSSII)-deficient mutant (Fontaine *et al.*, 1993) and double mutants deficient both in granule starch-bound starch synthase (GBSS) and in SSS II (Maddelein *et al.*, 1994). These studies have provided good information on the possible function of both these enzymes and their involvement in amylopectin biosynthesis. The SSSII mutant contained only 20 to 40% of the starch seen in the wild-type alga, and the amylose portion of the total starch increased from 25 to 55%. This mutant also contained a modified amylopectin which had an increased amount of very short chains (2 to 7 DP) and a concomitant decrease of intermediate size chains (8 to 60 DP). This suggested that the SSSII was involved in the synthesis or maintenance of the intermediate size chains (mainly B chains) in amylopectin. The higher amylose content could be explained if amylose were a precursor for amylopectin synthesis and, in the SSSII mutant, could not be effectively utilized.

The double mutants defective in SSSII and a GBSS ((Maddelein *et al.*, 1994) had an even lower starch content, 2 to 16%, of the wild-type and the amount of starch present was inversely correlated with the severity of the GBSS defect of the double mutant. The authors suggest that the GBSS is required to form the basic structure of the amylopectin, and these effects of the GBSS absence are exacerbated due to the diminished SSSII activity.

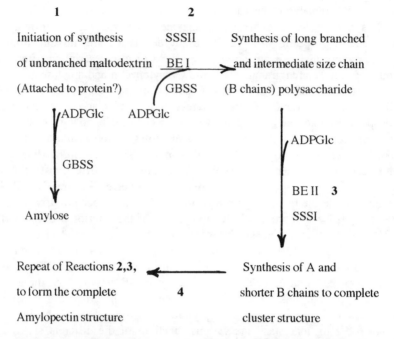

Figure 1. A proposed scheme for synthesis of amylose and amylopectin. Initiation may involve synthesis of a maltodextrin attached covalently to a protein. This putative protein-α-glucan then can accept glucose from ADP-Glc either via GBSS catalysis to form an amylose structure or in combination with BEI, SSSII, and possibly GBSS to form a polysaccharide having the internal structure of the final amylopectin product. BEII and SSSI carry out the reactions to form the exterior of the amylopectin structure. The enlargement of the amylopectin could proceed further by continuing participation of BEI, SSSII, and possibly GBSS.

These studies of the *Chlamydomonas* mutants, by Steven Ball and his colleagues, have been quite informative in that they provide good evidence for involvement of the GBSS in amylopectin synthesis and not just in amylose synthesis and suggest that an important function for SSSII would be in its involvement in synthesis of the intermediate size (B?) branches in amylopectin.

A tentative scheme of how amylose and amylopectin are synthesized is proposed in Figure 1, based on the information discussed above.

It is quite possible that initiation of α-1,4-glucan synthesis occurs via synthesis on an acceptor protein. It still remains to be determined whether only UDP-Glc or both UDP-Glc and ADP-Glc are the glucosyl donors in this process, which is the least known of all the reactions of starch synthesis. After formation of the unbranched maltodextrin of undetermined size, whether it is attached to a protein or not, there would be paths leading toward amylose or to amylopectin synthesis. The GBSS may be involved in both directions; in the synthesis of amylose, only GBSS would be involved, and at its site of synthesis, there would be restricted branching enzyme activity with the resultant amylose being minimally branched. It is possible that most of the amylose is produced in the internal part of the granule where branching enzyme may be present only to a small extent.

The higher rate of polysaccharide formation would occur at the surface of the developing granule, where SSSII and branching enzyme I are now interacting with the maltodextrin/amylose product synthesized via the GBSS reaction, to form a branched long chain polysaccharide also containing intermediate size chains. This hypothesis is based on the studies of the polysaccharides synthesized by the *Chlamydomonas* SSSII and GBSS mutants as well as the *ae* mutants of rice and maize (Boyer and Preiss, 1981; Mizuno *et al.*, 1993). Finally, SSSI and BEII become involved in the synthesis of the A-chains and exterior B-chains to produce the final amylopectin product. It should be noted that these reactions may not occur in perfect sequential order, but the present evidence (of the intermediate products formed by the various starch synthase and BE mutants of *Chlamydomonas* and of the higher plants) does suggest this is the sequence leading toward amylopectin biosynthesis. Although further experiments are certainly required to test this hypothesis, initial support is provided by results obtained with mutants and biochemical experiments.

ACKNOWLEDGMENTS

The work described was supported, in part, by the Department of Energy Grants DE-FG02-93ER20121 (J.P.), DE-F6-0687ER136 (T.W.O.), and by USDA Grant 9301525 (J.P.).

LITERATURE CITED

Ballicora MA, Laughlin MJ, Fu Y, Okita TW, Barry GF, Preiss J (1995) ADPglucose Pyrophosphorylase from potato tuber. Significance of the N-terminal of the small subunit for catalytic properties and heat stability. Plant Physiol (in press)

Boyer CD, Preiss J (1981) Evidence for independent genetic control of the multiple forms of maize endosperm branching enzymes and starch synthases. Plant Physiol 67: 1141-1145

Dickinson DB, Preiss J (1969) Presence of ADP-glucose pyrophosphorylase in *shrunken-2* and *brittle-2* mutants of maize endosperm. Plant Physiol 44: 1058-1062

Fontaine T, D'Hulst C, Maddelein M-L, Routier F, Pepin TM, Decq A, Wieruszeski J-M, Delrue B, Van Den Koornhuyse N, Bossu J-P, Fournet B, Ball S (1993) Toward an understanding of the biogenesis of the starch granule. Evidence that *Chlamydomonas* soluble starch synthase II controls the synthesis of intermediate size glucans of amylopectin. J Biol Chem **268**: 16223-16230

Guan H, Kuriki T, Sivak M, Preiss J (1995) Maize branching enzyme catalyzes synthesis of glycogen-like polysaccharide in glgB-deficient *Escherichia coli*. Proc Natl Acad Sci USA (in press)

Guan HP, Preiss J (1993) Differentiation of the properties of the branching isozymes from maize (*Zea mays*). Plant Physiol **102**: 1269-1273

Hizukuri S (1986) Polymodal distribution of the chain lengths of amylopectins and its significance. Carbohyd Res **147**: 342-347

Iglesias AA, Barry GF, Meyer C, Bloksberg L, Nakata PA, Greene T, Laughlin MJ, Okita TW, Kishore GM, Preiss J (1993) Expression of the potato tuber ADP-glucose pyrophosphorylase in *Escherichia coli*. J Biol Chem **268**: 1081-1086

Katz FR (1991) Starch. *In* I Goldberg, R Williams, eds, Biotechnology and Food Ingredients. Van Nostrand Reinhold, NY, pp 315-326

Li L, Preiss J (1992) Characterization of ADP-Glc pyrophosphorylase from a starch-deficient mutant of *Arabidopsis thaliana* (L.). Carbohyd Res **227**: 227-239

Maddelein M-L, Bellanger F, Delrue B, Libessart N, D'hulst C, Van Den Koornhuyse N, Fontaine T, Wieruszeski J-M, Decq A, Ball S (1994) Genetic dissection of starch metabolism in the monocellular alga *Chlamydomonas reinhardtii*: Determination of granule-bound and soluble starch synthases functions in amylopectin biosynthesis. J Biol Chem **269**: 25150-25157

Mizuno K, Kawasaki T, Shimada H, Satoh H, Kobayashi E, Okamura S, Arai Y, Baba T (1993) Alteration of the structural properties of starch components by the lack of an isoform of starch branching enzyme in rice seeds. J Biol Chem **268**: 19084-19091

Morell MK, Bloom M, Knowles V, Preiss J (1987) Subunit structure of spinach leaf ADPglucose pyrophosphorylase. Plant Physiol **85**: 185-187

Müller-Röber BT, Sonnewald U, Willmitzer L (1992) Inhibition of ADPglucose pyrophosphorylase in transgenic potatoes leads to sugar-storing tubers and influences tuber formation and expression of tuber storage protein genes. EMBO J **11**: 1229-1238

Nakata PA, Greene TW, Anderson JM, Smith-White BJ, Okita TW, Preiss J (1991) Comparison of the primary sequences of two potato tuber ADP-glucose pyrophosphorylase subunits. Plant Mol Biol **17**: 1089-1093

Okita T (1992) Is there an alternative pathway for starch synthesis? Plant Physiol **100**: 560-564

Preiss J (1988) Biosynthesis of starch and its degradation. *In* J Preiss, ed, The Biochemistry of Plants, Vol 14. Academic Press, New York, pp 181-254

Preiss J (1991) Starch biosynthesis and its regulation. *In* J Miflin, ed, Oxford Surv Plant Mol Cell Biol **7**: 59-114

Preiss J, Levi C (1980) Starch biosynthesis and degradation. *In* J Preiss, ed, The Biochemistry of Plants, Vol 3. Academic Press, New York, pp 371-423

Preiss J, Sivak MN (1995) Starch synthesis in sinks and sources. *In* E Zamski, AA Schaffer, eds, Photoassimilate Distribution in Plants and Crops: Source-Sink Relationships. Marcel Dekker, Inc, New York (in press)

Sivak MN, Preiss J (1995) Starch synthesis in seeds. *In* M Negbi, J Kigel, G Galili, eds, Seed Development and Germination. Marcel Dekker, Inc, New York, pp 139-168

Smith AM, Bettey M, Bedford ID (1989) Evidence that the *rb* locus alters the starch content of developing pea embryos through an effect on ADPglucose pyrophosphorylase. Plant Physiol **89:** 1279-1284

Smith-White BJ, Preiss J (1992) Comparison of proteins of ADP-glucose pyrophosphorylase from diverse sources. J Mol Evol **34:** 449-464

Sowokinos JR, Preiss J (1982) Pyrophosphorylases in *Solanum tuberosum*. III. Purification, physical and catalytic properties of ADPglucose pyrophosphorylase in potatoes. Plant Physiol **69:** 1459-1466

Stark DM, Timmerman KP, Barry GF, Preiss J, Kishore GM (1992) Role of ADPglucose pyrophosphorylase in regulating starch levels in plant tissues. Science **258:** 287-292

Takeda Y, Guan HP, Preiss J (1993) Branching of amylose by the branching isoenzymes of maize endosperm. Carbohydr Res **240:** 253-263

Tsai CY, Nelson OE (1966) Starch-deficient maize mutant lacking adenosine diphosphate glucose pyrophosphorylase activity. Science **151:** 341-343

Nitrogen Uptake and Its Regulation in Plants

Frank-Roman Lauter, Olaf Ninnemann, and Wolf B. Frommer

Institut für Genbiologische Forschung, Ihnestraße 63, D-14195 Berlin, Germany

For most plants, and especially for crop plants, nitrogen is one of the major important limiting factors in agricultural production. The importance of nitrogen is demonstrated by the fact that only oxygen, carbon, and hydrogen are more abundant in higher plants. Nitrogen is available in the biosphere primarily in three different forms: as molecular nitrogen (N_2), as mineral nitrogen (NO_3^- and NH_4^+), and as organic nitrogen (amino acids, peptides, etc.). In general, higher plants do not have the capacity for acquisition of molecular nitrogen from the atmosphere. Only in a few cases, e.g. the family of *Leguminosae* living in symbiotic association with nitrogen-fixing bacteria, is indirect access to atmospheric N_2 possible through bacterial symbiosis (Marschner, 1986; Long, 1989). For most plants, the major form taken up from the soil is mineral nitrogen, whereas ammonia uptake from the atmosphere into leaves or uptake of organic nitrogen under normal circumstances only play a minor role for plant nutrition.

The resorption of mineral nitrogen from the soil is one of the main functions of the root. Root axes and lateral roots are covered with root hairs which contribute about 70% of the total surface area of the root organ. The volume of the soil in contact with the roots is important for the uptake of mineral nitrogen. Controlling their root surface area is one of the strategies used by plants to cope with different availabilities of mineral nitrogen (Bloom *et al.*, 1993). Thus, the root requires specific transport systems at the plasma membrane that enable the plant to take up the various forms of mineral nitrogen across its outer surface which is in contact with the soil.

Nitrogen Uptake into Roots

Uptake of mineral nitrogen (mainly NO_3^- and NH_4^+) occurs across the membrane in the outer root cell layers, i.e. the root hairs and epidermal cells, respectively, and possibly also in the root cortex. The place of reduction, i.e.

root or shoot, is dependent on the environmental conditions, age of the plant, and plant species (Andrews, 1986). Therefore, reduction and assimilation may take place directly within the cells involved in the uptake from the soil, or the material may be transported through the long-distance distribution network to other plant organs. For the transport between the different root cells, principally, three routes are possible: (*i*) along the apoplastic space involving carrier proteins for uptake or release into and from individual cells; (*ii*) transport via symplastic connections, i.e. the plasmodesmata, or a transcellular route involving even transport in and out of the vacuoles of the respective cells. Across the cortex transport may be apoplastic, however, the casparian strip blocks further transfer to the stele via the apoplast. After symplastic transfer to the stele, the nutrients have to be transferred to the xylem by additional translocation systems (for review, cf. Redinbaugh and Campbell, 1991). Physiological studies support the view that multiple transport systems are involved in the uptake of mineral nitrogen into roots. Since plants have to cope with varying nitrogen supply under changing environmental conditions, one might expect that acquisition and metabolism are highly regulated processes involving multiple highly regulated isoforms of the different transporters.

Processing and Translocation of Nitrogen

In the case of nitrate being taken up from the soil, four different fates of this mineral ion can be envisaged. First, NO_3^- can be reduced to nitrite directly in the cytoplasm of root cells and, after transport into plastids (proplastids in nongreen tissues and chloroplasts in green leaves), is further reduced to ammonium. The reduction is catalyzed by nitrate (NR) and nitrite reductase (NiR), respectively (for review, cf. Caboche and Rouzé, 1990; Crawford and Campbell, 1990). Ammonium does not normally accumulate in plant cells, but is assimilated into amino acids. Assimilation of ammonia-nitrogen into carbon compounds proceeds through the reaction with glutamate to form its amide, glutamine; catalyzed by glutamine synthetase (GS). Glutamine can then be converted to glutamate by reacting with α-ketoglutarate, catalyzed by glutamate synthase (GOGAT). Once assimilated into glutamate, nitrogen can be further incorporated into other amino acids through transamination reactions. As an alternative for metabolization in the root, nitrate can be translocated into the xylem and is transported to the shoot. After reaching the shoot, the NO_3^- is unloaded from the xylem where it is translocated into cells for reduction and assimilation or storage (Redinbaugh and Campbell, 1991). In most plants, both roots and shoot have the capacity to carry out nitrate metabolism. However, the degree to which nitrate reduction takes place in the roots or the leaves depends on a number of factors, including the level of nitrate supplied to the roots (availability), plant species, and developmental stage of the individual plant (demand). In many plants, when the amount of nitrate supplied to the roots is low, nitrate reduction takes place primarily in the roots. When the supply of nitrate is increased, a greater proportion of nitrate metabolism occurs in the leaves because root nitrate reduction capacities become limited under these conditions (Marschner, 1986). Third, in addition to being metabolized in root or shoot cells, nitrate can be stored in root or shoot vacuoles (Granstedt and Huffaker, 1982). Finally, nitrate can efflux into the apoplast and into the soil environment. Therefore, it is important to determine the actual net influx for nitrogen into roots. If ammonium (NH_4^+) is taken up, assimilation into amino acids probably takes place directly in the root. Several authors have also reported that NH_4^+ can be transported in the xylem to the shoot (Shelp, 1987). Ammonium can be converted into organic nitrogen directly by GS and GOGAT, indicating that its use is less energy-requiring as compared to nitrate. Organic nitrogen is then distributed within the plant through both xylem and phloem in the form of amino acids, amides, and ureides (Pate, 1973).

Allocation of Nitrogen

Inorganic nitrogen that is not reduced directly can be stored in the vacuole, e.g. of the leaf epidermis, whereas organic nitrogen can be stored transiently in different vegetative organs, either in the form of soluble amino acids or as polypeptides, such as vegetative storage proteins (VSP), as well as in storage tissues of reproductive organs such as seeds. The nitrogen resources needed for the storage in reproductive organs only partially derive from direct uptake from the soil, but often are mainly derived from nitrogen that has been incorporated before. Therefore, the plant has to reallocate nitrogen in amino acids as the transport form during development. Exporting sources of transiently stored nitrogen can be roots or leaves or, in early stages of plant development, the endosperm and the cotyledons. The transport routes in this case are both xylem and phloem. Thus, in the case of plant nitrogen metabolism, the situation is much more complex as compared to carbon metabolism in that multiple nitrogen-compounds are translocated and cycle through the vascular network of the plant.

Regulation of Nitrogen Uptake

The uptake of nitrogen in plants seems to be controlled mainly by two parameters; availability and demand. The composition of nitrogen sources available in the soil and the specific nitrogen demand of the plant determines the mode of uptake system(s) which is utilized. Nitrogen in the soil is available as nitrate and ammonium, the major nitrogen sources, and, to a lesser extent, as amino acids and peptides (for review, see Higgins and Payne, 1980). External conditions have a strong impact on which amount and type of nitrogen is available for the plant. Nitrate varies up to 10,000-fold in the soil—typical values ranging from 0.1 μM to 1 mM;whereas, in the cytoplasm, concentrations vary between 5 to 30 mM (Lee and Clarkson, 1986). Ammonium concentrations vary between 8 to 50 mM in the root vacuole and between 3 and 90 mM in the cytoplasm. Block of GS leads to the accumulation of high ammonium concentrations; whereas in xylem sap, concentrations range between not detectable and 1 mM (Lee and Ratcliffe, 1991). Beginning with the work of Minotti et al. (1968a, b), nitrate uptake has been observed as being substrate-inducible. The induction varies depending on species, environmental conditions, and nutritional prehistory of the plant (Jackson et al., 1973). In most plants, low temperature, in general, increases the reliance upon ammonium as the mineral nitrogen source (Haynes and Goh, 1978). Ammonification is less temperature sensitive than nitrification, leading to an increased availability of ammonium versus nitrate in cold soils (Thiagalingham and Kanehiro, 1978). In addition, roots absorb ammonium more readily than nitrate at low temperatures, however, genotypic differences can exist between cultivars (Bloom and Chapin, 1981). A two-fold increase in cold-induced nitrate absorption and translocation to the shoot was observed in barley and *Brassica* species (Clarkson and Deane-Drummond, 1983; Deane-Drummond and Glass, 1983; Bigot and Boucaud, 1994). This internal temperature control is thought to be regulated indirectly through the shoot sink strength. It seems obvious that due to the requirement of carbon and energy for nitrogen metabolism, a coordinated regulation of carbon/ nitrogen metabolism is required.

The availability of nitrogen pools in the plants also strongly affects the uptake. Nitrogen withdrawal from the nutrient solution for limited periods of time often results in an increased absorption once the supply is restored. This induction was observed for a number of species, including *Arabidopsis* (Doddema and Otten, 1979), maize (MacKown and McClure, 1988), and tomato (Chapin et al., 1988). Split root experiments have demonstrated that the stimulus does not come from the root itself (Simpson et al., 1982). Products of nitrate assimilation in leaves, i.e. organic and amino acids seem to serve as long-distance signals for the nitrogen status of the plant (Touraine et al., 1992). The pH of the rhizosphere is a critical factor affecting nitrate uptake (Haynes, 1986). Nitrate uptake is subject to both positive and negative feedback regulation (Larsson and Ingemarsson, 1989; Redinbaugh and Campbell, 1991). In the absence of nitrate, a low constitutive level of nitrate uptake activity can be measured. Upon exposure to nitrate, the nitrate uptake activity increases. This increase is not only due to an increase in V_{max}, but also to the activation of new kinetic components (Jackson et al., 1973; MacKown and McClure, 1988; Siddiqi et al., 1989; Hole et al., 1990). Negative feedback inhibition was observed after nitrate exposure for extended periods of time (Larsson and Ingemarsson, 1989; Siddiqi et al., 1989). If nitrate is subsequently removed, the uptake activity again increases (Teyker et al., 1988; Larsson and Ingemarsson, 1989).

The concentration of different nitrogenous compounds can change in the soil and, therefore, plants have to be equipped with the option of changing both capacity and affinity of the respective uptake systems. In addition, nitrogen uptake seems to be controlled by the nitrogen demand of the plant, independent of the soil quality. The demand for nitrogen can vary dramatically during ontogeny and in response to environmental conditions such as light, temperature, or stress (for review, see Imsande and Touraine, 1994). It is thus apparent that transport and translocation systems for nitrogenous compounds should be present at different locations within a plant and should serve different nitrogen requirements. The activity of those transport systems should be regulated by nitrogen availability and nitrogen demand.

Physiological Studies of Nitrate Uptake

Most of the physiological data available are derived from NO_3^- uptake studies in maize, barley, wheat, tomato, and *Arabidopsis thaliana*. For maize and barley roots, three different modes of nitrate transport activity have been determined, i.e. constitutive, induced, and deinduced (Siddiqi *et al.*, 1989; Hole *et al.*, 1990). In the absence of nitrate, plants constitutively express a low-activity NO_3^- uptake system (constitutive mode). Upon exposure to exogenous nitrate, influx is greatly increased in NO_3^--induced roots (induction mode). Induction reaches maximum uptake capacity after about 6 h of continuous (or discontinuous) contact with NO_3^- in the case of maize (MacKown and McClure, 1988; Hole *et al.*, 1990) and 12 to 24 h of NO_3^- in the case of barley (Siddiqi *et al.*, 1989). Kinetic and transcription inhibitor studies suggest that constitutive and inducible NO_3^- uptake are mediated by two distinct 'carrier' systems. There is general agreement that induction of the NO_3^- uptake system specifically requires the presence of external NO_3^-. NH_4^+ is incapable of inducing the uptake system (Jackson *et al.*, 1973). Upon prolonged exposure to exogenous nitrate and as the nitrogen concentration in the root increases, expression of NO_3^- uptake declines (deinduced mode). Therefore, NO_3^- uptake is controlled by positive and negative feedback effects during induction and postinduction periods, respectively (Siddiqi *et al.*, 1989; Hole *et al.*, 1990). In contrast to the situation for induction, the signals responsible for negative feedback effects on NO_3^- uptake are not known with certainty. Potential candidates might include NO_3^- and products of NO_3^- reduction and assimilation such as NO_2^-, NH_4^+, and amino acids.

With respect to their substrate affinity, at least two nitrate transport systems can be distinguished in plants based on their kinetic properties (Doddema and Telkamp, 1979; Goyal and Huffaker, 1986; Siddiqi *et al.*, 1989). High-affinity, saturable, possibly constitutive (Aslam *et al.*, 1992), systems with low K_m values of 5 to 100 μM (HATS) have been identified, in addition to low-affinity, nonsaturable transport systems (high K_m values of >1 mM)

(LATS). HATS have low-transport capacity and LATS have high-transport capacity; in the case of *Arabidopsis*, 4 and 700 μmol/h, respectively. In the case of barley, nitrate influx across the plasmalemma into roots occurs below 100 μM [NO_3^-] via the saturable HATS, whereas from 100 μM to above 1000 μM, the second, nonsaturable LATS becomes apparent. Electrophysiological studies in barley and maize showed that nitrate transport by LATS and HATS occurs via $2H^+$: $1NO_3^-$ proton symport (McClure *et al.*, 1990; Glass *et al.*, 1992). One might speculate that the high-affinity system is constitutively active at low environmental NO_3^- concentrations, while low-affinity systems with high transport capacity are induced by raising NO_3^- levels.

In addition to being regulated by availability of nitrate present in the soil, the activity of nitrate transport is also controlled by the nitrogen demand of the plant (Imsande and Touraine, 1994). The demand can vary with environmental conditions (other than nitrogen availability) and the developmental phase of the plant. The nature of the signals that inform the nitrate uptake apparatus about the demand state of the plant is a matter of debate. Amino acids and malate are candidates for such signaling molecules. Some amino acids, the products of nitrate assimilation, strongly inhibit nitrate uptake when supplied directly to roots in nutrient medium, suggesting that amino acids may control the rate of nitrate uptake (Muller and Touraine, 1992).

Genetic and Molecular Studies of Nitrate Uptake

Genes for nitrate transporters have been cloned from the fungus *Aspergillus nidulans* (Unkles *et al.*, 1991) and from the green algae *Chlamydomonas reinhardtii* (Quesada *et al.*, 1994). In *Arabidopsis*, a monogenetic recessive, chlorate-resistant mutant, *chl-1*, was isolated which lacks a LATS component of nitrate uptake. It was suggested that the *CHL1* gene of *Arabidopsis* encodes the low-affinity, high-capacity nitrate uptake system, or at least parts of it (Doddema and Telkamp, 1979). The *CHL1* gene was cloned (Tsay *et al.*, 1993) by using T-DNA from *Agrobacterium tumefaciens* as an insertional mutagen for gene tagging (Feldmann, 1991). *CHL1* encodes an integral membrane protein with 12 putative membrane-spanning domains. Nitrate transport capacity of *chl-1* was shown by heterologous expression in *Xenopus* oocytes. *CHL1* mRNA is predominantly expressed in *Arabidopsis* roots and displays nitrate-inducible regulation. Plants grown on NH_4^+ as a nitrogen source express *CHL1* weakly. *CHL1* mRNA levels increase in response to nitrate and peak about 2 h after plants are transferred from nitrate-free to nitrate medium. Besides nitrate, CHL1 also mediates the transport of other anions such as sulfate, but not of phosphate or malate (Tsay *et al.*, 1993). In addition, two *CHL1* homologues have been isolated from *Arabidopsis*. Both homologues are nitrate-stimulated, root-dominant membrane proteins. However, both respond to nitrate more slowly than *CHL1*, and their mRNA levels remain high after a 16-h exposure to nitrate (Tsay *et al.*,

1994). Furthermore, two *CHL1* homologues have been isolated from oilseed rape. Both clones are homologous to the coding region of *CHL1*, both on amino acid and nucleotide levels. The clones do not hybridize to RNA isolated from rape that have not received any nitrate, but treatment of the plant with 10 μM to 2500 μM nitrate for 3 h results in significant accumulation of transcript (Muldin and Ingemarsson, 1994). Furthermore, mRNA of the *CHL-1* gene has been identified in six other plant species (Tsay *et al.*, 1993). It will be interesting to see whether transporters related to the *Aspergillus crnA* and the *Chlamydomonas nar3/nar4* transporter genes are also present in higher plants contributing to the complexity of nitrate uptake systems.

Physiological Studies of Ammonium Uptake

In contrast to nitrate, ammonium occurs mainly in bound forms in the soil, thus requiring efficient systems for release and uptake. In rice cultivation, in forest ecosystems, in Arctic tundra, and even in winter varieties of cereals growing in cold soils, NH_4^+ may represent the more important form of available mineral nitrogen (cited in Wang *et al.*, 1993*a*). An impressive set of NH_4^+ uptake data derived from studies on rice roots (Wang *et al.*, 1993*a*, *b*, 1994). Ammonium influx across the plasmalemma into rice roots exhibits a biphasic pattern: in the low range (below 1 mM NH_4^+), influx occurred via a saturable HATS, whereas from 1 to 40 mM NH_4^+, a second, nonsaturable LATS becomes apparent. The significance of HATS for NH_4^+ in rice roots is that it allows plants to absorb sufficient nitrogen (NH_4^+) from very low levels in the rhizosphere to meet the minimum requirements for plant growth. HATS shows a pH optimum in the neutral pH range. The biphasic pattern of uptake has been reported also for NH_4^+ uptake by *Lemna* (Ullrich *et al.*, 1984), for NO_3^- uptake, as mentioned above, and for K^+ uptake by maize roots (Kochian and Lucas, 1982). HATS and LATS of rice root NH_4^+ uptake have different pH optima at 6.0 to 7.5 and 4.5 to 6.0, respectively. Although the biphasic pattern of NH_4^+ influx is independent of the prior NH_4^+ exposure, the individual systems, particularly the HATS, are extremely sensitive to prior NH_4^+ exposure (Wang *et al.*, 1993*b*). Evidently NH_4^+ influx by the HATS is subject to regulation by negative feedback; with increasing exogenous $[NH_4^+]$, root $[NH_4^+]$ increases and NH_4^+ uptake decreases. The signals responsible for the strong negative down-regulation of influx by the HATS in response to elevated NH_4^+ supply during growth are unclear. Feedback signals may result from unmetabolized ammonium of root cells or reduced nitrogen. Lee and Rudge (1986) have suggested that in barley, the uptake of NH_4^+ and NO_3^- are under common negative feedback control from a product of NH_4^+ assimilation rather than NH_4^+ and/or NO_3^- accumulation *per se*. However, results from Wang *et al.* (1993*b*) indicated that the influx of NH_4^+, that can be attributed to the LATS, is higher in plants previously maintained at 1000 μM NH_4^+ than those at 2 μM NH_4^+. Therefore, NH_4^+ LATS are not under negative feedback control; the reverse was found for the NO_3^- LATS (Siddiqi *et al.*, 1990). It is apparent that regulation of HATS and LATS is different for NO_3^- and NH_4^+ uptake. For NO_3^-, the low-affinity uptake system is under negative feedback control, while for NH_4^+, the high-affinity uptake system is negatively feedback controlled. Results from electrophysiological studies (Wang *et al.*, 1994) indicate that HATS and LATS have different mechanisms of energy coupling. It was suggested that the HATS use a proton : NH_4^+ symport as a mechanism for NH_4^+ uptake, while NH_4^+ transport through LATS is a passive process. Passive entry of NH_4^+ might occur via an electrogenic uniport. This could be mediated either by specific NH_4^+ transporters or by unspecific cation channels, such as K^+ channels that also mediate ammonium uptake.

Genetic Studies on Ammonium Uptake

Saccharomyces cerevisiae uses at least three different ammonium uptake systems (Dubois and Grenson, 1979). Mutants that lack the two major ammonium uptake systems, MEP1 and MEP2, were identified by selection on the toxic ammonium analogue methylamine. Remaining uptake activities indicate that further transport systems must be present. *Chlamydomonas* seems to have at least two ammonium uptake systems: the constitutive component 1 with a K_m of 27 μM and high V_{max} for ammonium and the ammonium-repressible component 2 with a K_m of 7.5 μM and low V_{max}. Mutants in ammonium transport were identified in *Chlamydomonas* that lack the high-affinity component which has a pH optimum around pH 7.

Molecular Studies on Ammonium Uptake

Despite the fact that in several organisms, mutants had been identified that are involved in ammonium transport and despite extensive trials to identify these proteins, only genes encoding putative regulatory functions were identified. Only the yeast mutants allowed the isolation of transporter genes from yeast and *Arabidopsis* by complementation. As described above, yeast utilizes at least three different ammonium uptake systems. Genes for two transporters MEP1 and MEP2 with differing affinity and capacity have been cloned (Marini *et al.*, 1994; B. André, unpubl. results). Using heterologous complementation of a yeast mutant deficient in ammonium uptake, we have recently succeeded in isolating the first high-affinity ammonium transport system from the plasma membrane of plants, AMT1 (Ninnemann *et al.*, 1994). AMT1 operates in an energy-dependent manner, transports methylamine against a concentration gradient into the cells, and depends on the proton motive force. The transporter constitutes a high-affinity uptake system with high specificity for ammonium uptake. Whether AMT1 constitutes a typical channel or a transporter remains to be shown. The biochemical properties, including the neutral pH optimum, coincide nicely with the physiological data on ammonium uptake from a variety of plant species including green algae (see above). An interesting question concerns the number of systems involved. Under certain conditions, significant amounts of ammonium can be found in the xylem. Therefore, similar to nitrate uptake, transporters may be required for uptake into the cortex, transfer and release into/from the vessels, and in addition, for specific retrieval systems that prevent loss in the form of ammonia. The ammonium transporters of higher plants constitute a gene family consisting of at least three members (W.B. Ninnemann and O.W. Frommer, unpubl. data). A detailed analysis of the different transporters will be necessary to test if they differ in the expression pattern or kinetic properties possibly linked to different roles in the plant. Apart from the AMT1 type of transporter which is highly selective for ammonium, other transporters have been shown to also mediate ammonium transport. This includes potassium channels like KAT1 and the high-affinity potassium proton cotransporter HKT1 (Schachtman et al., 1992; Schachtman and Schroeder, 1994).

Interactions of Nitrogen Uptake with the Transport of Other Ions

In most soils, potassium concentrations typically vary from 0.2 to 5 mM (Marschner, 1986). Since both the size and charge of potassium ions are comparable to those of ammonium ions, cross-competition could occur (Buurman et al., 1991). This assumption is supported by the finding that ammonium inhibits potassium uptake (Smith and Epstein, 1964; Minotti et al., 1968b; Ajayi et al., 1970; Rufty et al., 1982; Deane-Drummond and Glass, 1983; Scherer et al., 1984; Vale et al., 1987, 1988). On the other hand, competition studies with AMT1 demonstrate that at least the high-affinity ammonium transport is only marginally affected by potassium. However, as pointed out above, both potassium channels and high-affinity potassium proton symporters mediate ammonium uptake in oocytes (Schachtman et al., 1992; Schachtman and Schroeder, 1994).

Nitrogen Uptake Via Symbiosis

Microorganisms contribute, to a large extent, to nitrogen acquisition of higher plants. In plants which are able to use atmospheric nitrogen via symbiosis with dinitrogen-fixing organisms, dinitrogen reduced in the bacteria must be transferred into the plant cytoplasm. As the rhizobial ammonium carriers are repressed in nodules, it is assumed that ammonia diffuses across the bacteroid membranes and is trapped in the apoplast due to protonation in the more acidic milieu (for review, see Kleiner, 1993). Subsequently, the ammonium has to be transported by channels or transporters into the cytoplasm of the adjacent cells. The assumption that ammonium is the major transport form for the transfer across the two membranes is supported by the finding of only low capacities for the uptake of various amino acids (Udvardi et al., 1990).

With respect to NH_4^+ uptake, one has to realize that roots of about 80% of all higher plants live in symbiotic association with mycorrhizal fungi which participate in the acquisition of mineral nutrients by host plants. In coach grass (*Agropyron repens*), approximately 25% of the total nitrogen uptake could be attributed to uptake and delivery by the external hyphae. Measurements of the nitrogen accumulation in the hyphal compartment indicate preferential uptake of NH_4^+-nitrogen. Up to now, information is lacking on the capacity of external hyphae for uptake and transport of NO_3^--nitrogen (Marschner and Dell, 1993). Ectomycorrhizae contribute to nitrogen nutrition of their host plants (Reid *et al.*, 1983; Rygiewicz *et al.*, 1984; Alexander, 1985, Finlay *et al.*, 1992). In most temperate forest soils characterized by profuse ectomycorrhizal development, ammonium is the predominant form of nitrogen nutrition and the competition for this nutrient is intense (Harley and Smith, 1983). In such conditions, ammonium assimilation by ectomycorrhizae probably plays a key role in nitrogen nutrition of forest trees (Dell *et al.*, 1989), particularly when soils are poor in nutrient elements. The rates of ammonium assimilation in ectomycorrhizal forest trees are usually higher than those measured for nitrate (Harley and Smith, 1983) and the same applies for the majority of ectomycorrhizal fungi (France and Reid, 1984; Littke *et al.*, 1984). Unfortunately, molecular studies on nitrogen uptake by these fungi have not yet been reported.

CONCLUSIONS AND PERSPECTIVES

Physiological analysis of nitrogen uptake has provided an excellent overview and understanding of the factors involved in nitrogen uptake from the soil. The next step will be to identify the individual transporters and their regulators that are responsible for the complex nitrogen uptake characteristics. In general, several different levels of regulating biochemical processes are used by plants. Regulation can be exerted on the transcriptional level via control on initiation rates, differential mRNA size and stability; on the translational level via control on translation rates and on the post-translational level via control on polypeptide maturation, targeting, and stability. Finally, the activity state of the mature transport protein can be regulated through modification, such as phosphorylation or glycosylation. Electrophysiological techniques should enable elegant studies of the regulation of electrogenic transporters or channels. Regulation of transporters involved in nitrogen uptake is well studied in yeast (Wiame *et al.*, 1985; Grenson, 1992). In filamentous fungi, nitrate seems to operate through regulatory genes specific to the pathway, *nit-2* in *Neurospora* and *nirA* in *Aspergillus* (Cove, 1979) that turn on the expression of genes encoding NR, NiR, and nitrate permeases. In higher plants, the analysis of the regulatory elements involved in nitrogen utilization is still at the beginning. The isolation of plant genes encoding nitrogen transporters has allowed researchers to get a first glimpse at the molecular complexity of nitrogen uptake systems, but a thorough analysis of all components will be necessary in order to obtain a full understanding of processes involved in the regulation of nitrogen uptake. In this context, the detailed study of root architecture (Benfey and Schiefelbein, 1994) will be helpful to complement the approaches using molecular physiology in order to reach a more complete understanding of nitrogen uptake and its regulation.

LITERATURE CITED

Ajayi O, Maynard DN, Barker AV (1970) The effect of potassium on ammonium nutrition of tomato (*Lycopersicon esculentum* Mill.). Agron J **62**: 818-821

Alexander A (1985) The significance of ectomycorrhizas in the nitrogen cycle. *In* JA Lee, S McNeill, IH Rorison, eds, Nitrogen as an Ecological Factor. Blackwell, Oxford, UK, pp 69-94

Andrews M (1986) The partitioning of nitrate assimilation between the root and shoot of higher plants. Plant Cell Environ **9**: 511-519

Aslam M, Travis RL, Huffaker RC (1992) Comparative kinetics and reciprocal inhibition of nitrate and nitrite uptake in roots of uninduced and induced barley seedlings. Plant Physiol **99**: 1124-1133

Benfey PN, Schiefelbein JW (1994) Getting to the root of plant development: the genetics of *Arabidopsis* root formation. Trends Genet **10**: 84-88.

Bigot J, Boucaud J (1994) Low-temperature pretreatment of the root system of *Brassica rapa* L. plants: effects on the xylem sap exudation and on the nitrate absorption rate. Plant Cell Environ **17**: 721-729

Bloom AJ, Chapin FS III (1981) Differences in steady-state net ammonium and nitrate influx by cold- and warm-adapted Barley varieties. Plant Physiol **68**: 1064-1067

Bloom AJ, Jackson LE, Smart DR (1993) Root growth as a function of ammonium and nitrate in the root zone. Plant Cell Environ **16**: 199-206

Buurman ET, Joost Teixeira de Mattos M, Neijssel ON (1991) Futile cycling of ammonium ions via the high affinity potassium uptake system (Kdp) of *E. coli*. Arch Microbiol **155**: 391-395

Caboche M, Rouzé P (1990) Nitrate reductase: a target for molecular and cellular studies in higher plants. Trends Genet **6**: 187-192

Chapin FS III, Fetcher N, Kielland K, Everett KR, Linkins AE (1988) Productivity and nutrient cycling of Alaskan tundra: enhancement by flowing soil water. Ecology **69**: 693-702

Clarkson DT, Deane-Drummond CE (1983) Thermal adaptation of nitrate transport. *In* JA Lee, S McNeill, IH Rorison, eds, Nitrogen as an Ecological Factor. Blackwell, Oxford, UK, pp 211-224

Cove DJ (1979) Genetic studies on nitrate assimilation in *Aspergillus nidulans*. Biol Rev **54**: 291-303

Crawford NM, Campbell WH (1990) Fertile fields. Plant Cell **2**: 829-835

Deane-Drummond CE, Glass ADM (1983) Short-term studies of nitrate uptake into barley plants using ion specific electrodes and $^{36}ClO_3^-$. II. Regulation of NO_3^- efflux by NH_4^+. Plant Physiol **73**: 105-110

Dell B, Botton B, Martin F, Le Tacon F (1989) Glutamate dehydrogenase in ectomycorrhizas of spruce and beech. New Phytol **111**: 683-692

Doddema H, Otten H (1979) Uptake of nitrate by mutants of *Arabidopsis thaliana*, disturbed in uptake or reduction of nitrate. III. Regulation. Physiol Plant **45**: 339-346

Doddema H, Telkamp GP (1979) Uptake of nitrate by mutants of *Arabidopsis thaliana*, disturbed in uptake or reduction of nitrate. II. Kinetics. Physiol Plant **45**: 332-338

Dubois E, Grenson M (1979) Methylamine/ammonia uptake systems in *Saccharomyces cerevisiae*: Multiplicity and regulation. Mol Gen Genet **175**: 67-76

Feldmann, KA (1991) T-DNA insertion mutagenesis in *Arabidopsis*: mutational spectrum. Plant J **1**: 71-82

Finlay RD, Frostegard A, Sonnerfeldt AM (1992) Utilization of organic and inorganic nitrogen sources by ectomycorrhizal fungi in pure culture and in symbiosis with *Pinus contorta* Dougl. ex Loud. New Phytol **120**: 105-115

France RC, Reid CPP (1984) Pure culture growth of ectomycorrhizal fungi on inorganic nitrogen sources. Microb Ecol **10**: 187-195

Glass ADM, Shaff JE, Kochian LV (1992) Studies of uptake of nitrate in barley. IV. Electrophysiology. Plant Physiol **99**: 456-463

Goyal SS, Huffaker RC (1986) A novel approach and a fully automated microcomputer-based system to study kinetics of NO_3^-, NO_2^- and NH_4^+ transport simultaneously by intact wheat seedlings. Plant Cell Environ **9**: 209-215

Granstedt RC, Huffaker RC (1982) Identification of the vacuole as a major nitrate storage pool. Plant Physiol **70**: 410-413

Grenson M (1992) Amino acid transporters in yeast: structure, function and regulation. *In* CCC DePont, ed, Molecular Aspects of Transport Proteins. Elsevier Publ, New York, pp 219-245

Harley JL, Smith SE (1983) Mycorrhizal Symbiosis. Academic Press, London, pp 1-483

Haynes RJ (1986) Uptake and assimilation of mineral nitrogen by plants. *In* RJ Haynes, ed, Mineral Nitrogen in the Plant-Soil System. Academic Press, San Diego, pp 303-378

Haynes RJ, Goh KM (1978) Ammonium and nitrate nutrition of plants. Biol Rev **53**: 465-510

Higgins CF, Payne JW (1980) Transport and utilization of amino acids and peptides by higher plants. *In* JW Payne, ed, Microorganisms and Nitrogen Sources. Wiley and Sons Inc, New York, pp 609-639

Hole DJ, Emran AM, Fares Y, Drew MC (1990) Induction of nitrate transport in maize roots, and kinetics of influx, measured with nitrogen-13. Plant Physiol **93**: 642-647

Imsande J, Touraine B (1994) N demand and the regulation of nitrate uptake. Plant Physiol **105**: 3-7

Jackson WA, Flesher D, Hageman RH (1973) Nitrate uptake by dark-grown corn seedlings: some characteristics of apparent induction. Plant Physiol **51:** 120-157

Kleiner D (1993) NH_4^+ transport systems. *In* EP Bakker, ed, Alkali Cation Transport Systems in Procaryotes. CRC Press, Boca Raton, FL, pp 379-396

Kochian LV, Lucas WJ (1982) Potassium transport in corn roots. Plant Physiol **70:** 1723-1731

Larsson CM, Ingemarsson B (1989) Molecular aspects of nitrate uptake in higher plants. *In* JR Kinghorn, JL Wray, eds, Molecular and Genetic Aspects of Nitrate Assimilation. Oxford Sci Publ, New York, pp 4-14

Lee RB, Clarkson DT (1986) Nitrogen-13 studies of nitrate fluxes in barley roots. I. Compartmental analysis from measurements of ^{13}N efflux. J Exp Bot **185:** 1753-1767

Lee RB, Ratcliffe RG (1991) Observations on the subcellular distribution of the ammonium ion in maize root tissue using *in vivo* ^{14}N-nuclear resonance spectroscopy. Planta **183:** 359-367

Lee RB, Rudge KA (1986) Effects of nitrogen deficiency on the absorption of nitrate and ammonium by barley plants. Ann Bot **57:** 471-486

Littke WR, Bledsoe CS, Edmonds RL (1984) Nitrogen uptake and growth *in vitro* by *Hebeloma crustuliniformae* and other northwest mycorrhizal fungi. Can J Bot **62:** 647-652

Long, S (1989) *Rhizobium*-legume nodulation: Life together in the underground. Cell **56:** 203-214

MacKnown CT, McClure PR (1988) Development of accelerated net nitrate uptake. Plant Physiol **87:** 162-166

Marini AM, Vissers S, Urrestarazu A, André B (1994) Cloning and expression of the *MEP1* gene encoding an ammonium transporter in *Saccharomyces cerevisiae*. EMBO J **13:** 3456-3463

Marschner H (1986) Mineral Nutrition in Higher Plants. Academic Press, London

Marschner H, Dell B (1993) Nutrient uptake in mycorrhizal symbiosis. Plant Soil **159:** 89-102

McClure PR, Kochian LV, Spanswick RM, Staff JE (1990) Evidence for cotransport of nitrate and protons in maize roots. I. Effects of nitrate on membrane potential. Plant Physiol **93:** 281-289

Minotti PL, Williams DC, Jackson WA (1968*a*) Nitrate uptake and reduction as affected by calcium and potassium. Soil Sci Am Proc **32:** 692-698.

Minotti PL, Williams DC, Jackson WA (1968*b*) Nitrate uptake by wheat as influenced by ammonium and other cations. Crop Sci **9:** 9-14

Muldin I, Ingemarsson B (1994) Cloning and characterization of putative nitrate transport proteins from oilseed rape, *Brassica napus* L. Intl Conf Plant Mol Biol (Abstract 1006), Amsterdam

Muller B, Touraine B (1992) Inhibition of NO_3^- uptake by various phloem-translocated amino acids in soybean seedlings. J Exp Bot **41:** 221-241

Ninnemann OW, Jauniaux JC, Frommer WB (1994) Identification of a ehigh affinity ammonium transporter from plants. EMBO J **13:** 3464-3471

Pate JS (1973) Uptake, assimilation and transport of nitrogen compounds by plants. Soil Biol Biochem **5:** 109-119

Quesada A, Galvan A, Fernandez E (1994) Identification of nitrate transporter genes in *Chlamydomonas reinhardtii*. Plant J **5**: 407-419

Redinbaugh MG, Campbell WH (1991) Higher plant responses to environmental nitrate. Physiol Plant **82**: 640-650

Reid CPP, Kidd FA, Ekwebelam SA (1983) Nitrogen nutrition, photosynthesis and carbon allocation in ectomycorrhizal pine. Plant Soil **71**: 415-432

Rufty TWJ, Jackson WA, Raper CDJ (1982) Inhibition of nitrate assimilation in roots in the presence of ammonium: the moderating influence of potassium. J Exp Bot **33**: 1122-1137

Rygiewicz PT, Bledsoe CS, Zasoski RJ (1984) Effects of ectomycorrhizae and solution pH on [^{15}N]ammonium uptake by coniferous seedlings. Can J For Res **14**: 885-892

Schachtman DP, Schroeder JI (1994) Cloning, transport mechanism and localization of a high affinity potassium uptake transporter from higher plants. Nature **370**: 655-658

Schachtman DP, Schroeder JI, Lucas WJ, Anderson JA, Gaber RF (1992) Expression of an inward-rectifying potassium channel by the *Arabidopsis* KAT1 cDNA. Science **258**: 1654-1658

Scherer HW, Mackown CT, Leggett JE (1984) Potassium-ammonium uptake interactions in tobacco seedlings. J Exp Bot **35**: 1060-1070

Shelp BJ (1987) The composition of phloem exudate and xylem sap from Broccoli (*Brassica oleracea* var. *italica*) supplied with NH_4^+, NO_3^- or NH_4NO_3. J Exp Bot **38**: 1619-1636

Siddiqi MY, Glass ADM, Ruth TJ, Fernando M (1989) Studies of the regulation of nitrate influx in barley seedlings using $^{13}NO_3^-$. Plant Physiol **90**: 806-813

Siddiqi MY, Glass ADM, Ruth TJ, Rufty TW Jr (1990) Studies on nitrate uptake in barley. Plant Physiol **93**: 1426-1432

Siddiqi MY, King BJ, Glass ADM (1992) Effects of nitrite, chlorate, and chlorite on nitrate uptake and nitrate reductase activity. Plant Physiol **100**: 644-650

Simpson RJ, Lambers H, Dalling MJ (1982) Translocation of nitrogen in a vegetative wheat plant (*Triticum aestivum*). Physiol Plant **56**: 11-17

Smith RC, Epstein E (1964) Ion absorption by shoot tissue. Kinetics of potassium and rubidium absorption by corn leaf tissue. Plant Physiol **39**: 992-996

Teyker RH, Jackson WA, Volk RJ, Moll RH (1988) Exogenous $^{15}NO_3^-$-influx and endogenous $^{14}NO_3^-$-efflux by two maize inbreds during nitrogen deprivation. Plant Physiol **86**: 778-781

Thiagalingham K, Kanehiro Y (1978) Effect of temperature on nitrogen transformation in Hawaiian soils. Plant Soil **38**: 177-189

Touraine B, Muller B, Grignon C (1992) Effect of phloem-translocated malate on NO_3^- uptake by roots of intact soybean plants. Plant Physiol **99**: 1118-1123

Tsay Y, Schroeder JI, Crawford NM (1994) Analysis of nitrate transport in *Arabidopsis* at the molecular level. Intl Conf Plant Mol Biol (Abstract 1005), Amsterdam

Tsay Y, Schroeder JI, Feldmann KA, Crawford NM (1993) The herbicide sensitivity gene *CHL*1 of *Arabidopsis* encodes a nitrate-inducible nitrate transporter. Cell **72**: 705-713

Udvardi MK, Yang LO, Young S, Day DA (1990) Sugar and amino acid transport across symbiotic membranes from soybean nodules. Mol Plant-Micr Inter **3**: 334-340

Ullrich WR, Larsson M, Larsson CM, Lesch S, Novacky A (1984) Ammonium uptake in *Lemna gibba* G1, related membrane potential changes, and inhibition of anion uptake. Physiol Plant **61**: 369-376.

Unkles SE, Hawker KL, Grieve C, Campbell EI, Montague P, Kinghorn JR (1991) *crn*A encodes a nitrate transporter in *Aspergillus nidulans*. Proc Natl Acad Sci USA **88**: 204-208

Vale FR, Jackson WA, Volk RJ (1987) Potassium influx into maize root systems 1. Plant Physiol **84**: 1416-1420

Vale FR, Volk RJ, Jackson WA (1988) Simultaneous influx of ammonium and potassium into maize roots: kinetics and interactions. Planta **173**: 424-431

Wang MY, Glass ADM, Shaff JE, Kochian LV (1994) Ammonium uptake by rice roots III. Electrophysiology. Plant Physiol **104**: 899-906.

Wang MY, Siddiqi MY, Ruth TJ, Glass ADM (1993*a*) Ammonium uptake by rice roots I. Fluxes and subcellular distribution of $^{13}NH_4^+$. Plant Physiol **103**: 1249-1258

Wang MY, Siddiqi MY, Ruth TJ, Glass ADM (1993*b*) Ammonium uptake by rice roots II. Kinetics of $^{13}NH_4^+$ influx across the plasmalemma. Plant Physiol **103**: 1259-1267

Wiame JM, Grenson M, Arst HN Jr (1985) Nitrogen catabolite repression in yeasts and filamentous fungi. Adv Micr Physiol **26**: 1-87

Carbon Partitioning and Source-Sink Interactions in Plants, *Monica A. Madore* and
William J. Lucas, eds, Copyright 1995, published by The American Society of Plant
Physiologists

Movement Protein Expression and
Carbohydrate Partitioning

Shmuel Wolf, Amnon A. Olesinski,
Suchandra Balachandran, and William J. Lucas

*Department of Vegetable Crops, Faculty of Agriculture, The Hebrew
University of Jerusalem, Rehovot 76-100, Israel (S.W.; A.A.O.); and
Section of Plant Biology, Division of Biological Sciences, University of
California, Davis, CA 95616, USA (S.B.; W.J.L.)*

Plasmodesmata are membrane-lined channels traversing the cell wall, and
as such, they provide continuous symplasmic connections throughout the tissues of the plant. These structures coordinate biochemical and physiological
processes by facilitating cell-to-cell diffusion of simple metabolites and ions.
Considering the internal dimensions of the plasmodesmata, large macromolecules are not expected to pass readily from one cell to another. However,
recent studies provide compelling evidence that higher plant plasmodesmata
can engage in cell-to-cell transport of macromolecules, including proteins and
nucleic acids (Fujiwara *et al.*, 1993; Lucas and Wolf, 1993; Lucas *et al.*,
1993*a*; Noueiry *et al.*, 1994; Waigmann *et al.*, 1994).

Molecular studies of plant viruses have established the generality of the
concept that many plant viruses code a protein(s) essential for their movement
through plasmodesmata from the site of replication to surrounding, uninfected
cells (Maule, 1991; Deom *et al.*, 1992; Lucas and Gilbertson, 1994). This
process requires interaction between the virally encoded protein, termed the
movement protein (MP), and proteins within the plasmodesmata of the host
plant. Immunogold cytochemical studies have shown that the MP of tobacco
mosaic virus (TMV-MP) is localized within the plasmodesmal channel in
recently infected tissue (Tomenius *et al.*, 1987).

Expression of viral MP genes in transgenic plants has greatly contributed
to the elucidation of both the viral mechanism [protein(s)] involved in conferring symplasmic mobility, and the function of the plasmodesmata (Deom *et
al.*, 1987; Wolf *et al.*, 1989). Immunolocalization studies of transgenic plants
expressing the TMV-MP indicate that the protein is localized exclusively in the

secondary (consisting of multiple branches united via a central cavity near the middle lamella) and not primary plasmodesmata, between various nonvascular cells, and between bundle-sheath and phloem-parenchyma cells. Interestingly, no plasmodesmata within the phloem-associated tissues were positively labeled in these plants (Ding *et al.*, 1992). Microinjection (dye-coupling) studies have established that the size exclusion limit (SEL) of plasmodesmata interconnecting mesophyll cells is greater than 9.4 kD in these transgenic plants, as compared to values of about 800 D in control plants. This change in plasmodesmal function occurred only in mesophyll and nonvascular tissues where secondary plasmodesmata had formed (Wolf *et al.*, 1989, 1991; Ding *et al.*, 1992).

RESULTS

Effect of the TMV-MP on Carbon Metabolism and Transport

The role of plasmodesmata in facilitating symplasmic transport is evidenced by their increased numbers at locations where considerable cell-to-cell transport occurs (van Bel, 1993). According to Tyree (1970), theoretical considerations alone dictate that such transfer of solutes must occur mainly by diffusion through plasmodesmata, even though the plasmodesmata themselves represent a high resistance to flow. Purely diffusive transport of dye through the symplasm was demonstrated by Tucker *et al.* (1989), so the rate-controlling factor of symplasmic transport should be diffusion through the plasmodesmata. Based on this hypothesis, changes in plasmodesmal SEL, as reflected in transgenic plants expressing the TMV-MP gene, should have an effect on the rate of diffusion through such modified plasmodesmata and, therefore, on the transport rate of small molecules, including sucrose.

An experimental system which includes different transformed tobacco plants was employed to investigate whether the expression of the TMV-MP has the predicted effect on the rate of carbon export from source leaves. Pulse-labeling experiments, performed on the youngest, fully expanded tobacco leaf (leaf #5 or 6) demonstrated that the rate of reduction in radioactivity was significantly lower in leaves of plant line 277 (TMV-MP expressing) than in those of control plant line 306 (Fig. 1A). These results were confirmed using another series of transgenic tobacco plants that express the TMV-MP in a different genetic background (Fig. 1B). Analyses of carbohydrate content in these leaves, as a function of the day/night cycle, revealed that leaves of tobacco plants expressing the TMV-MP accumulate much higher levels of glucose, fructose, sucrose, and starch during the day than control plants (Fig. 1C-F). Analysis of the distribution and turnover of ^{14}C-photosynthates within the source leaf was based on a determination of both concentration (mg cm^{-2}) and radioactivity of the various sugars and starch after predetermined intervals after $^{14}CO_2$ labeling (Olesinski *et al.*, 1995). Calculations based on these data

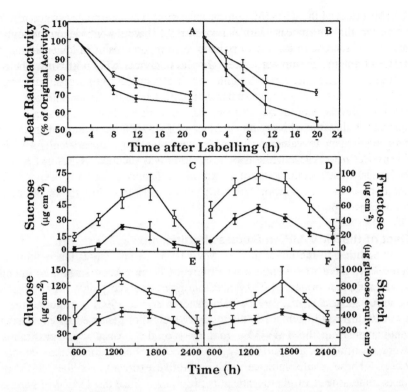

Figure 1. Diurnal changes in ^{14}C-photosynthate (A,B) and carbohydrate content [glucose (C), fructose (D), sucrose (E), and starch (F)] in fully expanded leaves of TMV-MP transgenic (lines 277[A] and 2004[B]) and vector control (lines 306[A] and 3001[B]) tobacco plants. Plants were grown in a greenhouse (25/18°C) under natural sunlight with a midday average photon flux density of 1500 μmol m^{-2} s^{-1}. Radioactivity within intact leaves was assayed nondestructively with a "Rotem" portable β-counter. ($\circ$ and $\bullet$ data obtained on TMV-MP transgenic and control tobacco plants, respectively.) (A,B - Data redrawn from Olesinski *et al.*, 1995; C-F - data redrawn from Lucas *et al.*, 1993*b*, with permission from Planta.)

revealed that ^{14}C-sucrose export from MP-expressing and control plants was 13.6 and 15.3 mg cm^{-2} h^{-1}, respectively (Olesinski *et al.*, 1995). It should be noted that these calculations were based on the assumption that newly synthesized ^{14}C-sucrose is able to mix with <u>all</u> unlabeled sucrose. If, however, the differences in sucrose levels between the two plant lines were due to storage in the vacuole and newly fixed ^{14}C-sucrose exchanged uniformly with similar levels of sucrose in the two plant lines, the differences in export rate would be even greater.

This effect of the TMV-MP on carbon export was unexpected, since it was anticipated that an increase in plasmodesmal SEL would enhance symplasmic transport of sucrose to the site of phloem loading, and result in lower levels of sugars within the mesophyll tissue. If plasmodesmal SEL within the mesophyll did not constitute a rate-limiting step in the process of sucrose transport, carbon metabolism would have remained unaffected by the TMV-MP, and carbohydrate levels would be similar for both plant lines. It should be emphasized that the photosynthetic rate in TMV-MP-expressing plants was nearly equivalent to values measured in control plants (Lucas *et al.*, 1993*b*; Olesinski *et al.*, 1995), while dark respiration was identical (Olesinski *et al.*, 1995), such that accumulation of sugars in the former must have been due to alterations in carbon transport and not to differences in carbohydrate assimilation or consumption.

Effect of the TMV-MP on Biomass Partitioning

In addition to the effect of the TMV-MP on carbon allocation within the source leaf, there was a significant difference in biomass distribution among the various plant organs of TMV-MP transgenic tobacco plants, as compared to controls (Lucas *et al.*, 1993*b*; Balachandran *et al.*, 1995). Although there was no significant difference in the total dry weight of plants either expressing or not expressing the TMV-MP, root mass of the former was significantly lower, resulting in a significantly lower root-to-shoot ratio (Lucas *et al.*, 1993*b*). These results indicate that constitutive expression of the TMV-MP affects some aspects of photosynthate partitioning. Since the TMV-MP gene is expressed in these transgenic tobacco plants under the control of the 35S cauliflower mosaic virus (CaMV) promoter and the protein is expressed in leaves, stems and roots (Deom *et al.*, 1990), we attempted to identify the specific site at which the TMV-MP exerts its effect on biomass distribution. Reciprocal grafts made between the control and TMV-MP-expressing plants established that expression of the MP was necessary only in leaf tissue. As shown in Figure 2A, when the scion (shoot) expressed the TMV-MP, the root-to-shoot ratio was low, whereas a high value of this ratio was obtained when the scion did not express the TMV-MP. Analysis of root mass (in a separate experiment) established that expression of the TMV-MP in the scion inhibits root development, while root mass was identical to that of control plants even though the protein was expressed in the root but was absent from the scion (Fig. 2B).

Interestingly, expression of the TMV-MP in the vasculature (under the control of a tissue-specific promoter [rolC]) resulted in control-type partitioning of assimilates as well as root-to-shoot ratios (Balachandran *et al.*, 1995). These results suggest that the TMV-MP need only be present in the mesophyll tissue to affect assimilate partitioning between the various plant organs.

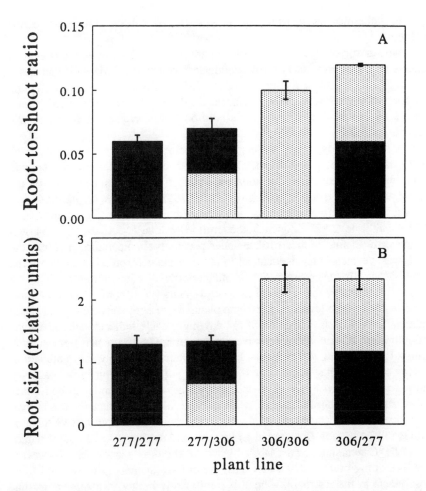

Figure 2. Root-to-shoot ratios (A) and root size (B) obtained from experiments performed on grafted transgenic tobacco plants expressing either the TMV-MP (line 277) or the vector control (line 306). Control plants were grafted with the stock and scion from the same line. Data for A was redrawn from Balachandran *et al*. (1995). Root size was determined using relative units with 1 and 3 representing the smallest and highest masses, respectively.

The Pleiotropic Nature of the TMV-MP

The significant differences between the vector control and TMV-MP-expressing plants, in terms of carbon metabolism, ^{14}C-photosynthate export from source leaves, and biomass distribution, clearly establish that constitutive expression of the TMV-MP gene within the tobacco plant influences, by some as yet unknown mechanism, the process(es) of carbon transport via the phloem.

Most surprisingly, an alteration in photosynthate distribution was evident after application of $^{14}CO_2$ to the young leaf before the TMV-MP had influenced plasmodesmal SEL (Lucas *et al.*, 1993*b*; Olesinski *et al.*, 1995). Young leaves of TMV-MP-expressing plants retained 76% of the newly fixed carbon 24 h after exposure to $^{14}CO_2$, while only 64% was retained in young control leaves.

A further study, aimed at determining the relationship between the TMV-MP's alteration of plasmodesmal SEL and its effect on carbon metabolism\ transport, included transgenic tobacco plants in which mutant forms of the TMV-MP were expressed (Olesinski *et al.*, 1995). Studies of plasmodesmal SEL in transgenic plants expressing a temperature-sensitive (ts) mutant TMV-MP (plant line 2-72), in which the proline residue at amino acid 154 was changed to alanine, indicated that under permissive temperatures (24°C), the SEL was elevated to levels identical to those of plants expressing the wild-type TMV-MP. However, after 6 h at nonpermissive temperatures (32°C), the SEL was similar to that detected in control plants (Wolf *et al.*, 1991). Analysis of carbohydrate levels in transgenic plants expressing the wild-type or the ts mutant TMV-MP as a function of the day/night cycle indicated similar values in both plant lines under permissive temperatures (24°C), which were significantly higher during the afternoon hours as compared to the values obtained in vector control plants (Olesinski *et al.*, 1995). The reduction in radioactivity during the first few hours after $^{14}CO_2$-labeling was also similar in both plant lines expressing the TMV-MPs, with the rate being significantly lower than that measured on vector control plants. Pretreatment at nonpermissive temperatures (32-34°C) for 72 h caused an increase and **similar** overall rate of reduction of ^{14}C remaining in the labeled leaves of the three plant lines. However, the interesting point is that under these conditions, sucrose, glucose, and fructose levels in the afternoon were still significantly higher in plants expressing the wild-type or ts mutant TMV-MP, as compared to the values obtained in the control line.

Results from the two systems, young leaves of transgenic plants expressing wild-type TMV-MP and mature leaves expressing a ts mutant form of the MP (at nonpermissive temperatures), demonstrated that carbohydrate metabolism and translocation in the leaf can be affected without significant changes in plasmodesmal SEL. These results indicate that the TMV-MP has a pleiotropic effect on the physiological functioning of the leaf.

Effect of TMV-MP Mutants on Carbohydrate Metabolism in Source Leaves

Mutational analysis of the TMV-MP gene in infectious clones and generation and analysis of transgenic plants expressing wild-type and mutant forms of this protein, as well as microinjection techniques, have been used to identify functional domains within the TMV-MP (Lucas and Gilbertson, 1994). The role of the C-terminus of the TMV-MP in dilation of plasmodesmal microchannels was investigated using transgenic plants expressing various C-terminal deletions (Berna et al., 1991). This study established that the C-terminus is not required for the TMV-MP-induced increase in plasmodesmal SEL. Dye-coupling studies showed that TMV-MP, from which up to 55 amino acids had been deleted, still allowed movement of a 9.4-kD F-dextran between mesophyll cells. However, this effect was eliminated when the protein was truncated by 77 or 108 amino acids. Carbohydrate analysis again indicated significantly higher levels of sucrose and starch, in the afternoon, in transgenic plants expressing the wild-type TMV-MP as compared to vector control lines. Interestingly, transgenic plants expressing TMV-MP which was truncated by only 10 amino acids exhibited similar (or slightly lower) levels of sucrose and starch as compared to vector control plants (Fig. 3). Analysis of biomass partitioning indicated that similar values of root-to-shoot ratio were present in two independent transformants expressing this 10 amino acid deletion mutant MP, with the value obtained from the control line being significantly higher than that obtained in plants expressing the wild-type MP (Balachandran et al., 1995). Transgenic plants expressing MP truncated by 73 or 108 amino acids (plant lines MP-4 and MP-5, respectively) exhibited significantly higher levels of carbohydrates than control plants (Fig. 3). It is important to note that both sucrose and starch levels in plant line MP-5 were similar to those in plant line 277 (expressing a wild-type MP), although in both MP-4 and MP-5, no influence of the mutant MP was detected on plasmodesmal function (Berna et al., 1991). The restoration of the MP's effect on carbohydrate levels when 35 or 55 amino acids were deleted from the C-terminus was evident when the MP was expressed in a different genetic background, N. tabacum Xanthi NN, (plant line 2004 expressed the MP, versus the vector control plant line 3001). Since the different mutated MPs were expressed in transgenic tobacco plants of different genetic backgrounds, the comparisons were made with their respective controls (plant lines MP-2 and MP-3 are Xanthi NN, while plant lines MP-1, MP-4 and MP-5 are Xanthi nn).

The most pronounced effect on phenotype of transgenic tobacco plants expressing the TMV-MP was observed in a mutant form (plant line MP-9) in which the N-terminal 3-5 amino acids had been deleted (Lapidot et al., 1993). These plants exhibited an overall reduction in plant morphology, including plant height, leaf number and total biomass as compared with either transgenic plants expressing the wild-type MP or vector controls (Balachandran et al., 1995). However, despite the significant reduction in total biomass of these plants, the root-to-shoot ratio resembled the value observed in plant line 277, which was significantly lower than that of plant line 306. Diurnal changes of

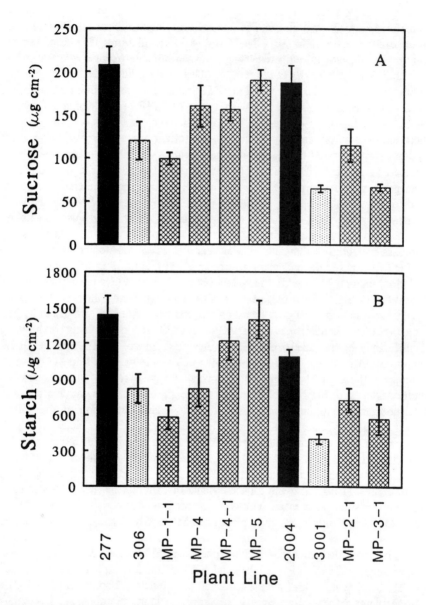

Figure 3. Sucrose (A) and starch (B) content within leaves of transgenic tobacco plants expressing wild-type (plant lines 277 and 2004), C-terminal deletion mutants (plant lines MP-1-1, MP-2-1, MP-3-1, MP-4, MP-4-1, and MP-5, and vector control (plant lines 306 and 3001). Plant lines 2004, 3001, MP-2, and MP-3 are Xanthi NN, while plant lines 277, 306, MP-1, MP-4, and MP-5 are Xanthi nn.

Table I. *Carbohydrate Content Within Source Leaves of Transgenic Tobacco Plants Expressing Wild-Type (line 277), a Vector Control (line 306), an N-Terminal 3-5 Amino Acids Deletion Mutant Plant (line MP-9), and a Control Line Mn-6 (contained the TMV-MP gene, but did not have detectable protein levels)*

Samples for carbohydrate analyses were taken at 1800 HR. Sugars and starch presented as μg cm^{-2} and μg glucose equivalent cm^{-2}, respectively. Six plants of each line were used and values represent mean $\pm$ SE.

Plant Line	Sucrose	Glucose	Fructose	Starch
277	177±9	194±46	163±36	992±127
306	116±7	107±15	126±15	758±74
MP-9	145±22	181±14	180±20	1020±61
Mn-6	60±9	37±11	53±13	548±72

carbohydrate level in source leaves of this plant line also resembled the pattern observed in plant line 277, resulting in significantly higher levels of sucrose and starch in the afternoon (Table I).

DISCUSSION

The data presented provide strong support for the hypothesis that the TMV-MP has pleiotropic effects on source tobacco leaves. The mode of action of this protein, in terms of altering biomass partitioning and carbohydrate metabolism in source leaves, is completely independent of the mechanism by which it acts to increase plasmodesmal SEL (Fig. 4A).

Our dye-coupling studies revealed that the C-terminus is not required for MP-induced increases in plasmodesmal SEL (Berna *et al.*, 1991). However, deletion of 10 amino acids from the C-terminus eliminated the effect of the MP on carbohydrate metabolism and root-to-shoot ratio. Interestingly, deletion of more than 10 amino acids gradually restored the wild-type TMV-MP phenotype (Fig. 4C). These results indicate that the site, via which the MP affects carbon metabolism/transport, is associated with the C-terminus, or with the tertiary structure of the protein which is determined by this region of the MP. It is also important to note that a region within the C-terminus contains a putative phosphorylation domain on the TMV-MP (Citovsky *et al.*, 1993). An 83-amino acid domain (130-213) was suggested to be essential for increasing plasmodesmal SEL (Fig. 4B). It is possible that this domain contains at least two motifs, one involved in targeting the MP to the plasmodesma, and a second that affects plasmodesmal function (alteration in SEL). Deletion of more

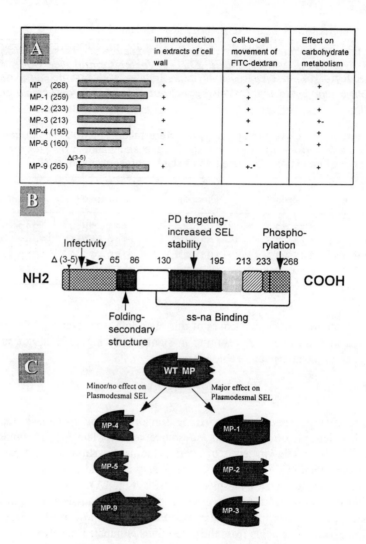

Figure 4. Characterization of the C-terminal truncated TMV-MP constructs, the detection of the respective proteins in cell walls of transgenic tobacco plants and functioning of these proteins in terms of effect on plasmodesmal SEL and on carbohydrate metabolism (A). Functional domains identified within the TMV MP (B). Model for the pleiotropic effect of the TMV-MP (C). Plant lines MP-1, MP-2, and MP-3 express a MP in which the site affecting plasmodesmal SEL is intact, while in plant lines MP-4, MP-5 and MP-9, this site is truncated/modified. The toothed pattern on the TMV-MP represents an active site which affects carbohydrate metabolism, while the blunt pattern represents a modification in the structure of this site which blocks the effect on carbohydrate metabolism.

than 55 amino acids from the C-terminus eliminated the effect of the MP on plasmodesmal SEL, without altering its influence on carbohydrate accumulation in source leaves, indicating that the two sites of action of this protein are independent. In this regard, it is interesting to note that deletion of three amino acids (3-5) from the N-terminus, caused an inhibition of viral systemic infection and reduced the extent of alteration in plasmodesmal SEL (Lapidot *et al.*, 1993). Although the level of MP in these transgenic plants (plant line MP-9) was approximately 1/20th of that detected in line 277, they still exhibited similar characteristics in terms of root-to-shoot ratio and source leaf accumulation of carbohydrates.

A relatively simple explanation for the inhibition of sucrose transport may relate to the mechanism of sugar transfer from cell to cell. Targeting of the MP to plasmodesmal proteins may cause **specific** inhibition of sucrose transport despite the increase in SEL. If this is the case, it may well be that sucrose transfer through plasmodesmata does not occur by diffusion alone. This explanation can be supported by a recent theoretical study of symplasmic transport of sucrose in the primary root tip of maize (Bret-Harte and Silk, 1994). These authors concluded that the current interpretation of plasmodesmal structure and function is incompatible with symplasmic diffusion as the sole transport mechanism for sucrose.

An alternative explanation for the pleiotropic effect of TMV-MP may relate to the recent findings that macromolecules can traffic through plasmodesmata. If carbon fixation, sucrose synthesis, starch accumulation, and sugar transport are coordinated in a programmed manner, which involves the transport of endogenous signaling protein through plasmodesmata, interaction of the TMV-MP with such proteins may affect their transport which could alter the manner by which this program functions (Wolf and Lucas, 1994; Balachandran *et al.*, 1995).

The fact that carbohydrate accumulation in source leaves was also evident in plants expressing a truncated form of the TMV-MP (73 and 108 amino acids) may suggest that this influence (function) of the MP is not associated with plasmodesmata, since the MP was not detected in the cell-wall fraction of plants expressing these mutants MPs (Berna *et al.*, 1991). It may well be that the detection procedure was not sensitive enough to identify the existence of such truncated MP in this fraction. However, since the MP is able to bind RNA and ssDNA (Citovsky *et al.*, 1990), we cannot rule out the possibility that the second function is due to interference of the MP with other cellular processes.

ACKNOWLEDGMENTS

This work was supported by United States-Israel Binational Science Foundation grant No. 90-00070 (S.W.; W.J.L), United States-Israel Binational

Agricultural Research and Development Fund (BARD) grant No. IS-1968-91R (S.W.; W.J.L), and National Science Foundation grant No. DCB-90-16756 (W.J.L.).

LITERATURE CITED

Balachandran S, Hull R, Vaadia Y, Wolf S, Lucas WJ (1995) Tobacco mosaic virus movement protein-induced change in carbon partitioning originates from the mesophyll and is independent of change in plasmodesmal size exclusion limit. Plant Cell Environ (in press)

Berna A, Gafny R, Wolf S, Lucas WJ, Holt CA, Beachy RN (1991) The TMV movement protein: role of the C-terminal 73 amino acids in subcellular localization and function. Virology 182: 682-689

Bret-Harte SM, Silk WK (1994) Nonvascular, symplasmic diffusion of sucrose cannot satisfy the carbon demands of growth in the primary root tip of Zea mays L. Plant Physiol 105: 19-33

Citovsky V, Knorr D, Schuster G, Zambryski P (1990) The P30 movement protein of tobacco mosaic virus is a single stranded nucleic acid binding protein. Cell 60: 637-647

Citovsky V, McLean BG, Zupan JR, Zambryski P (1993) Phosphorylation of tobacco mosaic virus cell-to-cell movement protein by a developmentally regulated plant cell wall-associated protein kinase. Genes Dev 7: 904-910

Deom CM, Lapidot M, Beachy RN (1992) Plant virus movement proteins. Cell 69: 221-224

Deom CM, Oliver MJ, Beachy RN (1987) The 30-kilodalton gene product of tobacco mosaic virus potentiates virus movement. Science 237: 389-394

Deom CM, Schubert K, Wolf S, Holt C, Lucas WJ, Beachy RN (1990) Molecular characterization and biological function of the movement protein of tobacco mosaic virus in transgenic plants. Proc Natl Acad Sci USA 87: 3284-3288

Ding B, Haudenshield JS, Hull RJ, Wolf S, Beachy RN, Lucas WJ (1992) Secondary plasmodesmata are specific sites of localization of the tobacco mosaic virus movement protein in transgenic tobacco plants. Plant Cell 4: 915-928

Fujiwara T, Geisman-Cookmeyer D, Ding B, Lommel SA, Lucas WJ (1993) Cell-to-cell trafficking of macromolecules through plasmodesmata potentiated by the red clover necrotic mosaic virus movement protein. Plant Cell 5: 1783-1794

Lapidot M, Gafny R, Wolf S, Ding B, Lucas WJ, Beachy R (1993) Transgenic plants that express a non-functional tobacco mosaic virus movement protein are resistant to virus infection. Plant J 4: 959-970

Lucas WJ, Ding B, Van der Schoot C (1993a) Plasmodesmata and the supracellular nature of plants. New Phytol 125: 435-476

Lucas WJ, Gilbertson RL (1994) Plasmodesmata in relation to viral movement within leaf tissues. Annu Rev Phytopath 32: 387-411

Lucas WJ, Olesinski A, Hull RJ, Haudenshield JS, Deom CM, Beachy RN, Wolf S (1993*b*) Influence of the tobacco mosaic virus 30-kDa movement protein on carbon metabolism and photosynthate partitioning in transgenic tobacco plants. Planta **190**: 88-96

Lucas WJ, Wolf S (1993) Plasmodesmata: the intercellular organelle of green plants. Trends Cell Biol **3**: 308-315

Maule AJ (1991) Virus movement in infected plants. Crit Rev Plant Sci **9**: 457-473

Noueiry AO, Lucas WJ, Gilbertson RL (1994) Two proteins of a plant DNA virus coordinate nuclear and plasmodesmata transport. Cell **76**: 925-932

Olesinski AA, Lucas WJ, Galun E, Wolf S (1995) Pleiotropic effects of TMV-MP on carbon metabolism and export in transgenic tobacco plants. Planta (in press)

Tomenius K, Clapham D, Meshi T (1987) Localization by immunogold cytochemistry of the virus-coded 30K protein in plasmodesmata of leaves infected with tobacco mosaic virus. Virology **160**: 363-371

Tucker JE, Mauzerall D, Tucker EB (1989) Symplastic transport of carboxyfluorescein in staminal hairs of *Setcreasea purpurea* is diffusive and includes loss to the vacuole. Plant Physiol **90**: 1143-1147

Tyree MT (1970) The symplast concept. A general theory of symplastic transport according to the thermodynamics of irreversible processes. J Theor Biol **26**: 181-214

van Bel AJE (1993) Strategies of phloem loading. Annu Rev Plant Physiol Plant Mol Biol **44**: 253-281

Waigmann E, Lucas WJ, Citovsky V, Zambryski P (1994) Direct functional assay for tobacco mosaic virus cell-to-cell movement protein and identification of a domain involved in increasing plasmodesmata permeability. Proc Natl Acad Sci USA **91**: 1433-1437

Wolf S, Deom CM, Beachy RN, Lucas WJ (1989) Movement protein of tobacco mosaic virus modifies plasmodesmatal size exclusion limit. Science **246**: 377-379

Wolf S, Deom CM, Beachy RN, Lucas WJ (1991) Plasmodesmatal functioning is probed using transgenic tobacco plants that express a virus movement protein. Plant Cell **3**: 593-604

Wolf S, Lucas WJ (1994) Virus movement protein and other molecular probes of plasmodesmatal function. Plant Cell Environ **17**: 573-585

Relationships Between Viral Infection and Carbohydrate Accumulation and Metabolism

Laszlö I. Técsi, Alison M. Smith, Andrew J. Maule, and Richard C. Leegood

Robert Hill Institute and Department of Animal and Plant Sciences, University of Sheffield, Sheffield S10 2UQ, UK (L.I.T.; R.C.L.); and John Innes Centre, Norwich Research Park, Colney Lane, Norwich NR4 7UH, UK (A.M.S.; A.J.M.)

The majority of investigations concerning plant viruses have been directed toward understanding the structure, genetics, transport, and localization of viruses in plants. However, far less is known about the physiological impact of virus infection on host plant metabolism (Zaitlin and Hull, 1987). From many examples (reviewed in Goodman *et al.*, 1986; Fraser, 1987), it is clear that virus infection alters both photosynthetic capacity and carbohydrate partitioning in leaves, often leading to an accumulation of starch (e.g. Cohen and Loebenstein, 1975; Roberts and Wood, 1982) and a shift in the partitioning of photosynthate toward starch and organic and amino acids, at the expense of soluble sugars (Goodman *et al.*, 1965; Bedbrook and Matthews, 1973). In spite of the large impact of many virus infections upon plant yield, the mechanisms by which these changes occur have not been systematically studied. Only a few attempts have been made to dissect the complex physiological processes which lead to symptoms characteristic of a susceptible virus/host interaction (e.g. Hodgson *et al.*, 1989; Reinero and Beachy, 1989; van Kooten *et al.*, 1990).

VIRUSES CAN ALTER SINK-SOURCE INTERACTIONS

Red clover mottle comovirus (RCMV) typically causes slight mosaic symptoms, followed by chlorosis, reduction, and malformation of shoot apices in pea plants. The 'O' strain specifically produces top necrosis on pea (Oxefelt, 1976). The pattern of infection of pea plants with RCMV-O is similar to that recognized for other plant viruses. In this process virus replicates in cells of the inoculated leaf, moves systemically through the vascular tissues and invades young leaves prior to a critical stage in development, probably when they are still acting as net sinks rather than sources for photosynthate (Leisner et al., 1993). Hence, RCMV-O multiplies extensively in the inoculated leaves and accumulates in the young tissues of the apex, but it does not infect intervening leaves (Tésci et al., 1992). Infection of pea plants with RCMV-O results in a large increase in the starch content of leaves between the inoculated leaf and the apex, in which no virus multiplication occurs. Thus, starch accumulation in these leaves is not a direct metabolic consequence of virus replication in photosynthesizing cells. Técsi et al. (1992) showed that the removal of the apex as a major sink also led to the retention of photosynthate in source leaves in the form of starch. Such observations emphasize that, in attempts to study metabolic changes in the leaves of virus-infected plants, it is important to determine the extent of both virus multiplication and virus invasion of the tissues. The interaction between pea and RCMV-O is an example where alterations in starch accumulation result not from a specific interference in the synthesis or breakdown of starch, but from a disturbance of sink-source relationships in the infected plant. This altered relationship within the infected whole plant is an important, but rather indirect, effect of the virus infection.

NATURE OF THE LESIONS CAUSED BY MOSAIC INFECTIONS

Starch is known to accumulate in lesions and in mosaic regions of tissue infected by mosaic viruses (Israel and Ross, 1967; Cohen and Loebenstein, 1975; Ehara and Misawa, 1975). Técsi et al. (1994a) studied host responses to viral infection during the interaction between cucumber mosaic virus (CMV) and the cotyledons of vegetable marrow (*Cucurbita pepo* L.). This susceptible host/virus combination results in chlorotic lesions on inoculated cotyledons and a chlorotic mosaic on systemically-infected young leaves, leading to significant yellowing and stunting of the mature plant.

Técsi et al. (1994a) defined the relationships between virus accumulation, starch, and photosynthetic activity within a single lesion. The first visible symptoms of inoculation of CMV onto the cotyledons of *C. pepo* are chlorotic lesions after 4 d. These expand and coalesce to give a generalized chlorosis after 10 d. However, appreciable starch accumulation (visualized by iodine staining) occurred in lesions even by 2 d after infection. Immunolocalization of the sites of virus accumulation (using an antibody to the viral coat protein) in tissue prints of inoculated cotyledons showed that sites of starch accumulation always coincided with the sites of virus accumulation 2 d after infection. As infection proceeded, starch became confined to particular regions of the lesion. At day 4, starch was visible in a small group of cells at the center of the lesion and in a ring which approximately coincided with the outer edge of the region of infected cells. The region between the central dot of starch and the outer ring contained little or no starch. By day 6, this dot and ring pattern of starch accumulation persisted but became diffuse as adjacent infected regions coalesced. Very occasionally, the region between the central dot and the outer ring of starch was not devoid of starch, but contained concentric rings of starch. The number of concentric rings corresponded to the number of days post-infection, consistent with a diurnal component to the synthesis and perhaps the degradation of starch in the lesion. Studies of the exact location of starch and virus were made both in adjacent sections of serially-sectioned, infected cotyledons and by micro-dissection of iodine-stained cotyledons. Analysis of tissue at 4 d post-infection revealed that lesions had a complex three-dimensional structure (Fig. 1). Virus was present in a region which extended through the cross-section of the cotyledon, but usually did not include the abaxial epidermis. Within this infected region, all cell types contained virus particles. Starch accumulation, in contrast, occurred only within mesophyll cells. The central dot of starch consisted of a region of cells of high starch content within the palisade mesophyll. The starch ring consisted of a

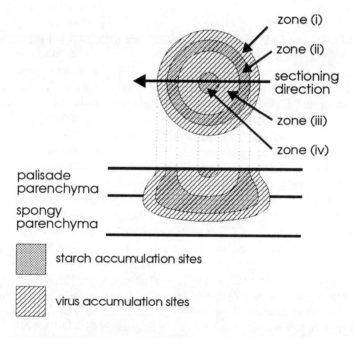

Figure 1. Schematic diagram of the distribution of virus and starch in a lesion on day 4 post-infection. From the outside in, the infected region consists of four zones of cells (see text).

zone of cells with high starch content positioned inside, but close to, the outer edge of the infected area. Técsi *et al.* (1994*a*) additionally measured chlorophyll fluorescence quenching (by image analysis) and $^{14}CO_2$ fixation. From the outside in, the infected region at about 4 d post-infection consists of (Fig. 1):

(*i*) a zone of cells which may have an elevated level of photosynthesis, but which does not yet have high levels of starch;

(*ii*) a zone which probably consists of cells with high photosynthetic activity (fast chlorophyll fluorescence quenching, high CO_2 assimilation) and low starch accumulation at its outer edge and cells of relatively low photosynthetic activity, but high starch content, at its inner edge;

(*iii*) a zone of largely starchless cells which are starting to become chlorotic and which have a low photosynthetic activity (slow chlorophyll fluorescence quenching, low CO_2 assimilation);

(*iv*) a relatively stable group of infected cells which has high photosynthetic activity and high starch content.

Clearly then, the CMV-induced lesion is not homogeneous, but is a dynamic structure composed of circular zones of cells of diverse physiology. At a later stage in senescing infected cotyledons, after about 10 d, chlorophyll is retained in the outer ring and occasionally in the central dot regions of the lesion, with clear parallels to the 'green islands' found in fungal infections. The arrangement of the lesion as a ring of chlorotic or necrotic tissue surrounding a central dot, frequently referred to as a 'ringspot', is a common feature for a wide range of host/virus interactions (Matthews, 1991). A ring and dot pattern of high $^{14}CO_2$ assimilation has been described for leaves of tobacco infected with tobacco mosaic virus (Doke and Hirai, 1970*a*). A similar low fluorescence quenching inner region surrounded by a zone of high fluorescence quenching has been observed in lesions in tobacco caused by tobacco mosaic virus (Balachandran *et al.*, 1994*a, b*).

The precise relationship between the zones of cells within the lesion remains unknown. However, the immediate proximity and partial coincidence of cells with high rates of photosynthesis and cells with high starch contents indicates strongly that starch accumulation is a direct result of elevated rates of photosynthesis caused by viral infection. This view is reinforced by the observation that starch accumulation in infected cells is dependent upon direct illumination of those cells (Técsi *et al.*, 1994*a*). The progressive expansion of the starch-free zone behind the starch ring indicates that starch is being mobilized within cells at the inner border of the starch ring. The fact that respiration rates increase in virus-infected tissues (see below) suggests that this starch may be simply respired. The starch-free zone then becomes chlorotic. In contrast, the central dot surrounding the initial point of infection retains photosynthetic activity and a high starch content for at least the first 4 to 6 d of the infection.

EFFECTS OF VIRAL INFECTION ON CARBOHYDRATE METABOLISM

In susceptible virus-host interactions, apart from changes in carbohydrate partitioning discussed above, there are generally localized changes in the rate of respiration (Menke and Walker, 1963) and increases in the synthesis of amino and organic acids (Bedbrook and Matthews, 1973; Magyarosy *et al.*, 1973). Historically, most studies of physiological changes associated with virus infection have regarded infected leaves as uniformly-responding tissues. The localized and metabolically-complex regions of infection illustrated in Figure 1 mean that such an approach can only give an average measure of the physiological responses of the host. However, if taken together with a knowledge of the nature and time-course of development of the lesions, these measurements on whole organs can increase our understanding of the metabolism of the lesions.

Recent measurements of metabolic changes occurring during infection of *C. pepo* by CMV provide a broader picture of metabolic perturbations during the development of infection than has previously been available for any virus infection (Técsi *et al.*, 1994*b*). They show:

(*i*) that infection has a large effect on the capacity for respiration and the respiratory flux. Activities of enzymes of the Krebs cycle (isocitrate dehydrogenase, fumarase) and electron transport (cytochrome oxidase) rose by between 20 and 40%, and respiration rates were significantly larger (by 70%) in infected than in uninfected cotyledons. Increased respiration rates have frequently been observed in virus-infected tissues (Owen, 1958; Jensen, 1968; Dwurazna and Weintraub, 1969; Leal and Lastra, 1984; Goodman *et al.*, 1986);

(*ii*) that infection clearly alters the carbohydrate metabolism of cotyledons. Enzymes involved in glycolysis, such as ATP- and PPi-dependent phosphofructokinases, increased in infected cotyledons (Fig. 2), consistent with the increase in respiratory capacity. Activities of enzymes unique to the oxidative pentose-phosphate pathway (Glu-6-P dehydrogenase and 6-phosphogluconate dehydrogenase) doubled in infected plants, which may reflect enhanced demand for reductants and precursors for the synthesis of amino and nucleic acids;

(*iii*) that at an early stage of infection the starch content was higher and the sucrose content lower in infected than in uninfected cotyledons (see also Goodman *et al.*, 1986). Despite the fact that starch accumulated in lesions, this was very localized and there was a decrease in the starch content of the cotyledon as a whole. This was accompanied by a decline in the activity of ADP-glucose pyrophosphorylase, an enzyme which is directly involved in starch synthesis, and an increase in the capacity for starch degradation. Consistent with this, in the later stages of infection, infected cotyledons incorporated more recently-assimilated $^{14}CO_2$ into soluble sugars and less into structural carbohydrates and starch than uninfected cotyledons;

(iv) that although there are no large overall changes in photosynthetic capacity, there are undoubtedly local changes in the rate of photosynthesis, as revealed by different patterns of chlorophyll fluorescence quenching discussed above. The activity of Rubisco also declined in infected tissue (see also Balachandran et al., 1994b).

These studies by Técsi et al. (1994a, b) indicate that increases in respiration and the capacity for oxidative carbohydrate metabolism of the whole cotyledon are associated with the period during which the inner chlorotic zone becomes the dominant feature of the lesions and occupies a large area of the cotyledons. If the increases were due to metabolic changes in inner-zone cells, in which loss of starch is followed by chlorosis, we would expect to find increases in the capacity for oxidative carbohydrate metabolism in these cells which are many times greater than those measured on a whole-cotyledon basis.

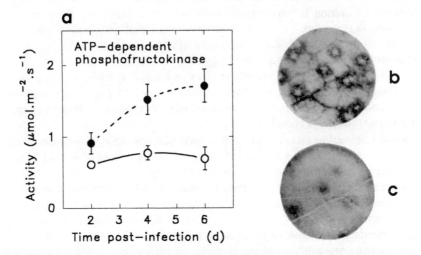

Figure 2. (a) Changes in maximum catalytic activity of ATP-dependent phosphofructokinase in CMV-infected marrow cotyledons following infection (from Técsi et al., 1994a). Infected cotyledons (●), healthy cotyledons (O). (b) Accumulation of starch and a corresponding tissue print of ATP-dependent phosphofructokinase activity (right) in CMV-infected marrow cotyledons 4 d after infection (shown 1.5 x actual size).

Such a hypothesis can be tested by studying changes in the biochemistry of small groups of cells within the expanding lesion, using such techniques as microdissection, immunolocalization, and *in situ* hybridization. Figure 2 shows measurements which illustrate the increase in activity during infection, together with a tissue print stained for activity of ATP-dependent phosphofructokinase in cotyledons of *C. pepo* 4 d after infection. It is clear that ATP-phosphofructokinase increases in the inner, chlorotic, region of the lesion. Increased activities of defence-related enzymes (peroxidase, polyphenol oxidase, α-glucosidase) have also been detected in the vicinity of lesions by using leaf tissue prints (Avidiushko *et al.*, 1993).

HOW DOES THE VIRUS EXERT ITS EFFECTS ON METABOLISM?

The complexity of mosaic lesions suggests that viral infection could interfere with normal carbohydrate metabolism of leaf cells in more than one way. The pattern of altered physiology is indicative of a series of metabolic events occurring over several days following viral replication within a cell. We need to know: (*i*) what factors are responsible for the increased rate of photosynthesis at the outer parts of the lesion and whether or not they are directly linked to virus replication; (*ii*) what factors are responsible for the decline in the rate of photosynthesis, the loss of starch and the development of chlorosis (senescence) in cells behind the zone of viral replication; (*iii*) if starch accumulation is caused by increased assimilation, by a blockage of export, by decreased degradation, or by a combination of these effects; and (*iv*) whether or not accumulation of the virus could act as a sink for photosynthate. Answers to these questions are now beginning to emerge.

The first concerns the role of the virus as a sink. If sufficient virus were to accumulate, it could act as a sink for carbon and nitrogen, with a resultant redirection of metabolism and a stimulation of photosynthesis. In many fungal infections, starch accumulates inside infected lesions, particularly those described as dark green islands. It is believed that this is because fungal growth causes the lesions to become sinks for photosynthate produced in surrounding uninfected regions of the leaf. This process may be different from that operating in CMV-induced lesions, where starch accumulation is dependent upon photosynthesis in the cells of the lesion rather than the import of photosynthate from uninfected regions. Most of the metabolic changes in such viral infections are unlikely to be related directly to the diversion of carbon from normal metabolism into the synthesis of viral components. Although a few previous studies (e.g. Doke and Hirai, 1970*b*) have quantified the amount of the virus and total protein of the same leaf during the infection process, viral synthesis may occur only in a narrow zone of cells at the periphery of the lesions (Técsi *et al.*, 1994*a*), and it has been shown that viral proteins represent less than 1% of the leaf protein after 6 d (Técsi *et al.*, 1994*b*). Despite this, there are significant alterations on a whole-cotyledon basis in the activities of enzymes involved in a range of primary metabolic processes (Técsi *et al.*, 1994*b*). Since these alterations are localized to specific regions of the lesions (Fig. 2), they must be very substantial within the affected cells (Avidiushko *et al.*, 1993). The synthesis and accumulation of virus must, therefore, interfere with normal metabolism in ways other than simply draining carbon for synthesis of viral particles in the cells in which viral synthesis is occurring.

The second consideration is the extent to which the presence of the viral movement protein and modification of the plasmodesmata (Ding *et al.*, 1992) could interfere with movement of photosynthate and the partitioning of carbon. Expression of the tobacco mosaic virus movement protein in transgenic tobacco led to an *increase* in soluble sugars and starch in source leaves, consistent with interference, by some unknown mechanism, of export of sugars from the phloem (Lucas *et al.*, 1993). However, while this observation could be causally related to starch accumulation in the CMV lesions, it does not explain the complexity of the lesions.

The third consideration is how replication of the virus might interfere with host gene expression. We know that the virus is more or less uniformly distributed throughout mosaic lesions (Fig. 1), but we also need to know in which of these cells virus replication is occurring because viral replication might interfere with gene expression in host cells and thereby interfere with host metabolism. This can be done using *in situ* hybridization techniques. Viruses with positive-strand RNA genomes, such as CMV, replicate via a complementary negative strand. Recent work with a different RNA virus has indicated that the presence of the negative strand of RNA is a good indicator of the location of recent virus replication, presumably because (-) RNA is turned over quickly (Wang and Maule, 1995). We are currently studying the location of viral replication in marrow cotyledons infected with CMV. Such techniques, together with immunolocalization, can also be utilized to study localized changes in amounts of transcript and protein of various enzymes whose activities change during infection.

Of course, there are other ways of approaching these problems by using mutants of the host (e.g. in starch synthesis) or variants of the virus. A feature such as chlorosis could be initiated by a localized buildup of carbohydrate (Stitt *et al.*, 1990), but it may be due to a more direct effect of viral infection, since genetically-defined strains of CMV have been isolated which vary in their ability to induce chlorosis. This characteristic is related to only one or a few nucleotide changes in either the satellite RNA (Sleat and Palukaitis, 1992) or the coat protein cistron (Shintaku *et al.*, 1992).

ACKNOWLEDGMENTS

This research was supported by research grants from the Agricultural and Food Research Council, U.K. (LRG 213 and PO1459).

LITERATURE CITED

Avidiushko SA, Ye XS, Kuc J (1993) Detection of several enzymatic activities in leaf prints of cucumber plant. Physiol Mol Plant Pathol **42**: 441-454

Balachandran S, Osmond B, Daley P (1994*a*) Diagnosis of the earliest strain-specific interactions between tobacco mosaic virus and chloroplasts of tobacco leaves *in vivo* by means of chlorophyll fluorescence imaging. Plant Physiol **104**: 1059-1065

Balachandran S, Osmond B, Makino A (1994*b*) Effects of two strains of tobacco mosaic virus on photosynthetic characteristics and nitrogen partitioning in leaves of *Nicotiana tabacum* cv Xanthi during photoacclimation under two nitrogen nutrition regimes. Plant Physiol **104**: 1043-1050

Bedbrook JR, Matthews REF (1973) Changes in the flow of early products of photosynthetic carbon fixation associated with the replication of TYMV. Virology 53: 84-91

Cohen J, Loebenstein G (1975) An electron microscope study of starch lesions in cucumber cotyledons infected with tobacco mosaic virus. Phytopathology **65**: 32-39

Ding B, Haudenshield JS, Hull RJ, Wolf S, Beachy RN, Lucas WJ (1992) Secondary plasmodesmata are specific sites of localization of the tobacco mosaic virus movement protein in transgenic tobacco plants. Plant Cell **4**: 915-928

Doke N, Hirai, T (1970) Effects of tobacco mosaic virus infection on photosynthetic CO_2 fixation and $^{14}CO_2$ incorporation into protein in tobacco leaves. Virology 42: 68-77

Doke N, Hirai T (1970) Radioautographic studies on the photosynthetic CO_2 fixation in virus-infected leaves. Phytopathology **60**: 988-991

Dwurazna MM, Weintraub M (1969) Respiration of tobacco leaves infected with different strains of potato virus X. Can J Bot **47**: 723-730

Ehara Y, Misawa, T (1975) Occurrence of abnormal chloroplasts in tobacco leaves infected systemically with the ordinary strain of cucumber mosaic virus. Phytopathology Z **84**: 233-252

Fraser, RSS (1987) Biochemistry of virus-infected plants. Research Studies Press, Letchworth, Hertfordshire

Goodman PJ, Watson MA, Hill ARC (1965) Sugar and fructosan accumulation in virus-infected plants: rapid testing by circular-paper chromatography. Ann Appl Biol **56**: 65-72

Goodman RN, Kiraly Z, Wood KR (1986) The biochemistry and physiology of plant disease. University of Missouri Press, Columbia

Hodgson RAJ, Beachy RN, Pakrasi HB (1989) Selective inhibition of photosystem II in spinach by tobacco mosaic virus: an effect of viral coat protein. FEBS Lett **245**: 267-270

Israel HW, Ross AF (1967) The fine structure of local lesions induced by tobacco mosaic virus in tobacco. Virology 33: 272-286

Jensen SG (1968) Photosynthesis, respiration, and other physiological relationships in barley infected with barley yellow dwarf virus. Phytopathology 58: 204-208

Leal N, Lastra R (1984) Altered metabolism of tomato plants infected with tomato yellow mosaic virus. Physiol Plant Pathol 24: 1-7

Leisner SM, Turgeon R, Howell SH (1993) Effects of host plant development and genetic determinants on the long-distance movement of cauliflower mosaic virus in Arabidopsis. Plant Cell 5: 191-202

Lucas WJ, Olesinski A, Hull RJ, Haudenshield JS, Deom CM, Beachy RN, Wolf S (1993) Influence of the tobacco mosaic virus 30-kDa movement protein on carbon metabolism and photosynthate partitioning in transgenic tobacco plants. Planta 190: 88-96

Magyarosy AC, Buchanan BB, Schürmann P (1973) Effect of systemic virus infection on chloroplast function and structure. Virology 55: 426-438

Matthews REF (1991) Plant Virology, Ed 2. Academic Press, London

Menke GH, Walker JC (1963) Metabolism of resistant and susceptible cucumber varieties infected with cucumber mosaic virus. Phytopathology 53: 1349-1355

Owen PC (1958) Photosynthesis and respiration rates of Nicotiana glutinosa infected with tobacco mosaic virus and of N. tabacum infected with potato virus X. Ann Appl Biol 46: 198-204

Oxelfelt P (1976) Biological and physiological characteristic of three strains of red clover mottle virus. Virology 74: 73-80

Reinero A, Beachy RN (1989) Reduced photosystem II activity and accumulation of viral coat protein in chloroplasts of leaves infected with tobacco mosaic virus. Plant Physiol 89: 111-116

Roberts P L, Wood KR (1982) Effects of severe (P6) and mild (W) strains of cucumber mosaic virus on tobacco leaf chlorophyll, starch and cell ultrastructure. Physiol Plant Pathol 21: 31-37

Shintaku MH, Zhang L, Palukaitis P (1992) A single amino acid substitution in the coat protein of cucumber mosaic virus induces chlorosis in tobacco. Plant Cell 4: 751-757

Sleat DE, Palukaitis P (1992) A single nucleotide change within a plant virus satellite RNA alters the host specificity of disease induction. Plant J 2: 43-50

Stitt M, von Schaewen A, Willmitzer L (1990) "Sink" regulation of photosynthetic metabolism in transgenic tobacco plants expressing yeast invertase in their cell wall involves a decrease of the Calvin-cycle enzymes and an increase in glycolytic enzymes. Planta 183: 40-50

Técsi LI, Wang D, Smith AM, Leegood RC, Maule AJ (1992) Red clover mottle virus infection affects sink-source relationships and starch accumulation in pea plants. J Exp Bot 43: 1409-1412

Técsi LI, Maule AJ, Smith AM, Leegood RC (1994a) Complex, localized changes in CO_2 assimilation and starch content associated with the susceptible interaction between cucumber mosaic virus and a cucurbit host. Plant J 5: 837-847

Técsi LI, Maule AJ, Smith AM, Leegood RC (1994*b*) Metabolic alterations in cotyledons of *Cucurbita pepo* infected by cucumber mosaic virus. J Exp Bot **45:** 1541-1551

van Kooten O, Meurs C, van Loon LC (1990) Photosynthetic electron transport in tobacco leaves infected with tobacco mosaic virus. Physiol Plant **80:** 446-452

Wang D, Maule AJ (1995) Inhibition of host gene expression associated with plant virus replication. Science (in press)

Zaitlin M, Hull R (1987) Plant virus-host interactions. Annu Rev Plant Physiol **38:** 291-315

Sugar-Modulated Expression of Genes for Sucrose Metabolism and Their Relationship to Transport Pathways

Karen E. Koch and Kurt D. Nolte

Plant Molecular and Cellular Biology - Horticultural Sciences, University of Florida, Gainesville, FL 32611, USA

Sucrose in phloem and importing structures can enzymatically enter cellular metabolism by only two known means. The reversible reaction of sucrose synthase often functions in the degradative direction, interchangeably converting sucrose and UDP to fructose and UDPGlc. Alternatively, the invertase reaction hydrolyzes sucrose and water to glucose and fructose. Modification of either of these reactions by sugar regulation of gene expression has the potential to adjust the capacity for sucrose use by importing cells. This possibility is further enhanced by the close relationship between these enzymes and long-distance transport processes.

SUCROSE IMPORT AND SUGAR-RESPONSIVE GENES

A specific group of genes is responsive to changes in sugar levels, yet until relatively recently there was little evidence for this in multicellular organisms. Many animal systems display a near homeostasis for sugars when compared to the wide variability observed among plant parts during development and in response to environmental changes. As immobile organisms, plants have evolved an impressive array of adaptive mechanisms including that of adjusting resource allocation among cells and organs relative to the available supplies (Williams and Farrar, 1990; Farrar and Williams, 1991). Long-distance information on the status of whole-plant carbohydrate availability is conveyed by photosynthetic products moving from exporting to importing regions. Their impact on expression of specific genes at sites of sugar utilization extends beyond their role as essential substrates for heterotrophic cells.

In contrast to the often repressive effects of sugars on genes for enzymes of photosynthesis (Sheen, 1990, 1994; Jang and Sheen, 1994; Thomas and Rodriguez, 1994, 1995), and processes of remobilization (Karrer and

Rodriguez, 1992; Graham *et al.*, 1994), elevated sugar levels typically enhance expression of genes related to processes of storage and/or utilization. These include synthesis of storage proteins such as patatin (Rocha-Sosa *et al.*, 1989; Wenzler *et al.*, 1989; Liu *et al.*, 1991; Grierson *et al.*, 1994), sporamin (Hattori *et al.*, 1990), and vsps (Mason *et al.*, 1992; Sadka *et al.*, 1994). Elevated sugars also up-regulate genes for enzymes involved in starch biosynthesis, including granule-bound starch synthase and branching enzyme (KoBmann *et al.*, 1991; Salehuzzaman *et al.*, 1994), sucrose synthase (Salanoubat and Belliard, 1989; Maas *et al.*, 1990; Karrer and Rodriguez, 1992; Koch *et al.*, 1992; Heim *et al.*, 1993) and one of the ADPG pyrophosphorylase subunits (Müller-Röber *et al.*, 1990). Together, these can presumably affect overall import through their indirect enhancement of capacity for carbon utilization and ultimately the source-to-sink turgor gradient.

A more direct influence of carbohydrate-responsive gene expression on import can be exerted through the sugar sensitivity of genes for enzymes of sucrose metabolism (Koch *et al.*, 1992; Thomas and Rodriguez, 1994). Activity of these enzymes (sucrose synthase and invertase) are closely related to the extent of sucrose import in many systems (Claussen, 1983; Morris and Arthur, 1984*a, b*; Sung *et al.*, 1988; Wang *et al.*, 1993). Sucrose synthase is considered a reasonable indicator of "sink strength" in a number of instances (Sung *et al.*, 1988), and in others, invertases appear to be more closely correlated with import (Morris and Arthur, 1984*a, b*; Shaffer *et al.* 1987*b*; Sung *et al.*, 1994). Capacity for sucrose utilization by a given tissue could therefore respond to changes in photosynthate availability through this mechanism (Koch *et al.*, 1992). Farrar and Williams (1991) have also proposed that the physiology of importing organs can be adjusted relative to carbon supply at the level of gene expression or "coarse control" in addition to the better known metabolic "fine tuning" by adenylates.

SUGAR MODULATION OF SUCROSE SYNTHASE GENES

Sugars and Differential Expression

Genes encoding sucrose synthase are markedly sugar-responsive, but a fascinating contrast is evident between this aspect of the two isozyme genes (*Sus1* and *Sh1*) (Koch *et al.*, 1992). [The isozymes themselves are otherwise very similar (Echt and Chourey, 1985)]. Levels of *Sus1* message (encoding SUS1 protein) rise with increasing levels of metabolizable sugars, reaching an apparent maximum at concentrations equivalent to 2.0% glucose (approximately 110 mM). In contrast, transcripts of the *Sh1* sucrose synthase (encoding SH1 protein) are most abundant at 10-fold lower glucose levels (0.2%, approximately 10 mM), and are reduced by elevated sugar availability. Message for the *Sh1* form also persists longer under conditions of carbohydrate starvation (Koch *et al.*, 1992).

These data help resolve an apparent discrepancy between results obtained earlier on the sugar inducibility of sucrose synthase, which was reported to be both repressed (Koch and McCarty, 1988; Maas et al., 1990), and enhanced by elevated carbon supply (Salanoubat and Belliard, 1989; Karrer and Rodriguez, 1992). The contrasting carbohydrate sensitivity of different sucrose synthase genes was probably responsible (Koch et al., 1992), and is consistent with the reciprocal responses to light treatments observed by Maraña et al. (1990). One impact of this differential expression is to provide a mechanism whereby the *Sus1* form could contribute to adjustment of import capacity in many cells and tissues, while the *Sh1* form could aid prioritization of specific cells or tissues as sucrose recipients during reproduction and/or stress.

Changes in Enzyme Activity and Localization

Long-term responses to sugar availability at the enzyme level are slow, but consistent with hypotheses regarding coarse adjustment of respiratory rates in importing cells/organs (Williams and Farrar, 1990; Farrar and Williams 1991). The entry of sucrose into the respiratory path could theoretically be influenced at the point of its initial breakdown through sucrose synthase or invertase reactions. Sucrose synthase in particular would be an effective link to respiration due to the inherent sensitivity of its reaction to adenylate balance (Geigenberger et al., 1993; Martin et al., 1993) and theoretical conservation of ATP (Huber and Akazawa, 1986; Sung et al., 1988). Data from *sh1* and *sus1* mutants indicates that shifts in enzyme activity at the whole organ level do not become evident until approximately 36 to 48 h (K.D. Nolte, E.R. Duke, D.R. McCarty, and K.E. Koch, unpubl. data).

Figure 1 shows that localization of sucrose synthase can be altered within 24 h of changes in sugar availability. If carbohydrates are depleted in root tips, sucrose synthase immunolabel decreases markedly in the cortex and increases in the epidermis (compare Fig. 3A to 3C). Protein radiolabeling studies indicate that altered localization involves formation of new sucrose synthase (SH1) and not solely a differential turnover (Nolte and Koch, unpubl. data). A contrasting localization is observed in sugar-fed root tips, where sucrose synthase immunolabel is enhanced in a range of cell types across the entire organ (compare Fig. 3A to 3D). This change is consistent with up-regulation of capacity for sucrose metabolism in regions not otherwise receiving elevated sugar supplies.

The shift in sucrose synthase localization observed under C-depletion may be a mechanism for conferring sink priority to the most essential cells and tissues in instances of starvation stress (Koch et al., 1992). Epidermis is considered a primary site of nutrient ion uptake in many species (especially grasses) and is often accompanied by development of casparian-like suberin deposits (Peterson, 1988). Specific ATPases are also localized in root epidermal cells (J. Harper and M. Sussman, unpubl. data), and in many grasses, extensive

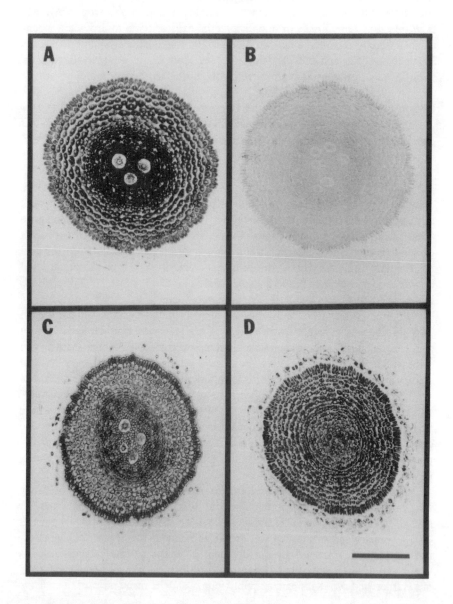

polysaccharide secretion binds soil particles to this surface in a mucigel sheath (McCully and Canny, 1989). A locally elevated demand for both UDPGlc and respiration are probable and these, in turn, could enhance expression of the *Sh1* sucrose synthase in individual cells.

Sucrose Synthase in Phloem

The immunolocalization of sucrose synthase was further investigated in phloem partly because the specific cellular expression of this enzyme could be altered by sugar availability, and also because previous studies indicated an overall phloem locale (see below). Results showed sucrose synthase to be specifically localized in companion cells both of importing structures [citrus fruit (Fig. 2)] and exporting organs [maize leaf (Fig. 3)]. The breadth of this observation is evident in its similarity among species ranging from monocot grasses (*Zea*) to dicot perennials (*Citrus*) (Nolte and Koch, 1993). This is not a result of differences in cytoplasmic density alone, because immunolabel is not evident in cytoplasmic regions of nearby phloem parenchyma cells.

Vascular strands are a complex arrangement of different cell types, therefore this cellular localization extended our previous understanding beyond that of the collective conducting tissues. The overall activity of sucrose synthase had been reported to be greater in vascular strands than adjacent tissues of sugar cane stems (Hawker and Hatch, 1965), citrus fruit (Lowell *et al.*, 1989; Tomlinson *et al.*, 1991), and in eggplant leaves (Claussen *et al.*, 1985). The enzyme was also active in exudates believed to arise primarily from phloem sap (Lehmann, 1973). More recent evidence has also indicated that promoters from maize sucrose synthase (*Sh1*) could drive a GUS reporter in phloem of transgenic tobacco (Yang and Russel, 1990); however, cell-level data were lacking, however.

The companion cell specificity of sucrose synthase in vascular strands may be due to both an elevated respiratory demand and a requirement for UDPGlc during callose biosynthesis. Geigenberger *et al.* (1993) used the freely

Figure 1. Altered localization of sucrose synthase in maize root tips with changes in carbohydrate availability. (A) Root tip from an intact, 6-d-old seedling. (B) Pre-immune control (preimmune rabbit immunoglobin G instead of sucrose synthase antisera). (C) Carbohydrate-depleted root tip incubated 24 h in 0.2% glucose [approximately 10 mM]. (D) Sugar-fed root tip incubated 24 h in 2.0% glucose [approximately 110 mM]. Root tips were fixed in formalin acetic acid and embedded in paraffin. Sections (8 μm) were probed with polyclonal antibodies to kernel sucrose synthase (cross-reactive to both the SH1 and SUS1 forms) and anti-rabbit immunoglobulin G conjugated to 5-nm gold particles. Sampled region was 1.0-1.5 mm behind the tip of the root cap. Bars = 50 μm. (After Koch *et al.*, 1992, with permission from the American Society of Plant Physiologists.)

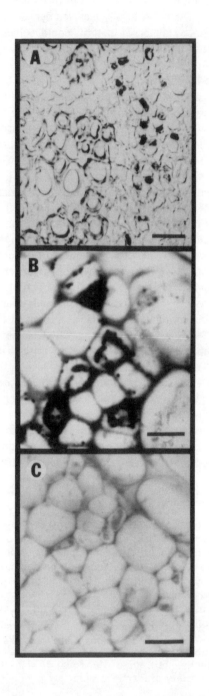

bleeding phloem sap of *Ricinus* to determine that the balance between UDP + sucrose versus UDPGlc + fructose in the translocation path is probably near equilibrium much of the time. A high respiratory demand is likely based on the densely packed mitochondria (Warmbrodt, 1987) and extensive ATPase localization in these cells (Parets-Soler *et al.*, 1990; DeWitt *et al.*, 1991). This is also consistent with data on the *Asus1* sucrose synthase of *Arabidopsis*, which is expressed in phloem and induced elsewhere when ATP supplies are limited (Martin *et al.*, 1993). In addition, the rapid formation of callose during injury-induced phloem plugging would require a massive or readily regenerated supply of UDPGlc, the preferred substrate for this synthesis (Morrow and Lucas, 1987; Wolf *et al.*, 1991). Clearly, the capacity for UDPGlc production exists in companion cells, and these are extensively interconnected with sieve tube elements.

The sucrose synthase localization and carbohydrate responsiveness of its transcripts indicate its probable importance to translocation and adjustment of import. However, this represents only one of the two known enzymatic reactions for sucrose entry into cellular metabolism. The invertase avenue remains, and has received comparatively little attention relative to its localization and sugar modulation.

INVERTASE AND THE TRANSPORT PATHWAY

Clones of maize invertase were sought to test the hypothesis that, like sucrose synthase, these genes could be especially sensitive to changes in carbohydrate availability. Such responsiveness could provide a means of coarse control for both avenues of sucrose breakdown, and a mechanism for adjustment of import capacity relative to photosynthate supply.

Both soluble and insoluble invertases can have marked effects on the transport and import pathways in plants despite the frequently observed association between sucrose synthase and sink strength (Claussen *et al.*, 1985; Sung

Figure 2. Companion cell localization of sucrose synthase in phloem of citrus fruit (*Citrus paradisi* Macf.). (A) Transverse section of a dorsal vascular bundle from the tangential face of a juice segment (site of phloem unloading for adjacent, nonvascular juice sacs). Bar = 20 μm. (B) Transverse section of companion cell-sieve tube element complexes from a dorsal strand in citrus fruit. Immunogold reaction is localized to companion cells and absent from densely cytoplasmic regions of parenchyma cells. Bar = 5 μm. (Companion cells are elongate in longitudinal sections not pictured.) (C) Pre-immune control of B (preimmune rabbit immunoglobin G instead of sucrose synthase antisera). Bar = 5 μm. Tissues and sections were treated as in Figure 1. (After Nolte and Koch, 1993, with permission from the American Society of Plant Physiologists.)

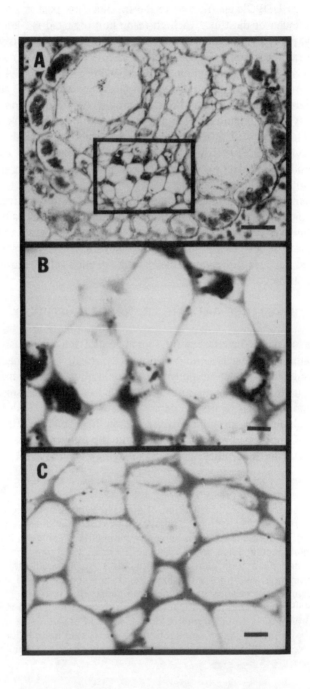

148

et al., 1988). Insoluble invertases have long been known for their role in hydrolysis of sucrose entering corn kernels (Shannon, 1972; Shannon and Dougherty, 1972), sugar cane stems (Hawker and Hatch, 1965; Glasziou and Gayler, 1972), and other systems where sucrose moves through the extracellular space (Avigad, 1982). The extent and essentiality of this hydrolysis to import has been debated, and does not occur in all apoplastic systems (Giaquinta, 1979; Avigad, 1982; Schmalstig and Hitz, 1987*b*). However, data indicate that a good portion of translocated sugars enter some organs and their cellular metabolism via this enzymatic reaction (Giaquinta *et al.*, 1983; Hitz *et al.*, 1985; Schmalstig and Hitz, 1987*a*). Studies of transgenic plants have also shown that although invertase can severely interfere with sucrose export from leaves (Sonnewald *et al.*, 1994), it can substantially increase the size of importing organs such as potatoes (Sonnewald *et al.*, 1994). Soluble acid invertases are present primarily in the cell vacuoles and to a lesser extent in the extracellular space of many tissues (Avigad, 1982). Their activity is generally much greater than that of the insoluble forms (Avigad, 1982; Morris and Arthur, 1984*b*; J. Xu, D.R. McCarty, and K.E. Koch, unpubl. data). The significance of these invertases to sugar composition in fruit [tomato (Klann *et al.*, 1993; Elliott *et al.*, 1993), blueberry (Darnell *et al.*, 1994), melon (Hubbard *et al.*, 1989; Schaffer *et al.* 1987*a*)], and possible contributions to osmotic adjustment (Sharp *et al.*, 1990), have tended to obscure their often dominant role in import (Giaquinta *et al.*, 1983; Hanft and Jones, 1986; Schmalstig and Hitz, 1987*a*; Sung *et al.*, 1994).

The significance of soluble invertases to transport has received comparatively little attention. This pathway of sucrose entry into metabolism appears to be particularly important to early growth of newly initiated organs (Hanft and Jones, 1986; Schmalstig and Hitz, 1987*a*). Recent data from Sung *et al.* (1994) show that soluble invertase activity rather than that of sucrose synthase correlates most closely with sucrose import during early growth of bean pods. Although the situation reverses as seed growth ensues, the early association

Figure 3. Companion cell localization of sucrose synthase in phloem of a fully expanded maize leaf (*Zea mays* L.). (A) Transverse section of a major vascular bundle showing sucrose synthase immunogold reactivity within phloem (boxed area). Bundle sheath chloroplasts appear dark in noncolor micrographs, but are not immunolabeled. Bar = 50 μm. (B) Transverse section of companion cell - sieve element complexes from phloem of the maize leaf bundle designated in A. Bar = 10 μm. (C) Pre-immune control of B (preimmune rabbit immunoglobin G instead of sucrose synthase antisera). Bar = 10 μm. Tissues and sections were treated as in Figure 1. (After Nolte and Koch, 1993, with permission from the American Society of Plant Physiologists.)

between soluble invertase and import is seen in a number of systems (Morris and Arthur, 1984a, b; Hanft and Jones, 1986; Schaffer et al., 1987b; Schmalstig and Hitz, 1987a; Lambrechts and Kolloffel 1994). Despite the value of osmotic contributions in rapidly expanding tissues, evidence also indicates that a large portion of the entering sucrose may pass through soluble invertase and the vacuolar compartment as it enters cellular metabolism (Giaquinta et al., 1983; Schmalstig and Hitz, 1987a). Expansion and rate of import are thus often tightly linked in such structures (Schmalstig and Cosgrove, 1990).

The maize invertase clones obtained thus far indicate a gene family of four to six members (Xu et al., 1995; J. Xu, B. Burr, S. Wright, D.R. McCarty, and K.E. Koch, unpubl. data) apparently encoding soluble isoforms of the enzyme (Xu et al., 1995). Direct biochemical evidence has indicated that other similar sequences encode soluble-acid invertases (Unger et al., 1994; Xu et al., 1995). These share not only overall similarity with the maize clones, but also specific key features (Unger et al., 1994; Xu et al., 1995), and a correlation between expression data and activity of the soluble enzyme (Xu, J. D.R. McCarty, and K.E.Koch, unpubl. data). A soluble-isozyme gene from tomato (Klan et al, 1992) was used to obtain the first of the maize invertases (Xu et al., 1995).

Two, differentially expressed subfamilies are distinguished by the Ivr1 and Ivr2 gene probes. Expression of these gene groups differs depending on tissue, organ, stage of development, and sugar status (Xu et al., unpubl. data). Moreover, response to sugars indicates a striking similarity to the contrasting carbohydrate modulation observed in expression of the two types of sucrose synthase [Sh1 and Sus1 as discussed above (Koch et al. 1992)]. The Ivr1 subgroup, like Sh1 sucrose synthase, is expressed in reproductive structures, and message is most abundant at relatively low levels of carbohydrate availability (approximately 0.5% glucose or equivalent). In contrast, both the Ivr2 subfamily and the Sus1 sucrose synthase are expressed in a wide array of sink tissues with mRNA levels rapidly depleted in the absence of available carbohydrate (Koch et al., 1992).

The high- and low-sugar response classes among genes for both sucrose synthase and invertase isozymes may correspond to contrasting cellular localizations and physiological function. Evidence favors this possibility for sucrose synthase genes (Koch et al., 1992). The low-sugar response form (Sh1) could aid the prioritization of vital cells as recipients of limited sucrose supplies under stress and/or during reproduction (Koch et al., 1992). Elevated C demands by specific cells could also be involved as for sucrose synthase in companion cells (Nolte and Koch, 1993). In contrast, the high-sugar response form present in a wide array of importing cells (Sus1) (McCarty et al., 1986), could facilitate a near organ-wide up-regulation of capacity for sucrose use when prioritization of individual cell types would be less important.

ACKNOWLEDGMENTS

Klann *et al.* (1992) provided the tomato invertase clone used to isolate the first of the maize invertase genes. Sucrose synthase antibodies were prepared in conjunction with D.R. McCarty and L.C. Hannah (Koch *et al.*, 1992). Research funds were provided through the National Science Foundation and the Florida Agricultural Experiment Station).

LITERATURE CITED

Avigad G (1982) Sucrose and other disaccharides. *In* FA Loewus, W Tanner, eds, Encyclopedia of Plant Physiology, New Series, Vol 13A. Springer-Verlag, New York, pp 217-347

Claussen W (1983) Investigations on the relationship between the distribution of assimilates and sucrose synthetase activity in *Solanum melongena* L. 2. Distribution of assimilates and sucrose synthase activity. Z. Pflanzen. **110:** 175-182

Claussen W, Hawker JS, Loveys BR (1985) Sucrose synthase activity, invertase activity, net photosynthetic rates and carbohydrate content of detached leaves of eggplants as affected by attached stems and shoots (sinks). J Plant Physiol **119:** 123-131

Darnell RD, Cano-Medrano R, Koch KE, Avery ML (1994) Differences in sucrose metabolism relative to accumulation of bird-deterent sucrose levels in fruits of wild and domestic *Vaccinium* species. Physiol Plant **92:** 336-342

DeWitt ND, Harper JF, Sussman MR (1991) Evidence for a plasmamembrane proton pump in phloem cells of higher plants. Plant J **1:** 121-128

Echt CS, Chourey PS (1985) A comparison of two sucrose synthase isozymes from normal and *shrunken-1* maize. Plant Physiol **79:** 530-536

Elliott KJ, Butler WO, Dickinson CD, Konno Y, Vedvick TS, Fitzmaurice L, Mirkov TE (1993) Isolation and characterization of fruit vacuolar invertase genes from two tomato species and temporal differences in mRNA levels during fruit ripening. Plant Mol Biol **21:** 515-524

Farrar JF, Williams JHH (1991) Control of the rate of respiration in roots: Compartmentation, demand, and the supply of substrate. *In* M Emmes, ed, Compartmentation of Metabolism. Butterworths, London, UK, pp 167-188

Geigenberger P, Langenberger S, Wilke I, Heineke D, Heldt HW, Stitt M (1993) Sucrose is metabolized by sucrose synthase and glycolysis within the phloem complex of *Ricinus communis* L. seedlings. Planta **190:** 446-453

Giaquinta, R (1979) Sucrose translocation and storage in the sugarbeet. Plant Physiol **63:** 828-832

Giaquinta RT, Lin W, Sadler NL, Franceschi VR (1983) Pathway of phloem unloading of sucrose in corn roots. Plant Physiol **72:** 362-367

Glasziou KT, Gayler KR (1972) Storage of sugars in stalks of sugar cane. Bot Rev **4:** 471-487

Graham IA, Denby KJ, Leaver CJ (1994) Carbon catabolite repression regulates glyoxylate cycle gene expression in cucumber. Plant Cell **6**: 761-772

Grierson C, Du JS, Zabala MD, Beggs K, Smith C, Holdsworth M, Bevan M (1994) Separate cis sequences and trans factors direct metabolic and developmental regulation of a potato-tuber storage protein gene. Plant J **5**: 815-826

Hanft JM, Jones RJ (1986) Kernel abortion in maize. I. Carbohydrate concentration patterns and acid invertase activity of maize kernels induced to abort in vitro. Plant Physiol **81**: 503-510

Hattori T, Nakagawa S, Nakamura K (1990) High-level expression of tuberous root storage protein genes of sweet potato in stems of plantlets grown in vitro on sucrose medium. Plant Mol Biol **14**: 595-604

Hawker JS, Hatch MD (1965) Mechanism of sugar storage by mature stem tissue of sugarcane. Physiol Plant **18**: 444-453

Heim U, Weber H, Bäumlein H, Wobus U (1993) A sucrose-synthase gene of *Vicia faba* L.: Expression pattern in relation to starch synthesis and metabolic regulation. Planta **191**: 394-401

Hitz WP, Schmitt MR, Card PJ, Giaquinta, RT (1985) Transport and metabolism of 1'-fluorosucrose, a sucrose analog not subject to invertase hydrolysis. Plant Physiol **77**: 292-295

Hubbard NL, Huber SC, Pharr DM (1989) Sucrose phosphate synthase and acid invertase as determinants of sucrose concentration in developing muskmelon (*Cucumis melo* L.) fruits. Plant Physiol **91**: 1527-1534

Huber SC, Akazawa T (1986) A novel sucrose synthase pathway for sucrose degradation in cultured sycamore cells. Plant Physiol **81**: 1008-1013

Jang J-C, Sheen J (1994) Sugar sensing in higher plants. Plant Cell **6**: 1665-1679

Karrer EE, Rodriguez RL (1992) Metabolic regulation of rice α-amylase and sucrose synthase genes in planta. Plant J **4**: 517-523

Klann E, Chetelat RT, Bennett AB (1993) Expression of acid invertase gene controls sugar composition in tomato (*Lycopersicon*) fruit. Plant Physiol **103**: 863-870

Klann E, Yelle S, Bennett AB (1992) Tomato fruit acid invertase complementary DNA: Nucleotide and deduced amino acid sequences. Plant Physiol **99**: 351-353

KoBmann J, Visser RGF, Müller-Röber BT, Willmitzer L, Sonnewald U (1991) Cloning and expression analysis of a potato cDNA that encodes branching enzyme: Evidence for coexpression of starch biosynthetic genes. Mol Gen Genet **230**: 39-44

Koch KE, McCarty DR (1988) Induction of sucrose synthase by sucrose depletion in maize root tips. Plant Physiol **86**: 35

Koch KE, Nolte KD, Duke ED, McCarty DR, Avigne WT (1992) Sugar levels modulate differential expression of maize sucrose synthase genes. Plant Cell **4**: 59-69

Lambrechts H, Kolloffel C (1994) Soluble and insoluble invertase activity in elongating tulipa-gesneriana flower stalks. Physiol Plant **89**: 830-834

Lehmann J (1973) Untersuchungen am phloemexsudate von *Cucurbita pepo* L. 2. Enzymaktivitaten der gluconeogenese und des Aufund Abbaus von Di-und polysacchariden. Planta **114**: 51-61

Liu X-Y, Rocha-Sosa M, Hummel S, Willmitzer L, Frommer WB (1991) A detailed study of the regulation and evolution of the two classes of patatin genes in *Solanum tuberosum* L. Plant Mol Biol **17**: 1139-1154

Lowell CA, Tomlinson PT, Koch KE (1989) Sucrose-metabolizing enzymes in transport tissues and adjacent sink structures in developing citrus fruit. Plant Physiol **90**: 1394-1402

Maas C, Schaal S, Werr W (1990) A feedback control element near the transcription start site of the maize *Shrunken* gene determines promoter activity. EMBO J **9**: 3447-3452

Maraña C, Garcia-Olmedo F, Carbonero P (1990) Differential expression of two types of sucrose synthase-encoding genes in wheat in response to anaerobiosis and light. Gene **88**: 167-172

Martin T, Frommer WB, Salanoubat M, Willmitzer L (1993) Expression of an *Arabidopsis* sucrose synthase gene indicates a role in metabolization of sucrose both during phloem loading and in sink organs. Plant J **4**: 367-377

Mason H, Dewald DB, Creelman RA, Mullet JE (1992) Coregulation of soybean vegetative storage protein gene expression by methyl jasmonate and soluble sugars. Plant Physiol **98**: 859-867

McCarty DR, Shaw JR, Hannah LC (1986) The cloning, genetic mapping, and expression of the constitutive sucrose synthase locus of maize. Proc Natl Acad Sci USA **83**: 9099-9103

McCully ME, Canny MJ (1989) Pathways and processes of water and nutrient movement in roots. *In* BC Loughman *et al.*, eds, Structural and Functional Aspects of Transport in Roots. Kluwer Academic Publ, Dordrecht, Netherlands, pp 3-4

Morris DA, Arthur ED (1984*a*) Invertase and auxin-induced elongation in internodal segments of *Phaseolus vulgaris*. Phytochemistry **23**: 2163-2167

Morris DA, Arthur ED (1984*b*) An association between acid invertase activity and cell growth during leaf expansion in *Phaseolus vulgaris* L. J Exp Bot **35**: 1369-1379

Morrow DL, Lucas WL (1987) (1-3)-β-D-glucan synthase from sugar beet. Plant Physiol **84**: 565-567

Müller-Röber BT, KoBmann J, Hannah LC, Willmitzer L, Sonnewald U (1990) One of two different ADP-glucose pyrophosphorylase genes from potato responds strongly to elevated levels of sucrose. Mol Gen Genet **224**: 136-146

Nolte KD, Koch KE (1993) Companion-cell specific localization of sucrose synthase in zones of phloem loading and unloading. Plant Physiol **101**: 899-905

Parets-Soler A, Pardo JM, Serrano R (1990) Immunocytolocalization of plasma membrane ATPase. Plant Physiol **93**: 1654-1664

Peterson CA (1988) Exodermal casparian bands: Their significance for ion uptake by roots. Physiol Plant **72**: 204-208

Rocha-Sosa M, Sonnewald U, Frommer W, Stratmann M, Schell J, Willmitzer L (1989) Both developmental and metabolic signals activate the promoter of a class I patatin gene. EMBO J 8: 23-29

Sadka A, DeWald DB, May GD, Park WD, Mullet JE (1994) Phosphate modulates transcription of soybean vspB and other sugar-inducible genes. Plant Cell 6: 737-749

Salanoubat M, Belliard G (1989) The steady-state level of potato sucrose synthase mRNA is dependent on wounding, anaerobiosis and sucrose concentration. Gene 84: 181-185

Salehuzzaman SNIM, Jacobsen E, Visser RGF (1994) Expression patterns of 2 starch biosynthetic genes in in-vitro cultured cassava plants and their induction by sugars. Plant Sci 98: 53-62

Schaffer AA, Aloni BA, Fogelmann E (1987a) Sucrose metabolism and accumulation in developing fruit of Cucumis. Phytochemistry 26: 1883-1887

Schaffer AA, Sage O, Goldschmidt, EE, Goren R (1987b) Invertase and sucrose synthase activity, carbohydrate status and endogenous IAA levels during Citrus leaf development. Physiol Plant 69: 151-155

Schmalstig JG, Cosgrove DJ (1990) Coupling of solute transport and cell expansion in pea stem. Plant Physiol 94: 1625-1633

Schmalstig JG, Hitz WD (1987a) Contributions of sucrose synthase and invertase to the metabolism of sucrose in developing leaves: Estimation by alternate substrate utilization. Plant Physiol 85: 407-412

Schmalstig JG, Hitz WD (1987b) Transport and metabolism of a sucrose analog (1'-fluorosucrose) into Zea mays L. endosperm without invertase hydrolysis. Plant Physiol 85: 902-905

Shannon JC (1972) Movement of ^{14}C-labelled assimilates into kernels of Zea mays L. I. Pattern and rate of sugar movement. Plant Physiol 49: 198-202

Shannon JC, Dougherty TC (1972) Movement of ^{14}C-labelled assimilates into kernels of Zea mays L. II. Invertase activity in the pedicel and placento-chalazal tissues. Plant Physiol 49: 203-206

Sharp RE, Hsiao TC, Silk WK (1990) Growth of the maize primary root at low water potentials II. Role of growth and deposition of hexose and potassium in osmotic adjustment. Plant Physiol 93: 1137-1346

Sheen J (1990) Metabolic repression of transcription in higher plants. Plant Cell 2: 1027-1038

Sheen J (1994) Feedback-control of gene-expression. Photosyn Res 39: 427-438

Sonnewald U, Lerchl J, Zrenner R, Frommer W (1994) Manipulation of sink-source relations in transgenic plants. Plant Cell Environ 17: 649-658

Sung S-J, Xu D-P, Black CC (1988) Identification of actively filling sucrose sinks. Plant Physiol 89: 1117-1121

Sung SS, Sheih WJ, Geiger DR, Black CC (1994) Growth, sucrose synthase, and invertase activities of developing Phaseolus vulgaris L. fruits. Plant Cell Environ 17: 419-426

Thomas BR, Rodriguez RL (1994) Metabolite signals regulate gene expression and source/sink relations in cereal seedlings. Plant Physiol 106: 1235-1239

Thomas BB, Rodriguez RL (1995) Metabolic regulation of source/sink relations in cereal seedlings. *In* MA Madore, WJ Lucas, eds, American Society of Plant Physiologists, Rockville, MD, this volume

Tomlinson PT, Duke ER, Nolte KD, Koch KE (1991) Sucrose synthase in isolated vascular bundles. Plant Physiol **97**: 1249-1252

Unger C, Hardegger M, Lienhard S, Sturm A (1994) cDNA cloning of carrot (*Daucus catota*) soluble acid β-fructofuranosidases and comparing with the cell wall isoenzyme. Plant Physiol **104**: 1351-1357

Wang F, Sanz A, Brenner ML, Smith A (1993) Sucrose synthase, starch accumulation, and tomato fruit sink strength. Plant Physiol **101**: 321-327

Warmbrodt RD (1987) Solute concentrations in the phloem and apex of the root of *Zea mays*. Am J Bot **74**: 394-402

Wenzler HC, Mignery GA, Fisher LM, Park WD (1989) Analysis of a chimeric class-I patatin-GUS gene in transgenic potato plants: High-level expression in tubers and sucrose-inducible expression in cultured leaf and stem explants. Plant Mol Biol **12**: 41-50

Williams JHH, Farrar JF (1990) Control of barley root respiration. Physiol Plant **79**: 259-266

Wolf S, Deom CM, Beachy R, Lucas WJ (1991) Plasmodesmatal function is probed using transgenic tobacco plants that express a virus movement protein. Plant Cell **3**: 593-604

Xu J, Pemberton GH, Bihn EA, Almira EC, McCarty DR, Koch KE (1995) The *Ivr1* gene for invertase in *Zea mays* L. Plant Physiol (in press)

Yang NS, Russel D (1990) Maize sucrose synthase-1 promoter directs phloem cell-specific expression of *Gus* gene in transgenic tobacco plants. Proc Natl Acad Sci USA **87**: 4144-4148

Assimilate Delivery Pathways in the Developing Wheat Grain and Their Implications for Control of Carbon Transport

Hong Li Wang, John W. Patrick, and Christine E. Offler

*Section of Plant Biology, University of California, Davis, CA 95616,
USA (H.L.W.); and Department of Biological Sciences, The University
of Newcastle, New South Wales 2308, Australia (J.W.P.; C.E.O.)*

Crop yield is mainly determined by a crop's ability to produce high levels of photosynthate over a wide range of environmental conditions and to efficiently transport and accumulate a high proportion of the photosynthate into the economically important organs (Wardlaw, 1990). The amount of photosynthate flow from the various sources to a specific sink organ is influenced by photosynthesis and phloem loading in the source, translocation from source to sink along the axial path, as well as phloem unloading and utilization within the sink (Wardlaw, 1990). Especially in modern agriculture, the improvement of crop yield has been associated, not with an increase in total biomass production, but with a greater partitioning of the available carbon to the organs being harvested (Wardlaw, 1990). However, although individual biochemical and physiological processes have been extensively studied, the factors and their dynamic interactions primarily responsible for the control of carbon partitioning in crop plants have not been well understood.

Today, wheat is one of the most important cultivated crop plants with respect to human nutrition. Therefore, photoassimilation, carbon partitioning, and their regulation in wheat have been widely studied. Development of the wheat grain may be divided into two stages: A phase of cell division that extends from fertilization up to 14 to 20 d after anthesis, overlapped and followed by a phase of grain filling starting 10 to 15 d after anthesis and continuing until the grain ripens (Jenner et al., 1991; Martinez-Carrasco and Thorne, 1979). Experiments that reduce photosynthesis indicate that grain growth is influenced strongly by the supply of photosynthate during the cell division phase (Singh and Jenner, 1984). However, these effects occur against a background in which excess photosynthate is produced during this phase. These photosynthates are stored in the stem as nonstructural carbohydrates and may be remobilized to the grain during the filling phase (Pheloung and Siddique, 1991; Schnyder, 1993). Thus, the factors limiting photosynthate supply to the grain are unlikely to be localized in the source and the stem transport path, but are more likely to be in the developing tissues of the ear. In contrast, grain growth is little affected by the supply of photosynthate during the filling stage. For instance, under adequate growing conditions during the filling stage, photosynthate production by the ear and flag leaf can meet the requirement of grain filling, and carbon dioxide enrichment does not increase grain growth (Jenner *et al.*, 1991). Furthermore, under conditions that reduce the photosynthetic activity of the flag leaf and ear, photosynthate supply to the grain can be maintained in nonlimiting amounts by one or more compensatory mechanisms. For instance, a decreased supply of photosynthate from the flag leaf by shading was found to be compensated for by photosynthate supplied from the lower leaves (Marshall and Wardlaw, 1973). More of the nonstructural carbohydrate in the stem is remobilized to sustain grain growth when the current photosynthate becomes limiting (Pheloung and Siddique, 1991). Wardlaw and Moncur (1976) found that cutting half the vascular bundles of the peduncle did not affect grain growth, indicating that the stem phloem has spare transport capacity. In addition, Fisher and Gifford (1986, 1987) found that there is little, if any, gradient in osmolality and solute composition from the peduncle to the crease phloem of the grain. These studies indicate that there is no restriction to photosynthate transport in the phloem from the peduncle to the grain. Together, these observations lead to the conclusion that grain growth during the filling stage is likely to be regulated by the grain itself.

In general, the nature of the controls regulating photosynthate transfer are determined by the cellular pathway and transport mechanism (Offler and Patrick, 1986). Moreover, sink transport and transfer processes are currently believed to be the predominant factors controlling photosynthate partitioning. Hence, those different features of photosynthate transport and their controlling patterns at the different developmental stage of wheat grain may be dictated by the cellular pathways and mechanisms of photosynthate transfer in the developing grain. This paper attempts to elucidate the cellular pathways of assimilate transport in the developing wheat grain and integrate with the control features of carbon transport at its different developmental stages. The implications of these pathways for control of carbon transport are also discussed.

CELLULAR PATHWAYS OF ASSIMILATE DELIVERY

Cell Division Stage

The wheat grain, from the time of fertilization to cessation of cell division within the endosperm, undergoes a rapid ontogeny and cell differentiation, with respect to its embryo, endosperm, and vascular systems (Frazier and

Appalanaidu, 1965; Fineran *et al.*, 1982; Lingle and Chevalier, 1985), and may experience great changes in assimilate transfer.

At the time of anthesis, four vascular strands are present in the wheat ovary: three bundles contain sieve elements, but no xylem vessels connect from the vascular tissue in the pedicel region. Two of these bundles, consisting of four to seven sieve elements each, are embedded in the lateral wall of the ovary and extended into the stigma. The third, consisting of one or two sieve elements, is embedded in the dorsal ovary wall opposite the crease and extends only a short distance toward the distal end of the ovary (Lingle and Chevalier, 1985; Fisher, 1990). These tissues are stretched and torn during the initial elongation of the grain and are obliterated by 12 d after anthesis (Lingle and Chevalier, 1985). These three bundles are considered to be important paths for the delivery of assimilate to the developing pericarp. However, the two lateral strands have been found to persist through approximately half or a large part of the grain-filling period and appear to be involved in the absorption of solutes produced during degeneration of the pericarp (Fisher, 1990).

The most important vascular strand, a large bundle of mostly provascular tissue, is embedded in the crease region. It links the pedicel vascular bundle to the nucellus and embryo sac through the chalaza cells (Fig. 1a; Zhang *et al.*, 1984). This provascular bundle develops into xylem and phloem tissue at the base of the ovary. Abundant plasmodesmata, 50 nm in diameter, interconnect the cells of the provascular bundle, chalaza, and nucellus (Zhang *et al.*, 1984). The wheat embryo sac is pear-shaped and deeply imbedded in fleshy nucellus of uneven thickness, which in turn, is enclosed partially by two layers of integument and is in intimate connection with the procambium around the chalaza region (Fig. 1a; Zhang *et al.*, 1984). The nucellus is transitory in existence, cells in the outer layers multiply by mitosis; cells in the intermediate layers begin to exhibit intercellular movement of protoplasmic constituents; and cells in the innermost layer, embracing the embryo sac, actively undergo disintegration, showing ruptured walls and cellular contents in disarray (Zhang *et al.*, 1984, 1988). While assimilate is transferred into the nucellus, a portion of imported assimilate may be transferred directly into the embryo sac through the symplasm (enlarged channel between nucellus and antipodal cells, Zhang *et al.*, 1980, 1984, 1988) or apoplasm by diffusion (Zhang *et al.*, 1984). Another portion of this imported assimilate is utilized to form protoplasmic constituents, partly for proliferation and differentiation within the nucellus, and partly for the developing embryo sac. The latter appears to involve a complex nurturing between the nucellar tissue and the embryo sac, mediated by intercellular movement of protoplasmic constituents through open channels (H.L. Wang and Z.H. Lou, unpubl. data; Zhang *et al.*, 1980, 1984, 1988). Accordingly, the nucellus is the direct sink for imported assimilate from the crease vascular bundle (Fig. 1a).

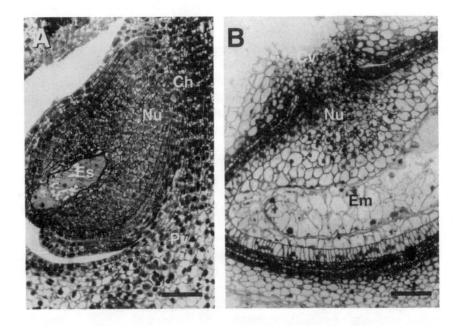

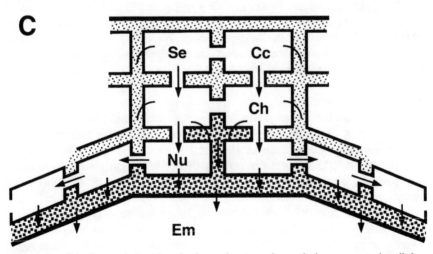

Figure 1. Sections of the developing wheat grain and the proposed cellular pathway of photosynthate transfer during cell division stage. A, light micrograph of a longitudinal section of the wheat grain at anthesis; B, transverse section of the wheat grain at 3 d after anthesis; Bar = 100 μm; C, schematic representation of the cellular pathway followed by assimilate transport in the developing grain from 3 d after anthesis during the cell division stage. Cc, companion cell; Ch, chalaza; Em, embryonic tissues; Es, embryo sac; Nu, nucellus; Pv, provascular bundle; Se, sieve element; → assimilate flow.

During the first week after anthesis, the grain begins to elongate, and the crease vascular bundle rapidly differentiates into xylem and phloem. It appears to be fully differentiated at 6 d after anthesis (Lingle and Chevalier, 1985). Light microscopy studies indicate that, after fertilization, the central cell expands rapidly and the nucellus collapses, except for the epidermis (Fig. 1b). Differentiation and cellularization of the endosperm are also in the central cell (Fig. 1b; Fineran et al., 1982). The movement of a membrane-permeable fluorochrome, fluorescein, which was induced from a flag leaf at 3 and 6 d after anthesis, appeared to move along the crease vascular bundle, chalaza, nucellar projection and subsequently spread through the nucellar epidermis into the embryo sac (H.L. Wang and Z.H. Lou, unpubl. data). These studies established the route of assimilate transfer from the crease vascular bundle to the endosperm.

Post-phloem transport of photosynthates in sink regions of higher plants involves two cellular pathways, the symplasm and apoplasm (Patrick, 1990). Our electron microscopy observations show that numerous plasmodesmata interconnect the cells from sieve element-companion cell complexes to the nucellar projection and nucellar epidermis (H.L. Wang and Z.H. Lou, unpubl. data), indicating a possible symplasmic pathway of photosynthate transfer. Alternatively, walls of the chalaza (pigment strand) cells only become progressively lignified (Zee and O'Brien, 1970) and phenolic substances accumulate from 15 d after anthesis (Cochrane, 1983). Therefore, solutes can also move through the apoplasm in the post-phloem region at this developmental stage. Accordingly, photosynthate is likely transferred via a combination of symplasmic and apoplasmic pathways (Fig. 1c).

Grain-Filling Stage

Many structural and physiological investigations on assimilate transport in the developing wheat grain at filling stage have been made at both the cellular and whole plant levels, such as structural studies (Zee and O'Brien, 1970; Cochrane, 1983; Lingle and Chevalier, 1985), $^{14}CO_2$ and [^{14}C]sucrose-labeling studies (Sakri and Shannon, 1975; Ho and Gifford, 1984; Ugalde and Jenner, 1990a, b), fluorescent tracer studies (Cook and Oparka, 1983), etc. These previous studies have led to the conclusion that photosynthate enters the developing wheat grain longitudinally along the crease phloem from where it is evenly unloaded for radial transfer through the vascular parenchyma, pigment strand, and nucellar projection into the endosperm cavity. Subsequently, photosynthate is taken up by and accumulated in the endosperm cells (Fig. 2a). However, these studies did not clearly define the cellular pathway, nor do they characterize the mechanisms responsible for moving photosynthate through the various components of the cellular pathway.

In order to test the operativity of the symplasmic and apoplasmic pathways for assimilate transfer, membrane-permeable and -impermeable dyes were

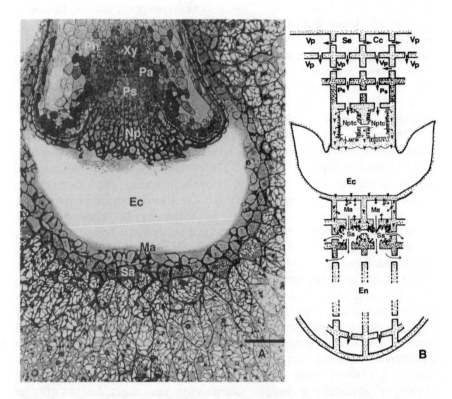

Figure 2. Section of the developing wheat grain and proposed cellular pathway of photosynthate transfer during grain-filling stage. A, light micrograph of a transverse section through the middle of the developing wheat grain at 25 ± 3 d after anthesis, Bar = 100 μm; B, schematic representation of the cellular pathway followed by assimilate transport in the developing grain during grain filling stage. Cc, companion cell; Cu, cuticular layer; Ec endosperm cavity; En, starchy endosperm; Ma, modified aleurone layer; Np, nucellar projection; Pa, vascular parenchyma cells; Ph, phloem; Ps, pigment strand; Sa, sub-aleurone cell; Se, sieve element; Xy, xylem ; → assimilate flow.

introduced into developing grain through the crease phloem, the endosperm cavity, or the dorsal surface of the endosperm (Wang *et al.*, 1994*a*). The movement of the symplasmic tracers, 6-carboxyfluorescein and sulphorhodamine G, indicated that symplasmic pathways operated from the crease phloem to the nucellar projection and from the modified aleurone to the starchy endosperm. In contrast, high resistance to the movement of the apoplasmic tracers, trisodium, 3-hydroxy-5,8,10-pyrentrisulfonate, and Calcofluor White, were localized in the walls of the pigment strand and the sub-aleurone cells (Wang *et al.*, 1994*a*). These results suggest that photosynthate is transferred from the crease phloem via a symplasmic route to the nucellar projection and then unloaded into the endosperm cavity through membrane exchange. The same pathway was also proposed by Wang and Fisher (1994*a*), based on their fluorescent tracer study on the crease region. The subsequent photosynthate uptake from the endosperm cavity is likely located at the modified aleurone, followed by symplasmic transfer into the starchy endosperm (Wang *et al.*, 1994*a*).

The proposed cellular pathway of photosynthate movement from the crease phloem to the endosperm cavity was further assessed by histochemical studies and structural analyses (Wang *et al.*, 1995*a*). Histochemical studies revealed that an apoplasmic barrier, composed of lignin, phenolics, and suberin, exists in the cell walls of the pigment strand. The significance of an apoplasmic barrier within the pigment strand is heightened by the continuity of the impregnating substances with the cell walls of the cuticular layer. As a result, these tissues together form a continuous apoplasmic barrier that isolates the endosperm from the surrounding pericarp. This accounts for the selective channeling of photosynthates radially through the pigment strand *en route* to the endosperm cavity with the apoplasmic barrier diverting the transported photosynthates to a symplasmic path. In addition, the apoplasmic barrier could block, or at least restrict, the back leakage of photosynthates released from the nucellar projection into the endosperm cavity. It could provide an independent osmolality status in the apoplasm on both sides of the barrier. Numerous plasmodesmata interconnect cells in the crease region from the phloem to the nucellar projection. Collectively, these plasmodesmata offer an adequate cross-sectional area to support photosynthate transport through a symplasmic pathway at rates sufficient for normal grain growth. Moreover, the nucellar projection cells exhibit progressive development and degeneration of secondary wall ingrowths of the transfer cell. These extensive wall ingrowths of the nucellar projection transfer cells increase the plasma membrane surface area by 22-fold (Wang *et al.*, 1994*b*, 1995*a*). Only the nucellar projection transfer cells were found to provide sufficient plasma membrane surface area to support *in vivo* rates of sucrose transfer into the endosperm cavity. In addition, the dense cytoplasm and abundant mitochondria within these specialized cells (Wang *et al.*, 1994*b*) indicate a high level of metabolic activity which may provide the necessary energy to drive the transport of photosynthate to the endosperm cavity across the plasma membrane. This is consistent with the findings by Wang and Fisher (1994*b*) that sucrose unloading can occur against its concentration gradient and is sensitive to the carbonyl cyanide m-chloro-phenylhydrazone (CCCP) treatment. Together, these observations support the hypothesis that photosynthate moves via the symplast from the sieve element/companion cell complexes of the crease phloem to the nucellar projection, from whence it is transferred actively across the amplified plasma membrane of the nucellar projection into the endosperm cavity (Fig. 2b).

Photosynthate is finally transferred from the endosperm cavity into the starchy endosperm through the modified aleurone and/or sub-aleurone cells. The cells of these modified tissues are characterized by a dense cytoplasm that contains a substantial network of ER and abundant mitochondria, many of which are aligned adjacent to the plasma membrane. Furthermore, the sub-aleurone cells exhibit irregularly-shaped wall ingrowth, characteristic of transfer cells (Wang et al., 1994b). Moreover, transport studies in which [14C]sucrose solutions were infused through the endosperm cavity of detached intact grain (Wang et al., 1993) demonstrated that the activity of a putative sucrose-proton symporter was restricted to the modified aleurone and possibly the sub-aleurone cells (Wang et al., 1995b). These findings agree with the cytochemical localization of ATPase activity (Baker et al., 1991) and the accumulation of a weak acid fluorescent dye, SRG, a probe for the presence of intensive proton extrusion (Canny, 1988; Wang et al., 1995b) in the modified aleurone and sub-aleurone cells. Quantitative structural analyses indicated that only the combination of the modified aleurone and sub-aleurone cells provides sufficient membrane surface area for active transfer of sucrose at the in vivo rate of grain growth. Since the modified aleurone and sub-aleurone cells exhibit active sucrose uptake (Wang et al., 1995b), and are well interconnected by plasmodesmata, this tissue likely functions as the major site for sucrose uptake from the endosperm cavity apoplasm. Finally, as plasmodesmata interconnect between all the cell types from the modified aleurone/sub-aleurone complex to the starchy endosperm, symplasmic transport appears to be the pathway of choice.

The cellular pathway of photosynthate transfer from the endosperm cavity to the starchy endosperm is depicted in Figure 2b. Sucrose is taken up actively by the modified aleurone/sub-aleurone complex from the endosperm cavity. Subsequently, the accumulated sucrose is transferred through the symplasm into the starchy endosperm cells where it is converted into starch. A small component of the total sucrose flux may move through the aleurone/endosperm apoplasm into the starchy endosperm cells where it is taken up by passive diffusion (Wang et al., 1995b).

IMPLICATIONS ON CONTROL OF CARBON TRANSPORT

The cellular pathway of photosynthate transfer in the wheat grain is shifted following the transition from cell division stage to the filling stage. Coincidentally, the control pattern of photosynthate transport in wheat plants also exhibits a remarkable change following the development of the source-path-sink system. The important question that needs to be addressed is, "Does the cellular pathway of photosynthate transport in the developing grain dictate the control pattern of carbon transport?"

At the cell division stage, photosynthate is transferred from the crease phloem to the nucellar projection and the nucellar epidermal cells via both the symplasmic and apoplasmic pathways, and is then followed by an apoplasmic transfer into the embryonic tissues (Fig. 1c). Potentially, symplasmic transfer of photosynthate from the crease sieve elements to the nucellus (at anthesis) or the nucellar projection and nucellar epidermis (from 3 d after anthesis) may occur by either mass flow or diffusion, and it is then followed by apoplasmic transfer along the assimilate gradient into the embryonic tissues; along this pathway, solute transfer would be driven by diffusion. As a result, the ulti-mate rate of photosynthate transfer (R_t) from the crease phloem into the grow-ing embryonic tissues could be expressed as:

$$R_t = K (C_{se} - C_{em})$$ [1]

where K is a transport constant, C_{se} and C_{em} are the photosynthate concentra-tion in the grain sieve elements and embryonic tissues, respectively. Photo-synthate concentration (C_{em}) in the sink cells is the balance between input from transport and output by utilization. Fast growth of the embryonic tissues will deplete more assimilates and, therefore, decrease the C_{em}. Thus, it could lead to an increase in the rate of photosynthate transfer (R_t). On the other hand, elevation of C_{se}, through increasing the supply of photosynthate, will amplify available assimilate in the embryonic tissues for their development. Conse-quently, the growth of the embryonic tissues will be increased, unless the uti-lization and compartmentation of the embryonic tissue has been saturated. In this case, the accumulation of photosynthate will establish a high C_{em} and may also produce a high photosynthate level along the path. Such high photosyn-thate levels would induce the operation of reserve pools in the leaf as well as in the stem along the transport path (Schnyder, 1993).

Several lines of physiological evidence are consistent with the above anal-ysis. Experiments on the effect of relative sink size on ^{14}C partitioning indi-cate a bias in favor of the larger sink grain in securing current assimilate from a nearby source (Cook and Evens, 1983). Grain increase in weight, in response to increased assimilate supply, only occurred before the time when grain volume was maximal, and shading the plants soon after anthesis decreased grain size (Martinez-Carrasco and Thorne, 1979). Conditions at anthesis and during the subsequent days determine how many grains are set, high temperature, low illuminance, and water stress at this stage being partic-ularly important in terms of setting grain number and size (Sofield et al., 1977). In other words, photosynthate supply to the developing grain during the cell division stage will control the development of sink potential.

In contrast, grain growth is largely independent of the supply of photosynthate during the filling stage. At this developmental stage, photosynthate transfer is restricted to the symplasmic pathway (Fig. 2b). Symplasmic transfer of photosynthate from the crease sieve elements to the nucellar projection may occur via diffusion (Wang and Fisher, 1994a) or mass flow (Wang and Fisher, 1994b). In the case of diffusion, the rate of diffusion (R_d) through the symplasm may be described by Fick's First Law:

$$R_d = n \{DA (C_{se} - C_{np})\}/d \tag{2}$$

where D is the diffusion coefficient; A, the plasmodesmatal cross-sectional area; d, the length of transfer path; n, the number of plasmodesmata; C, the sucrose concentration in the sieve element (C_{se}) and cytosol of the nucellar projection (C_{np}). This equation shows that the sucrose concentration gradient (ΔC) between the crease sieve elements (C_{se}) and the nucellar projection (C_{np}) is the driving force for solute transfer.

Alternatively, in the case of mass flow, the transport rate (R_f) may be described by the following rate equation:

$$R_f = (AC) \, Lp \, (P_{se} - P_{np}) \tag{3a}$$

where, A is the cross-sectional area of the path, C is the photosynthate concentration of the flowing solution, Lp is the hydraulic conductivity of the path, and P is the turgor potential of the sieve elements (P_{se}) and the nucellar projection (P_{np}). Here,

$$\text{As} \quad P_{se} = \pi_{se\text{-}s} - \pi_{se\text{-}a} \tag{3b}$$
$$\text{and} \quad P_{np} = \pi_{np\text{-}s} - \pi_{np\text{-}a} \tag{3c}$$

the turgor potential is determined by the osmotic potential ($\pi\Delta$) difference between the symplasm (π_s) and apoplasm (π_a). From Eq. 3a, transport is driven by the turgor difference (ΔP) between the sieve elements (P_{se}) and nucellar projection (P_{np}).

As compared with the cell division stage, significant changes in the cellular pathway of assimilate transfer occur during the grain-filling stage: (i) progressive development of an apoplasmic barrier in the cell walls of the pigment strand and the boundary between the sub-aleurone and starchy endosperm cells; and (ii) progressive development of intensive wall ingrowths of the nucellar projection transfer cells. Because of the existence of an apoplasmic barrier in the cell walls of the pigment strand, which restricts solute exchange in the apoplasm between the crease vascular bundle and the endosperm cavity, the osmotic potential in the apoplasm of the sieve elements ($\pi_{se\text{-}a}$) and the nucellar projection cells ($\pi_{np\text{-}a}$) can be independently maintained. Moreover, the high resistance for solute apoplasmic transfer in the boundary between the sub-aleurone and starchy endosperm cells would separate the endosperm of the developing grain into two apoplasmic domains: one for solute uptake and the other for storage. On one hand, at nonsaturating sucrose concentrations in the endosperm cavity, uptake by the sucrose-proton symporter in the modified aleurone and sub-aleurone domain, followed by symplasmic transfer to the starchy endosperm, offers an effective mechanism of sucrose delivery to the starch biosynthetic machinery, and hence, could contribute to the expression of the endosperm sink potential even under conditions of limited sucrose supply to the grain (Wang et al., 1995b). Alternatively, the composition and osmotic status in the endosperm cavity is able to be controlled by plasma membrane transfer processes across both the nucellar projection and the modified aleurone and sub-aleurone complex. In fact, attached wheat grains showed considerable capacity for regulating osmolality of the endosperm cavity sap (Wang and Fisher, 1994b). Together with our finding that no discernible change in osmolality of the cavity sap occurs, although there is marked change of osmolality in the crease sieve element during the diurnal cycle (Wang, 1993), it would seem that the osmotic status in the endosperm cavity is maintained at a constant value. Hence, the P_{np} would be mainly determined by the π_{np-s} (see Eq. 3b).

Sucrose concentration in the nucellar projection transfer cells (C_{np}) will be governed by the transfer rate of sucrose into the nucellar projection and the release rate of sucrose into the endosperm cavity. Wang and Fisher (1994b) reported that the release rate of sucrose into the endosperm cavity was unaffected over much wider in vivo ranges of osmotic and sucrose concentrations in the endosperm cavity. This suggests that a relative constant sucrose sym-/apoplasmic membrane exchange is accommodated by the nucellar projection cells, with their carrier-mediated active membrane transport mechanism and large plasma membrane surface area (Wang et al., 1995b). Hence, C_{np} will be changed following the change of photosynthate supply to the grain. As a result, the sucrose gradient (ΔC) will be restored and maintained, as will be the value of R_d (see Eq. 2).

The change of solute concentration in the nucellar projection (C_{np}) will lead to an adjustment in the osmolality of these cells (π_{np-s}) and, therefore, the value of P_{np} (Eq. 3b). For mass flow, the lowered value of π_{np-s} and, thus, of P_{np} may be oriented toward maintaining the turgor gradient (ΔP) between the sieve elements (P_{se}) and the nucellar projection (P_{np}) to drive photosynthate transfer into the nucellar projection at a constant rate; e.g. when π_{se-s} declines during the dark period of a diurnal cycle, or when photosynthate supply is decreased by stress or senescence of the leaf. In turn, further reduction in P_{se} and C_{se} will lead to the establishment of a "demand" force to drive photosynthate transfer to the grain. As a result, photosynthate transport from the source to, and within, the grain is controlled by the grain itself.

In conclusion, although the above analyses contain some speculative aspects, it is clear that the cellular pathway of photosynthase transfer can have a major impact on the control of carbon transport in the developing grain. At the cell division stage, the cellular pathway and the mechanism involved in photosynthate transfer in the developing grain cannot provide the driving force for photosynthate transfer to the grain, rather it leads to a situation in which assimilate supply determines the development of grain sink potential. Subsequently, the developed cellular pathway and potential mechanism of assimilate transfer, during the filling stage, produce a demand force to drive photosynthate transfer to and within the developing grain. This knowledge may provide new insights that can now be applied in terms of developing new strategies to improve wheat yield. In this respect, interactions among source-path-sink need to be further studied to refine our understanding of the cellular pathway and mechanisms of assimilate transport.

LITERATURE CITED

Baker DA, Poustini K, Didehvar F (1991) Effect of salinity on unloading of photoassimilates in the wheat caryopsis. *In* JL Bonnemain, S Delrot, WJ Lucas, J Dainty, eds, Recent Advances in Phloem Transport and Assimilate Compartmentation. Ouest Editions, Paris, pp 286-293

Canny MJ (1988) Bundle sheath tissues of legume leaves as a site of recovery of solute from the transpiration stream. Physiol Plant **73**: 457-464

Cochrane MP (1983) Morphology of the crease region to assimilate uptake and water loss during caryopsis development in barley and wheat. Aust J Plant Physiol **10**: 473-491

Cook H, Oparka KJ (1983) Movement of fluorescein into isolated caryopsis of wheat and barley. Plant Cell Environ **6**: 242-293

Cook MG, Evans LT (1983) The roles of sink size and location in the partitioning of assimilates in wheat ears. Aust J Plant Physiol **10**: 313-327

Fineran BA, Wild DJC, Ingerfeld M (1982) Initial wall formation in the endosperm of wheat, *Triticum aestivum*: a reevaluation. Can J Bot **60**: 1776-1795

Fisher DB (1990) Persistence of non-crease protophloem strands in the developing wheat grain. Aust J Plant Physiol **17**: 223-227

Fisher DB, Gifford RM (1986) Accumulation and conversion of sugars by developing wheat grains. VI. Gradients along the transport pathway from the peduncle to the endosperm cavity during grain filling. Plant Physiol **82**: 1024-1030

Fisher DB, Gifford RM (1987) Accumulation and conversion of sugars by developing wheat grains. VII. Effect of changes in sieve tube and endosperm cavity sap concentrations on the grain filling rate. Plant Physiol **84**: 341-347

Frazier JC, Appalanaidu B (1965) The wheat grain during development with reference to nature, location, and role of its translocatory tissues. Am J Bot **52**: 193-198

Ho LC, Gifford RM (1984) Accumulation and conversion of sugars by developing wheat grain. V. The endosperm apoplast and apoplastic transport. J Exp Bot **35:** 55-73

Jenner CF, Ugalde TD, Aspinal D (1991) The physiology of starch and protein deposition in the endosperm of wheat. Aust J Plant Physiol **18:** 211-226.

Lingle SE, Chevalier P (1985) Development of the vascular tissue of the wheat and barley caryopsis as related to the rate and duration of grain filling. Crop Sci **25:** 123-128

Marshall C, Wardlaw IF (1973) A comparative study of the distribution and speed of movement of ^{14}C assimilates and foliar-applied ^{32}P-labelled phosphate in wheat. Aust J Biol Sci **26:** 1-13

Martinez-Carrasco R, Thorne GN (1979) Physiological factors limiting grain size in wheat. J Exp Bot **30:** 669-679

Offler CE, Patrick JW (1986) Cellular pathway and hormonal control of short-distance transfer in sink regions. *In* J Cronshaw, WJ Lucas, RT Giaquinta, eds, Phloem Transport, Plant Biology, Vol I. Alan R. Liss, Inc, New York, pp 295-306

Patrick JW (1990) Sieve element unloading: cellular pathway, mechanism and control. Physiol Plant **78:** 298-308

Pheloung PC, Siddique KHM (1991) Contribution of stem dry matter to grain yield in wheat cultivars. Aust J Plant Physiol **18:** 53-64

Sakri FAK, Shannon JC (1975) Movement of ^{14}C-labelled sugars into kernels of wheat (*Triticum aestivum* L.). Plant Physiol **55:** 881-889

Schnyder, H (1993) The role of carbohydrate storage and redistribution in the source-sink relations of wheat and barley during grain filling - a review. New Phytol **123:** 233-247

Singh BK, Jenner CF (1984) Factors controlling endosperm cell number and grain dry weight in wheat: Effects of shading on intact plants and variation in nutritional supply to detached, cultured ears. Aust J Plant Physiol **11:** 151-163

Sofield I, Evans LT, Cook MG, Wardlaw IF (1977) Factors influencing the rate and duration of grain filling in wheat. Aust J Plant Physiol **4:** 785-797

Ugalde TD, Jenner CF (1990*a*) Substrate gradients and regional patterns of dry matter deposition within developing wheat endosperm. I. Carbohydrates. Aust J Plant Physiol **17:** 377-394

Ugalde TD, Jenner CF (1990*b*) Route of substrate movement into wheat endosperm. I. Carbohydrates. Aust J Plant Physiol **17:** 693-704

Wang HL (1993) The cellular pathway of photosynthate transfer in the developing grain of wheat (*Triticum turgidum*). PhD Thesis, Univ Newcastle

Wang HL, Offler CE, Patrick JW (1994*b*) Nucellar projection transfer cell in the developing wheat grain. Protoplasma **182:** 39-52

Wang HL, Offler CE, Patrick JW (1995*a*) Cellular pathway of photosynthate transfer in the developing wheat grain. II. A structural analysis and histochemical studies of the transfer pathway from the crease phloem to the endosperm cavity. Plant Cell Environ **18:** 373-388

Wang HL, Offler CE, Patrick JW, Ugalde TD (1994*a*) Cellular pathway of photosynthate transfer in the developing wheat grain. I. Delineation of the potential transfer pathway using fluorescent dyes. Plant Cell Environ **17**: 257-266

Wang HL, Patrick JW, Offler CE, Wang XD (1995*b*) Cellular pathway of photosynthate transfer in the developing wheat grain. III. A structural analysis and physiological studies of transfer from the endosperm cavity to the endosperm. Plant Cell Environ **18**: 389-407

Wang HL, Patrick JW, Offler CE, Wardlaw IF (1993) A novel experimental system for studies of photosynthate transfer in the developing wheat grain. J Exp Bot **44**: 1177-1184

Wang N, Fisher DB (1994*a*) The use of fluorescent tracers to characterize the post-phloem transport pathway in maternal tissues of developing wheat grains. Plant Physiol **104**: 17-27

Wang N, Fisher DB (1994*b*) Monitoring phloem unloading and post-phloem transport by microperfusion of attached wheat grains. Plant Physiol **104**: 7-16

Wardlaw IF (1990) The control of carbon partitioning in plants. New Phytol **116**: 341-381

Wardlaw IF, Moncur L (1976) Source, sink and hormonal control of translocation in wheat. Planta **128**: 93-100

Zee SY, O'Brien TP (1970) Studies on the ontogeny of the pigment strand in the caryopsis of wheat. Aust J Biol Sci **23**: 1153-1171

Zhang W, Yang W, Lou ZH (1984) Transport of disassembled protoplasm from degenerated nucellus into embryo sac and its role in feeding the proliferating antopodals in wheat. Acta Bot Sinica **26**: 11-18

Zhang W, Yang W, Lou ZH (1988) The structural changes during the degeneration process of antipodal complex and its function to endosperm formation in wheat caryopsis. Acta Bot Sinica **30**: 457-462

Zhang W, Yang W, Wu S (1980) Intercellular migration of protoplasm and its relation to the development of embryo sac in nucellus of wheat grain. Acta Bot Sinica **22**: 32-36

Carbon Partitioning and Source-Sink Interactions in Plants, *Monica A. Madore* and *William J. Lucas*, eds, Copyright 1995, published by The American Society of Plant Physiologists

Sugar Alcohol Metabolism in Source Leaves

**Wayne H. Loescher, John D. Everard,
Claudio Cantini, and Rebecca Grumet**

*Department of Horticulture, Michigan State University, East Lansing,
MI 48824-1325, USA (W.H.L.; J.D.E.; R.G.); and Istituto
Propagazione Specie Legnose, Consiglio Nazionale Ricerche,
Florence, Italy (C.C.)*

Roles in Photosynthesis, Transport, and Storage

Sugar alcohols account for as much as 30% of global primary photosynthetic production (Bieleski, 1982). Sugar alcohols were first shown to be primary photosynthetic products in higher plants approximatelty 35 years ago, after earlier work had established similar roles in algae. Rapid glucitol labeling was demonstrated in apple and plum leaves, as was rapid $^{14}CO_2$ incorporation into mannitol in *Fraxinus* and *Syringa* and into allitol in *Itea*. These, and later studies, showed that $^{14}CO_2$ assimilation generally resulted in two major soluble products, e.g. in apple, approximately 70% of the fixed carbon was distributed between sucrose and glucitol, and in celery, 80 to 90% between mannitol and sucrose. When galactosyl-sucrose oligosaccharides were significant products, sucrose and the sugar alcohol collectively accounted for less of the newly fixed carbon (Bieleski and Redgwell, 1977; Flora and Madore, 1993; Loescher et al., 1992). In all sugar-alcohol-producing higher plants studied to date, sucrose is present and is frequently the major photoassimilate. This dual, or multiple, pattern of primary products is not, however, universal; in diatoms and brown algae, mannitol may be the sole soluble product.

Like sucrose, sugar alcohols are also phloem transported, and frequently serve as storage compounds in fungi, algae, and higher plants. They may also be major photosynthetic carbon pools in leaves and other vegetative tissues, as well as in fruits and other storage organs. Sugar alcohols are additionally involved in heterotrophic nutrition, osmoregulation, and transport, occurring in mammals, bacteria, yeasts, fungi, parasitic plants, and in nonphotosynthetic stages of green plants, e.g. developing and germinating seeds and seedlings. However, space does not permit covering these topics here. For further discussion and for a list of extensive reviews of sugar alcohol physiology, distribution, and chemistry, see Loescher and Everard (1995).

Sugar Alcohol Biosynthesis

Compared to 15 years ago, sugar alcohol enzymology in higher plants is now better understood. Numerous synthetic and degradative enzymes have been identified—some have been purified, with antibodies available, and two critical genes in plant mannitol and glucitol biosynthesis have been sequenced, as has a step in mannitol degradation. Progress began when it was shown that glucitol synthesis in the family Rosaceae was accompanied by the appearance of hexose and hexitol phosphates (Bieleski and Redgwell, 1977). An NADPH-dependent aldose 6-phosphate reductase (A6PR) was discovered in *Eriobotrya* (Hirai, 1979), in apple cotyledons (Yamaki, 1980), and mature leaves of apple, peach, pear, and apricot (Negm and Loescher, 1981). A similar enzyme was found in *Trollius* in the Ranunculaceae (Chen and Negm, unpubl. data). An NADPH-dependent mannose 6-phosphate reductase (M6PR) was reported in celery in the Apiaceae (Loescher *et al.*, 1982; Rumpho *et al.*, 1983) and a ribitol-synthesizing NADPH-dependent ribose 5-phosphate reductase in *Adonis* in the Ranunculaceae (Negm and Marlow, 1985). Other reductases include a galactitol-synthesizing, NADPH-dependent aldose reductase in *Euonymus* leaves in the Celastraceae (Negm, 1986), and an NADH-dependent ketose reductase in maize endosperm (Doehlert, 1987). For further discussion of these and related enzymes, see Loescher and Everard (1995). Also, although A6PR has been cloned, sequenced, and otherwise well characterized (Kanayama *et al.*, 1992, only M6PR will be discussed in any detail here.

Mannitol is the most widely distributed of the sugar alcohols (Bieleski, 1982), and M6PR is the critical step in higher plant mannitol biosynthesis (Loescher *et al.*, 1992). M6PR has been isolated, characterized, and purified (Loescher *et al.*, 1992), polyclonal antibodies prepared, and the gene cloned and sequenced (J. Everard, C. Cantini, R. Grumet, and W. Loescher, unpubl. data). M6PR is predominantly cytosolic and not at all vacuolar or associated with any membrane system or organelle, although it may be present in nuclei. M6PR (and thus mannitol biosynthesis) is also primarily restricted to green, palisade, and spongy parenchyma tissues and bundle sheath cells in celery, but not vascular parenchyma (Everard *et al.*, 1993). Similarly, labeling studies in olive (*Olea*) suggested spatial separation of stachyose and mannitol biosynthesis, with rapid mannitol synthesis occurring within the photosynthetic mesophyll tissues and slower raffinose synthesis occurring closer to, probably within, minor veins (Flora and Madore, 1993).

Conclusions regarding sugar alcohol synthesis are supported by several kinds of evidence, e.g. the above-mentioned localization studies, as well as developmental, source-sink transition studies in celery (Davis and Loescher, 1990) and peach (Merlo and Passera, 1991) and studies of the parasites *Orobanche* in the Orobanchaceae (Harloff and Wegmann, 1993) and *Thesium* in the Santalaceae (Simier *et al.*, 1994). But, very little is known about regulation at the enzyme level, even less is known about regulation of transport and utilization, and nothing is known about regulation at the gene level.

Roles of Sugar Alcohols in Stress Tolerance in Higher Plants

Although sugar alcohols are clearly involved in photosynthesis, transport, and storage, in most species, these roles are played by sucrose and starch, and sucrose is apparently translocated in all higher plants (Zimmerman and Ziegler, 1975). What then is the advantage of sugar alcohols? Work on algae (Cowan *et al.*, 1992), lichens (Honegger, 1991), and fungi (Brown, 1978) suggests roles as compatible solutes in tolerance of environmental stresses, especially those related to salinity and drought. Several biophysical explanations have been proposed for compatible solutes and their interactions with biological structures (Galinski, 1993). The prevailing view suggests uneven distribution of compatible solutes in a protein solution where compatible solutes are excluded from protein hydration spheres; in some way, bulk water structure is ordered so that biological structures become preferentially hydrated and conformation is maintained as the bulk water activity is otherwise lowered.

Plants adapted to high salts have various mechanisms by which deleterious effects are avoided or minimized. Exclusion is one mechanism, but in most tolerant species, inorganic ions entering the cells are usually sequestered in the vacuole. In such salt-tolerant plants, ions may accumulate such that the water potential of the vacuole balances that of external milieu, thus maintaining turgor. In the cytoplasm, however, ions are usually maintained at low concentrations, yet this compartment must remain in osmotic equilibrium with the vacuole and the external medium. Compatible solutes play a role since they may accumulate in the cytoplasm without disrupting biological processes.

In theory, compatible solutes preferentially accumulate in the cytoplasm, but sugar alcohols are apparently predominantly stored in the vacuole (Keller and Matile, 1989). This implies that salt stress causes a reallocation of sugar alcohol to the cytoplasm. Although little is known about reallocation of sugar alcohols in response to stress, the extravacuolar/vacuolar ratio of proline has been reported to increase with water stress in tobacco protoplasts (Pahlich *et al.*, 1983). In celery, petiole parenchyma mannitol is stored predominantly in the vacuole (81%), with lesser amounts in the cytosol (19%), but cytosolic concentrations may reach 300 mM (Keller and Matile, 1989).

Evidence that sugar alcohols play roles in plant stress tolerance, especially to salt stress, is compelling in marine algae (Kirst, 1990) and in the euryhaline green algal flagellate *Dunaliella*, where glycerol is involved in osmoregulation across the entire NaCl solubility range (see Ginzburg, 1987, and Cowan *et al.*, 1992, for reviews). However, few studies link the acyclic hexitols to salt tolerance in higher plants. In a distributional study, mannitol (as well as cyclitols) dominated instead of sugars in several salt-secreting mangrove species; whereas, their nonmangrove counterparts typically lacked hexitols and cyclitols, but there was little correlation between accumulation and increasing salt load (Popp, 1984). In salt-tolerant members of the Plantaginaceae, however, glucitol accumulated strikingly with salinity stress and declined when the stress was relieved (Briens and Larher, 1983).

Several recent studies show that salt or nutrient stress increases sugar alcohol accumulation in higher plants, i.e. mannitol in celery (Stoop and Pharr, 1994*a*, *b*) and olive (Romani *et al.*, 1992) and glucitol in *Plantago* (Briens and Larher, 1983), but the cellular mechanisms involved were not investigated. In another celery study, however, increasing salt (NaCl) stress not only increased mannitol pools (and decreased other carbohydrates), but also increased relative levels of M6PR (Everard *et al.*, 1994). That study also showed that in mature leaves, the rate of mannitol biosynthesis was maintained at control levels even at 300 mM NaCl, despite a 70% reduction in photosynthesis. Labeling of sucrose and starch declined commensurate with photosynthesis. In another study, celery exposed to high macronutrient levels also showed increases in mannitol and M6PR in mature leaves and, in addition, decreases in mannitol 1-oxidoreductase in sink tissues (Stoop and Pharr, 1994*b*).

RESULTS AND DISCUSSION

Here, we report some results of a developmental study which shows that salt effects depend distinctly on leaf age. Salt treatments had no effect on total assimilation rates in young leaves, although older leaves senescenced prematurely (Fig. 1), but ^{14}C-labeling patterns in young leaves were altered dramatically with the proportion in mannitol increasing from 10% in controls to 23 and 37% in 150- and 300-mM treated plants, respectively (Table I). As in mature leaves (Everard *et al*, 1994), increased mannitol labeling occurred at the expense of sucrose, but the difference between the two leaf ages was that the rate of mannitol biosynthesis in young leaves increased 1.8- and 3-fold over controls in 150- and 300-mM treated plants, respectively. Increased mannitol synthesis in young leaves was also associated with much higher M6PR activities (Everard *et al.*, 1994) and M6PR protein (data not shown). Our conclusion is that salt treatments induced earlier expression of mannitol biosynthesis in leaf tissues.

Table I. *14C-Labeling of Young, Still Expanding Celery Leaves*

See Everard *et al.* (1994) for experimental protocols. Values followed by the same letter are not significantly different at the 5% level.

Treatment	14C-Labeling		Rate	
	Sucrose	Mannitol	Sucrose	Mannitol
	%		$(\mu Ci/g$ fresh wt) x 10^3	
Control	82.2 a	10.2 a	44.3 a	5.6 a
150 mM NaCl	68.4 b	23.3 b	29.9 a	10.2 ab
300 mM NaCl	59.1 c	36.9 c	26.7 a	16.7 b

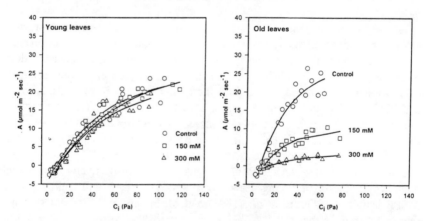

Figure 1. Salt effects on A-Ci curves for young (expanding) and old celery leaves. See Everard *et al.* (1994) for experimental protocols and further descriptions of leaf ages.

174

These results suggest a role for mannitol in stress tolerance, but do not resolve whether it is in osmoregulation or as a compatible solute. Genetic transformations have begun to address these same questions. For example, a mannitol 1-phosphate dehydrogenase, from the *E. coli mtl* operon, was recently introduced into tobacco. Although transformants produced only very low (micromolar) levels of mannitol in most tissues, the plants apparently showed enhanced salt tolerance (Tarczynski *et al.*, 1993). However, an important next step will be genetic transformation of a salt-tolerant, sugar-alcohol-synthesizing species to see if lack of the hexitol diminishes salt tolerance.

As compatible solutes, sugar alcohols may play a general role in stress tolerance. Work on insects strongly suggests a role in cold hardiness (Storey and Storey, 1991). The evidence in plants is less convincing (see review by Loescher and Everard, 1995). However, glucitol content and A6PR activity increased in late autumn and decreased in spring in evergreen leaves of loquat (*Eriobotrya*) and in seedlings exposed to low temperatures (Hirai, 1983). Low-temperature acclimation in *Opuntia* increased soluble sugars two- to nine-fold, including a nearly three-fold increase in mannitol in the hardiest species (Goldstein and Nobel, 1994).

Various salt, drought, and cold stress effects suggest that sugar alcohol metabolism might be highly regulated by stress at the gene level. Such relationships are clear in other organisms (Jennings and Burke, 1990), but in higher plants, the evidence more often involves increased capacity for cyclitol synthesis (Vernon and Bohnert, 1992). In barley embryos, however, desiccation tolerance was accompanied by expression of an ABA- and GA-promoted gene with high structural homology to mammalian genes encoding NADPH-dependent aldose reductases involved in sorbitol synthesis (Bartels *et al.*, 1991), but the barley gene product's substrate specificity and product were undefined, and presence of sorbitol in barley has not been established. Interestingly, the celery M6PR sequence also has similarities to several aldose

---

Table II. *DNA Similarities Between Celery M6PR and Genes Catalogued in the BLAST Nonredundant Database*

81%	-	rat aldose reductase
71%	-	*C. elegans* cDNA sequence
66%	-	apple aldose 6-phosphate reductase
60%	-	rat dihydrodiol dehydrogenase
60%	-	rat lens aldose reductase
60%	-	rat hydroxysteroid dehydrogenase
58%	-	mouse aldose reductase

---

reductases (Table II), but further relationships to stress tolerance mechanisms remain to be determined.

Conclusions and Considerations for Future Research

Understanding of sugar alcohol metabolism has progressed significantly in the last 15 years for both glucitol and mannitol. Nonetheless, little is yet known about regulation of biosynthesis or degradation, and even less is known about the basic metabolism of other sugar alcohols in higher plants. Sugar alcohol metabolism is very tightly controlled developmentally, but we have yet to describe any of the mechanisms involved. The systems involved are complex for two major reasons: (*i*) The need to regulate carbon partitioning in plants has been discussed in detail at this and other conferences, and all the arguments for the need to regulate carbon flow in starch and sucrose synthesizers are equally relevant to sugar alcohol synthesizers, with the added complication of another synthetic pathway (with additional regulatory steps) competing for the same substrates and intermediates. And (*ii*), with the increasing probability that sugar alcohols are involved in stress tolerance in higher plants, this almost certainly requires still further modulation of metabolism, storage, and transport. However, despite the complexities and difficulties, as we answer these problems we should develop insight not only into regulation of carbon partitioning, but also into mechanisms of stress tolerance, with the result the potential to increase crop productivity.

ACKNOWLEDGMENTS

This work was supported in part by a USDA-NRI grant #940-1439 to W.H.L., J.D.E., and R.G.

LITERATURE CITED

Bartels D, Engelhardt K, Roncarati R, Schneider K, Rotter M, Salamini F (1991) An ABA and GA modulated gene expressed in the barley embryo encodes an aldose reductase related protein. EMBO J **10**: 1037-1043

Bieleski RL (1982) Sugar alcohols. *In* FA Loewus, W Tanner, eds, Plant Carbohydrates I. Intercellular Carbohydrates. Encyclopedia of Plant Physiology, New Series, Vol 13A. Springer-Verlag, New York, pp 158-192

Bieleski RL, Redgwell RJ (1977) Synthesis of sorbitol in apricot leaves. Aust J Plant Physiol **4**: 1-10

Briens M, Larher F (1983) Sorbitol accumulation in Plantaginaceae: further evidence for a function in stress tolerance. Z Pflanzen **110**: 447-458

Brown AD (1978) Compatible solutes and extreme water stress in eukaryotic micro-organisms. Adv Microbiol Physiol **17**: 181-242

Cowan AK, Rose PD, Horne LG (1992) *Dunaliella salina*: a model system for studying the response of plant cells to stress. J Exp Bot **43**: 1535-1547

Davis JM, Loescher WH (1990) [14C]-Assimilate translocation in the light and dark in celery (*Apium graveolens*) leaves of different ages. Physiol Plant **79**: 656-662

Doehlert DC (1987) Ketose reductase in developing maize endosperm. Plant Physiol **84**: 830-834

Everard JD, Franceschi VR, Loescher WH (1993) Mannose-6-phosphate reductase, a key enzyme in photoassimilate partitioning, is abundant and located in the cytosol of photosynthetically active cells of celery (*Apium graveolens* L) source leaves. Plant Physiol **102**: 345-356

Everard JD, Gucci R, Kann SC, Flore JA, Loescher WH (1994) Gas exchange and carbon partitioning in the leaves of celery (*Apium graveolens* L.) at various levels of root zone salinity. Plant Physiol **106**: 281-292

Flora LL, Madore MA (1993) Stachyose and mannitol transport in olive (*Olea europaea* L). Planta **189**: 484-490

Galinski EA (1993) Compatible solutes of halophilic eubacteria - molecular principles, water-solute interaction, stress protection. Experientia **49**: 487-496

Ginzburg M (1987) *Dunaliella*: a green alga adapted to salt. Adv Bot Res **14**: 93-183

Goldstein G, Nobel PS (1994) Water relations and low-temperature acclimation for cactus species varying in freezing tolerance. Plant Physiol **104**: 675-681

Harloff HJ, Wegmann K (1993) Evidence for a mannitol cycle in *Orobanche ramosa* and *Orobanche crenata*. J Plant Physiol **141**: 513-520

Hirai M (1979) Sorbitol-6-phosphate dehydrogenase from loquat fruit. Plant Physiol **63**: 715-717

Hirai M (1983) Seasonal changes in sorbitol-6-phosphate dehydrogenase in loquat leaf. Plant Cell Physiol **24**: 925-931

Honegger R (1991) Functional aspects of the lichen symbiosis. Annu Rev Plant Physiol Plant Mol Biol **42**: 553-578

Jennings DH, Burke RM (1990) Compatible solutes - the mycological dimension and their role as physiological buffering agents. New Phytol **116**: 277-283

Kanayama Y, Mori H, Imaseki H, Yamaki S (1992) Nucleotide sequence of a cDNA encoding NADP-sorbitol-6-phosphate dehydrogenase from apple. Plant Physiol **100**: 1607-1608

Keller F, Matile P (1989) Storage of sugars and mannitol in petioles of celery leaves. New Phytol **113**: 291-299

Kirst GO (1990) Salinity tolerance of eukaryotic marine algae. Annu Rev Plant Physiol Plant Mol Biol **41**: 21-53

Loescher WH, Everard JD (1995) Metabolism of carbohydrates in sinks and sources: sugar alcohols. *In* E Zamski, A Schaffer, eds, Photoassimilate Distribution in Plants and crops: Source-sink relationships. Marcel Dekker, Inc, New York (in press)

Loescher WH, Redgwell R, Bieleski R (1982) Mannitol biosynthesis in higher plants: detection and characterization of a NADPH-dependent mannose 6-phosphate reductase. Plant Physiol **69S**: 51

Loescher WH, Tyson RH, Everard JD, Redgwell RJ, Bieleski RL (1992) Mannitol synthesis in higher plants: evidence for the role and characterization of a NADPH-dependent mannose 6-phosphate reductase. Plant Physiol 98: 1396-1402

Merlo L, Passera C (1991) Changes in carbohydrate and enzyme levels during development of leaves of *Prunus persica*, a sorbitol synthesizing species. Physiol Plant 83: 621-626

Negm FB (1986) Purification and properties of an NADPH-aldose reductase (aldehyde reductase) from *Euonymus japonica* leaves. Plant Physiol 80: 972-977

Negm FB, Loescher WH (1981) Characterization of aldose 6-phosphate reductase (alditol 6-phosphate: NADP 1-oxidoreductase) from apple leaves. Plant Physiol 67: 139-142

Negm FB, Marlow GC (1985) Partial purification and characterization of D-ribose-5-phosphate reductase from *Adonis vernalis* L. leaves. Plant Physiol 78: 758-761

Pahlich E, Kerres R, Jäger HJ (1983) Influence of water stress on the vacuole/extravacuole distribution of proline in protoplasts of *Nicotiana rustica*. Plant Physiol 72: 590-591

Popp M (1984) Chemical composition of Australian mangroves. II. Low molecular weight carbohydrates. Z Pflanzen 113: 411-421

Romani A, Baldi A, Vincieri FF, Tattini M, Cimato A (1992) Analisi Quali-Quantitativa di Oligosaccharidi in Piante di Olivo (cv. Leccino) Sottoposte a Stress da NaCl. Intl Conf on Olive Oil Quality 77-86

Rumpho ME, Edwards GE, Loescher WH (1983) A pathway for photosynthetic carbon flow to mannitol in celery leaves: activity and localization of key enzymes. Plant Physiol 73: 869-873

Simier P, Renaudin S, Fer A (1994) Characteristics of the mannitol pathway in a root hemiparasitic species, *Thesium humile* Vahl. (Santalaceae). J Plant Physiol 143: 33-38

Stoop JMH, Pharr DM (1994a) Growth substrate and nutrient salt environment alter mannitol-to-hexose partitioning in celery petioles. J Am Soc Hort Sci 119: 237-242

Stoop JMH, Pharr DM (1994b) Mannitol metabolism in celery stressed by excess macronutrients. Plant Physiol 106: 503-511

Storey KB, Storey JM (1991) Biochemistry of cryoprotectants. *In* RE Lee Jr, DL Denlinger, eds, Insects at Low Temperature. Chapman and Hall, New York, pp 64-93

Tarczynski MC, Jensen RG, Bohnert HJ (1993) Stress protection of transgenic tobacco by production of the osmolyte mannitol. Science 259: 508-510

Vernon DM, Bohnert HJ (1992) Increased expression of a myo-inositol methyl transferase in *Mesembryanthemum crystallinum* is part of a stress response distinct from Crassulacean Acid Metabolism induction. Plant Physiol 99: 1695-1698

Yamaki S (1980) Property of sorbitol-6-phosphate dehydrogenase and its connection with sorbitol accumulation in apple. HortScience 15: 268-270

Zimmerman MH, Zeigler H (1975) List of sugars and sugar alcohols in sieve-tube exudates. *In* MH Zimmerman, JA Milburn, eds, Transport in Plants, Encyclopedia of Plant Physiology, New Series, Vol 1. Springer-Verlag, New York, pp 480-503

Carbon Partitioning and Source-Sink Interactions in Plants, *Monica A. Madore* and *William J. Lucas*, eds, Copyright 1995, published by The American Society of Plant Physiologists

Mannitol Catabolism in Plant Sink Tissues

D. Mason Pharr, Johan M. H. Stoop, Monika E. Studer Feusi, John D. Williamson, Mara O. Massel, and Mark A. Conkling

Departments of Horticultural Science (D.M.P.; J.M.H.S.; M.E.S.F.; J.D.W.; M.O.M.) and Genetics (M.A.C.), North Carolina State University, Raleigh, NC 27695-7609, USA

Mannitol, a six-carbon, noncyclic alcohol, is a photosynthetic product along with sucrose that is translocated in the phloem to nonphotosynthetic, so-called sink tissues. In these heterotrophically growing tissues, either carbohydrate may be stored or metabolized to yield energy and carbon skeletons for the synthetic reactions of growth. There is increasing evidence that mannitol also may serve as an important osmolyte and compatible solute alleviating osmostress and stress resulting from excess salinity (Tarczynski *et al.*, 1993; Everard *et al.*, 1994; Stoop and Pharr, 1994*a*). Compatible solutes are thought to accumulate in the cytosol where they prevent inactivation of metabolic processes by protecting enzymes (Greenway and Munns, 1980). It has been suggested that polyols, because of their water-like OH-groups, may mimic the structure of water and maintain an artificial sphere of "hydration" around macromolecules (Schobert, 1977). Mannitol may also function as a scavenger of hydroxyl radicals that damage cells by initiating peroxidation of lipids. Hexitols are more effective in this role than glycine betaine, another common compatible solute in plants (Smirnoff and Cumbes, 1989).

Down regulation of mannitol catabolism in sink tissues of celery and the resulting mannitol accumulation plays a major role in mannitol accumulation during osmotic and salt stress (Stoop and Pharr, 1994*a*, *b*; Pharr *et al.*, 1995). This paper discusses the enzymology of mannitol catabolism in sink tissues of celery plants and celery suspension-cultured cells. Emphasis is given to mannitol dehydrogenase (MTD), the key enzyme regulating mannitol use or accumulation in celery.

Enzymes of Mannitol Catabolism

It was previously demonstrated that ^{14}C-mannitol is metabolized to $^{14}CO_2$ and other products in sink tissues of numerous species of plants (Trip *et al.*, 1964). Catabolism of mannitol in celery is restricted to actively growing sink tissues (Fellman and Loescher, 1987). Tissues such as mature petioles of celery do not catabolize mannitol, but accumulate hexitol (Keller and Matile, 1989). Until recently, the enzymatic route by which mannitol was catabolized was not known. Mannitol dehydrogenase, an NAD-dependent mannitol: mannose 1-oxidoreductase (MTD), that oxidizes mannitol to mannose was discovered in roots of celeriac, *Apium graveolens* L. var *rapaceum*, and celery, *Apium graveolens* L. var *dulce*, [Mill.] Pers. (Stoop and Pharr, 1992). This constituted the first report of a mannitol dehydrogenase in vascular plants. MTD catalyzes the reaction shown in Figure 1.

In the reversal of this reaction, MTD catalyzes an NADH-dependent reduction of mannose to mannitol and does not utilize either glucose or fructose in this reaction, verifying the specificity for mannose and the oxidation and reduction of carbon-1. All previously identified mannitol dehydrogenases in microorganisms are 2-oxidoreductases that catalyze oxidation of either mannitol to fructose, or mannitol-1-P to Fru-6-P. Biosynthesis of mannitol in higher plants involves mannose-6-P reduction to mannitol-1-P by mannose-6-P

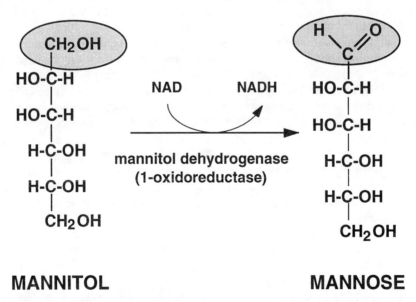

MANNITOL **MANNOSE**

Figure 1. The reaction catalyzed by celery mannitol dehydrogenase, MTD.

reductase. Thus, both the biosynthesis and catabolism of mannitol by vascular plants apparently involve 1-oxidoreductases rather than 2-oxidoreductases, as in bacteria, fungi, algae, and lichens. MTD isolated from celeriac roots (Stoop and Pharr, 1992) exhibited specificity for NAD rather than NADP. The enzyme was much more active on mannitol as a substrate than on other hexitols, although there was low apparent activity on sorbitol and galactitol, but not *myo*-inositol. MTD was recently purified to homogeneity from mannitol-grown celery suspension-cultured cells, and polyclonal antibodies directed against the protein were raised in rabbits (Stoop *et al.*, 1995).

Root tips contained higher activity of MTD than other tissues of celeriac and celery (Stoop and Pharr, 1992, 1994*a*, *b*). MTD activity was present in other tissues such as fibrous roots, young petioles, and young leaves, but was barely detectable in mature petioles and not detected in mature leaves. Thus, the enzyme is active primarily in rapidly growing tissues, a fact that correlates well with the observation that these are the tissues able to catabolize mannitol (Fellman and Loescher, 1987). In general, there was an inverse relationship between mannitol concentration and MTD activity in tissues throughout the plant. These observations suggest that the enzyme functions physiologically in an assimilatory pathway to consume mannitol during growth. The enzyme was also found in suspension-cultured cells of celery which provide a model system for heterotrophically growing tissues (Stoop and Pharr, 1993).

MTD constitutes the initial enzymatic step by which mannitol enters the central metabolic pathways that supply carbon skeletons and energy for growth in sink tissues of celeriac, celery, parsley (Stoop *et al.*, 1995), possibly other vascular plants, and in heterotrophically growing celery cells cultured on mannitol as the carbon source (Stoop and Pharr, 1993). The initial reactions of mannitol utilization leading to the central metabolite Fru-6-P are depicted in Figure 2. Mannose, the product of mannitol oxidation, is phosphorylated by hexokinase and subsequently isomerized to Fru-6-P. Celery cell cultures and sink tissues of celery plants have very high phosphomannose isomerase activity (Stoop and Pharr, 1993, 1994*a*, *b*). Plants that do not contain phosphomannose isomerase or plants that contain very low levels of the enzyme typically are unable to utilize exogenously supplied mannose. In these plants, sequestration of Pi results from accumulation of mannose-6-P that is formed through the action of hexokinase (Herold and Lewis, 1977). Unlike the broad specificity of plant hexokinases, the activity of phosphohexose isomerases appears to be highly specific to a particular hexose-P (Herold and Lewis, 1977).

MANNITOL UTILIZATION BY CELERY CELL CULTURES

Growth on Different Carbon Sources

Celery cells grow well in suspension culture on basal medium (Murashige and Skoog, 1962) supplemented with hormones, vitamins, and an appropriate

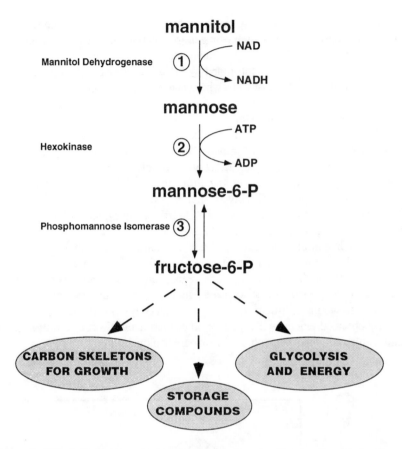

Figure 2. The initial steps of mannitol catabolism leading to the production of the central metabolite Fru-6-P.

carbohydrate source.   Unlike cultures of many species that will not utilize mannitol or mannose, celery cells grow well on mannitol, mannose, or sucrose as the sole carbon source as indicated by increases in packed cell volume. Culture growth was associated with depletion of each of the carbohydrates from their growth media (Stoop and Pharr, 1993).   The ability of the cells to utilize mannitol and mannose supports the route of mannitol metabolism shown in Figure 2.   Mannitol is actually utilized more effectively in dry weight production than is sucrose by these cells.   Cells growing on mannitol consumed an average of 2.93 mg mannitol per mg dry weight of cells produced, whereas 3.72 mg sucrose was consumed per mg dry weight of cells produced (Pharr *et al.*, 1995).   The differences in efficiency with which the carbohydrates are used may be related to the production of energy in the form of reduced pyridine nucleotide in the initial step of mannitol catabolism (Fig. 2) and the availability of the NADH for ATP production. This is not true of sucrose catabolism, wherein ATP is consumed by kinase reactions in the initial steps of sucrose utilization as discussed elsewhere (Pharr *et al.*, 1995).

MTD Activity in Cultured Cells

MTD activity in cells exhibited a characteristic pattern during each culture cycle, first increasing upon transfer to fresh medium and subsequently decreasing (Fig. 3). Activity of MTD was strongly influenced by the available carbon source and was highest in mannitol-grown cells (Fig. 3). These effects of carbon source appear formally similar to substrate induction observed for mannitol-1-P dehydrogenase in bacteria (Martinez De Drets and Arias, 1970), and it is tempting to speculate that MTD is induced by mannitol. Upon transfer to fresh mannitol-containing medium, the initial high mannitol concentration might induce MTD activity followed by a decline as mannitol is depleted during growth of the cultures. Such regulation would, however, present a dilemma in being inconsistent with the pattern observed in intact plants, where MTD and tissue mannitol concentration are inversely related. In fact, we have recently obtained evidence that factors other than mannitol concentration in the cultures play an important role in this apparent induction.

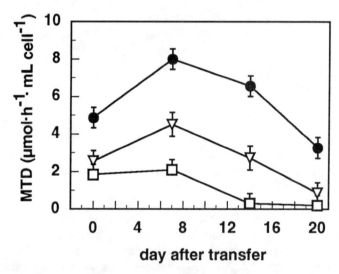

Figure 3. Mannitol dehydrogenase activity of cultured celery cells grown on (●) mannitol, (▽) sucrose or (□) mannose as a carbon source. Reproduced from Stoop and Pharr (1993) with permission from the American Society of Plant Physiologists.

Phosphate Nutrition Influences Cultured Cell MTD Activity

Phosphate nutritional status of the culture strongly influences the pattern of MTD activity observed during the culture cycle. Data from an experiment in which the Pi concentration initially present in mannitol-containing cultures was adjusted to either 0, 0.52, or 1.04 mM Pi, the concentration normally present in MS medium after addition of cells, is summarized in Figures 4 and 5. Growth, MTD activity and concentrations of Pi in cells and media were measured. Cells from 2-week-old cultures transferred into the fresh media differed in growth depending upon Pi concentration in the cultures. Media that did not contain Pi did not support growth, and MTD activity did not increase (Fig. 4). MTD activity was maintained at a higher level for a longer time in cultures initially containing 1.04 mM Pi than in those initially containing 0.52 mM Pi (Fig. 4B). Pi in culture media was rapidly depleted (Fig. 5A) and was associated with a marked increase in internal Pi followed by a decline (Fig. 5B). Presumably, the internal Pi was metabolized as well as redistributed to newly formed cells as the cells divided and culture density increased with time (Fig. 4A). Thus, adequate Pi is essential for high MTD activity in the cultured cells, and becomes limiting toward the end of the culture cycle, or sooner if the initial concentration of Pi is lower than normally present in the MS medium. By the 10th d of the culture cycle, mannitol concentration was still high in the media at 26, 18, and 16 mg per mL of media initially containing 0, 0.52, and 1.04 mM Pi, respectively. Thus, the decline in MTD activity occurring late in the culture cycle (Fig. 3) cannot be attributed to limited mannitol availability in the media.

Further evidence that Pi is important for maintenance of high MTD activity was obtained from experiments in which Pi was added to 2-week-old cultures (Table I). Sufficient Pi was added to 2-week-old, mannitol-grown cultures to bring the culture Pi concentration to a minimum of 1.04 mM. Two different phosphate salts were used, and all additions were made in a minimal volume of 1.5 to 150 mL cultures. Cultures to which H_2O was added served as the control. Pi addition resulted in a four- to five-fold rise in MTD activity during the next 4 d relative to control cultures. The increased MTD activity was observed with either NaH_2PO_4 or KH_2PO_4 as the source of Pi, and the magnitude of this rise is comparable to that typically observed when mannitol-grown cells are subcultured to fresh media containing mannitol. No specific role for Pi in inducing expression of MTD is necessarily suggested from these experiments other than the multiple and essential roles of Pi in general metabolism.

Sugars Suppress Cultured-Cell MTD Activity

While these experiments with Pi indicate that culture factors other than carbon source influence MTD activity, it is clear that carbon source has a major effect on MTD expression. The cultures in Figure 3 contained equal Pi,

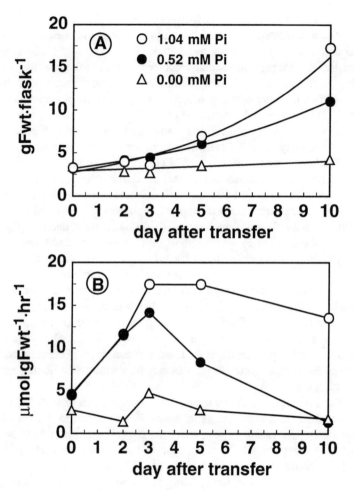

Figure 4. Effect of culture medium phosphate concentration on (A) growth and (B) mannitol dehydrogenase activity of cultured celery cells. Mannitol-grown cells were subcultured in complete growth media with mannitol as the carbon source in which the initial phosphate concentration was either 1.04, 0.52, or 0.00 mM.

but MTD activity was lower in sucrose- and mannose-grown cultures. Mannitol *per se* may not induce expression of MTD, rather sugars may suppress MTD expression. Several observations strongly support this contention. First, transfer of cells from 2-week-old, mannitol-grown cultures to a complete growth medium, minus carbohydrate, resulted in an approximate four-fold increase in MTD activity during the next 4 d (data not shown). Second, subculture of mannitol-grown cells onto sorbitol, which does not support growth,

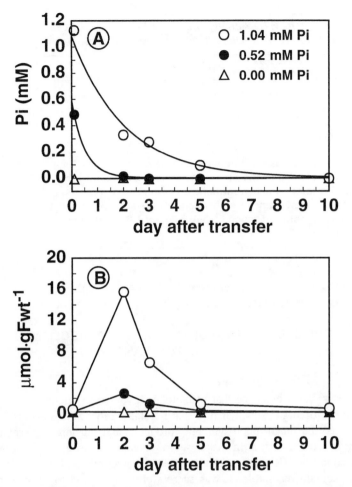

Figure 5. Change in phosphate concentration in the culture media (A) and inside celery cells (B) as influenced by initial media phosphate concentration. Mannitol-grown cells were subcultured in complete growth media with mannitol as the carbon source in which the initial phosphate concentration was either 1.04, 0.52, or 0.00 mM.

also resulted in an increase in MTD activity (data not shown). Cultures containing no carbohydrate or sorbitol did not grow and showed brown discoloration after 5 or 6 d. Third, it was shown previously that celery cultures containing mannose plus mannitol, or sucrose plus mannitol, expressed less MTD activity than cultures with mannitol alone as the carbon source (Stoop and Pharr, 1993). Thus, transfer of celery cells to culture media containing mannitol, sorbitol, or to media without carbohydrate, may result in high MTD

Table I. *Change in MTD Activity 4 D After Restoration of Original Phosphate Concentrations in 2-Week-Old, Mannitol-Grown Celery Cultures*

Treatment	Fold-Increase in MTD Activity[a]	SE
H_2O control	1.48	± 0.35
KH_2PO_4	5.19	± 1.28
NaH_2PO_4	4.35	± 0.58

[a] Fold-increase in MTD activity was calculated as the units of MTD per g fresh weight of cells at the time of treatment divided into the MTD activity of the cells 4 d later. Each treatment was replicated three times with a single culture flask constituting a replication. MTD activity of the 2-week-old cultures prior to treatment ranged from 0.63 to 2.68 units per g fresh weight of cells.

because these conditions are permissive of high MTD expression, while sugars or products of their metabolism may suppress the expression of MTD.

THE SPECIAL ROLE OF MANNITOL CATABOLISM IN STRESS TOLERANCE

Salt Tolerance in Intact Plants

There is ample evidence that mannitol is involved in tolerance to salinity in a number of organisms. In the marine alga *Platymonas subcordiformis*, mannitol is the main photosynthetic product, and mannitol increases or declines in concentration in response to changes in external salinity and osmotic conditions (Richter and Kirst, 1987). Tobacco is a plant that does not normally contain mannitol. It was successfully engineered to form mannitol through the introduction of a single gene, *mtlD*, from *Escherichia coli* under the control of the 35S cauliflower mosaic virus promoter (Tarczynski *et al.*, 1992). The gene encodes an NADH-dependent mannitol-1-P dehydrogenase that catalyses a reversible reduction of Fru-6-P to mannitol-1-P. A phosphatase normally present in tobacco apparently releases mannitol that accumulates throughout the plant. Interestingly, it was demonstrated that transformed mannitol accumulating tobacco was more tolerant to salinity than was wild-type tobacco (Tarczynski *et al.*, 1993). These experiments unequivocally established that the presence of mannitol can promote salt tolerance in vascular plants. Celery, a species normally containing mannitol, also exhibits substantial salt tolerance.

Modern celery cultivars are said to have been developed from *Apium graveolens* L. var *silvestre*, a species that is native to saline coastal habitats of

Europe, North Africa, and Asia (Yamaguchi, 1993). Recent studies have focused on the regulation of mannitol concentration in celery plants in response to elevated salinity in the rhizosphere (Everard *et al.*, 1994; Stoop and Pharr, 1994*a*, *b*). Celery, irrigated with 0.3 M NaCl, has been shown to maintain its ability to form photosynthetic mannitol, whereas the capacity to form photosynthetic sucrose is suppressed (Everard *et al.*, 1994). In analogous studies, hydroponically growing celery plants were stressed with excess macronutrient salts (Stoop and Pharr, 1994*b*). Total salinity of hydroponic solutions was varied by increasing the concentrations of all macronutrients simultaneously while maintaining micronutrients constant. The plants were grown for 35 d under varying levels of salinity ranging in electrical conductivity of 1.0 dS·m⁻¹ to an electrical conductivity of 11.9 dS·m⁻¹. The higher value corresponds to about 30% of the salinity of sea water. Plants exposed to differing concentrations of macronutrients did not respond by taking up excess nutrients. Nitrate, phosphate, potassium, calcium, magnesium, and sodium concentrations on a per gram dry weight of tissue basis were equal in plants after growth for 35 d at all salinity levels. Relative growth rate expressed on a fresh weight basis was progressively reduced as salinity of the hydroponic solution increased above 1.7 dS·m⁻¹. However, dry weight of plants at all salinities were equal at the end of 35 d. Thus, total assimilatory ability of the plants was unaffected by the nutrient solution salinity, but the water content of plants decreased as salinity increased.

Mannitol concentration progressively increased throughout the plants as the total salinity of the growth solution was increased. This was due primarily to a down regulation of MTD in sink tissues, including young roots, young leaves, and young petioles, resulting in less mannitol utilization and increased pool size. The dramatic decrease in MTD activity in the salinity-stressed roots was found to be associated with decreased amounts of MTD protein in western blots of SDS gels of extracted root proteins challenged with MTD-antiserum (Pharr *et al.*, 1995). Sucrose-metabolizing enzyme activities in the same sink tissues were totally unaffected by salinity stress as was sugar concentration, presumably indicating that the plants retain the ability to assimilate translocated sucrose while accumulating translocated mannitol.

Salt Tolerance in Celery Cultures

Direct evidence that mannitol can enhance salt tolerance of celery cells has been obtained through studies of the effects carbohydrates on the sensitivity of cultured cells to salinity. Inhibition of growth of cells cultured on either sucrose or mannitol by NaCl is shown in Figure 6. Cells growing on mannitol were about twice as resistant to growth inhibition by NaCl ($I_{50}=0.32$ M) as cells growing on sucrose ($I_{50}=0.17$ M). In another experiment, cells were grown on mannitol or sucrose in the presence and absence of 0.3 M NaCl. An analysis of the internal soluble carbohydrates in these cells on the 7th d of

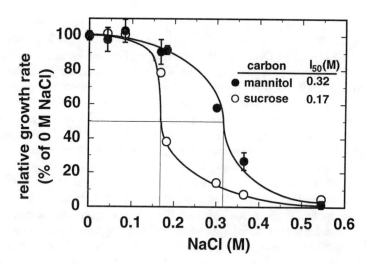

Figure 6. Inhibition of growth rate of cultured celery cells by NaCl as influenced by culture medium carbon source.

culture is shown in Table II. Mannitol-grown cells contained little sucrose and hexose compared to cells grown on sucrose, whereas sucrose-grown cells contained a substantial sucrose and hexose pool, but minimal mannitol. This agrees with previous observations (Stoop and Pharr, 1993). Cells on either carbon source accumulated total soluble carbohydrate in response to the NaCl, but the composition of these carbohydrate pools was very different. Cells grown on mannitol primarily accumulated mannitol, whereas cells grown on sucrose primarily accumulated sucrose.

This carbohydrate accumulation apparently represents osmotic adjustment of the cells in response to the media NaCl. Solutions of pure carbohydrates mixed at the concentrations identical to the internal concentrations were prepared, and their osmolalities were determined in a vapor pressure osmometer. The milliosmolality of the soluble carbohydrates of the mannitol- and sucrose-grown cells were 53 and 51 mmol/kg, respectively. Thus, the total osmotic contribution of soluble carbohydrates in the salt-stressed cells was about equal for cells on either carbohydrate source. Despite this, the growth rate of cells on sucrose was inhibited 86% by 0.3 M NaCl, while growth of cells on mannitol was only inhibited 42%. These data clearly point to a function of mannitol as an osmoprotectant in salt tolerance rather than a simple function as an osmolyte.

MTD activity, as expected, was higher in mannitol-grown cells than in sucrose-grown cells (Table III). NaCl resulted in about a 50% decrease in MTD activity in the mannitol-grown cells, and MTD was not detected in cells on sucrose in the presence of 0.3 M NaCl. It is possible that the decreased

Table II. *Mannitol, Sucrose, Hexose, and Total Carbohydrate Concentration (TCHO) of Celery Suspension Cultures Grown on Mannitol (Mt) or Sucrose (S) as the Carbon Source, Supplemented with 0.0 and 0.3 M NaCl*

Data represents mean ± SE of three replications. Cells were sampled 7 d after subculture.

Internal Carbohydrates	Mt		S	
	NaCl (M)		NaCl (M)	
	0.0	0.3	0.0	0.3
	mg/mL cell		*mg/mL cell*	
TCHO	4.78 ± 0.35	8.16 ± 1.20	5.95 ± 0.07	9.55 ± 0.67
Mannitol	3.69 ± 0.30	7.37 ± 1.03	0.02 ± 0.01	0.17 ± 0.01
Sucrose	0.89 ± 0.06	0.71 ± 0.14	2.12 ± 0.07	8.15 ± 0.75
Hexose	0.21 ± 0.01	0.08 ± 0.03	3.81 ± 0.04	1.23 ± 0.11

MTD activity and, thus, decreased catabolism of mannitol facilitates the increased mannitol concentration in the cells as discussed above for sink tissues in intact salt-stressed plants. In this regard, it is important that MTD activity be regulated independently of mannitol concentration in the cells. If MTD was up-regulated in direct proportion to mannitol concentration, this would limit the ability of tissues to accumulate mannitol. Regulation of this nature would be in opposition to the observed high accumulation of mannitol in tissues expressing low MTD activity such as petioles and mature leaves of intact plants (Stoop and Pharr, 1992), sink tissues of salinity-stressed plants (Stoop and Pharr, 1994*a*, *b*), and NaCl-stressed cells observed here.

CARBON SOURCE AND SALINITY AFFECT MTD TRANSCRIPT ABUNDANCE

Isolation of a cDNA for MTD

A 1.3-kb cDNA encoding MTD was recently isolated from a cDNA library produced from poly(A+) RNA extracted from mannitol-grown celery cells (Williamson *et al.*, 1995). Transformed bacteria containing cDNAs encoding and expressing MTD peptide sequences were identified with MTD antiserum produced against purified MTD (Stoop *et al.*, 1995). The clone contains consensus sequences for a zinc-binding site and an NAD/NADH-binding site, both of which are features common among many dehydrogenases. The open reading frame of the cDNA predicts a peptide translation product

Table III. *MDH Activity of Celery Suspension Cultures Grown on Mannitol (Mt) or Sucrose (S) as the Carbon Source, Supplemented with Either 0.0 or 0.3 M NaCl*

Data represents mean ± SE of three replications.

| NaCl | Mannitol Dehydrogenase | |
	Mt	S
M	$\mu mol \cdot h^{-1} \cdot mL^{-1}$ *cell*	
0.0	4.11 + 0.12	0.62 + 0.21
0.3	2.12 + 0.36	0.00 + 0.00

with a molecular mass of 39.7 kD which is very close to the experimentally determined molecular mass of 40 kD for celery MTD (Stoop *et al.*, 1995). Three tryptic peptides, obtained as cleavage products from purified MTD and containing a total of 39 amino acids, had amino acid sequences that matched amino acid sequences predicted by the celery cDNA (Stoop *et al.*, 1995; Williamson *et al.*, 1995). These data provide strong confirmation that the cDNA encodes MTD.

A computerized search of protein sequence data revealed no further significant homology beyond the zinc and NAD consensus sequences to any known dehydrogenases. Unexpectedly, the deduced MTD protein sequence was almost identical to a group of pathogenesis-related (PR) proteins known as ELI3, or elicitor-induced proteins. These ELI3 proteins are induced in parsley and *Arabidopsis* leaves upon infection with *Pseudomonas* (Kiedrowski *et al.*, 1992). Among the deduced amino acid sequences for the ELI3 and MTD proteins, there is 83% identity and an additional 10% similarity. The PR proteins were previously of unknown function, but are now clearly identified as MTD (Williamson *et al.*, 1995).

MTD Transcript Abundance

The full-length *Mtd* cDNA was labeled with ^{32}P and used as a probe to determine the relative abundance of *Mtd* RNA in response to carbon source and salinity in cultured celery cells (Williamson *et al.*, 1995). MTD activity and transcript amount were compared for cells grown on mannitol, sucrose, mannose, and sucrose plus 0.3 M NaCl. MTD activities were as previously reported for these treatments (Stoop and Pharr, 1993) with mannitol highest, sucrose and mannose intermediate, and sucrose plus NaCl lowest. MTD transcript either in equal total RNA or in poly(A[+]) RNA from each treatment paralleled the observed enzyme activity (Williamson *et al.*, 1995). It was also shown that MTD activity increased 20-fold within 24 h after treatment of sucrose-grown celery cells with 1 mM salicylic acid (Williamson *et al.*, 1995), a compound that is known to induce several PR proteins (Yalpani and Raskin, 1993). Salicylic acid treatment resulted in similar increase in *Mtd* transcript (Williamson *et al.*, 1995). Thus, MTD activity is regulated, at least in part, at the level of transcript abundance.

The important roles of mannitol as a phloem-translocated photoassimilate and as an osmoprotectant are apparent from the above-presented data and discussion. It now appears that another role for mannitol metabolism in response to plant pathogen attack has been discovered. Induction of MTD in leaves during pathogen attack may promote use of stored mannitol for energy and carbon skeletons for synthesis of compounds needed for a successful hypersensitive response to limit the advance of the invading organism (Williamson *et al.*, 1995). The fact that plants have already been engineered to form mannitol and that these plants exhibit increased tolerance to salinity (Tarczynski *et al.*, 1993) provides an incentive to also incorporate the mannitol-utilizing enzyme into plants. The ability to use, as well as make, mannitol might provide additional advantages. MTD, the mannitol-catabolizing enzyme, is a monomeric protein that requires no apparent special cofactors for activity. Introducing this enzyme into plants not normally containing *Mtd* appears to be an achievable objective in the immediate future. Additionally, the availability of the *Mtd* cDNA will facilitate cloning a full genomic sequence and assist further studies of the regulation of mannitol catabolism.

ACKNOWLEDGMENTS

This work was supported in part by Grant No. 9302250 from the U.S. Department of Agriculture to D.M.P. and M.A.C.

LITERATURE CITED

Everard JD, Gucci R, Kann SC, Flore JA, Loescher WH (1994) Gas exchange and carbon partitioning in the leaves of celery (*Apium graveolens* L.) at various levels of root zone salinity. Plant Physiol **106:** 281-292

Fellman JK, Loescher WH (1987) Comparative studies of sucrose and mannitol utilization in celery (*Apium graveolens*). Physiol Plant **69:** 337-341

Greenway H, Munns R (1980) Mechanisms of salt tolerance in nonhalophytes. Annu Rev Plant Physiol **31:** 149-190

Herold A, Lewis DH (1977) Mannose and green plants: occurrence, physiology and metabolism, and use as a tool to study the role of orthophosphate. New Phytol **79:** 1-40

Keller F, Matile P (1989) Storage of sugars and mannitol in petioles of celery leaves. New Phytol **113:** 291-299

Kiedrowski S, Kawalleck P, Hahlbrock K, Somssich IE, Dangle J (1992) Rapid activation of a novel plant defence gene is strictly dependent on the *Arabidopsis* RPM1 disease resistant locus. EMBO J **11**: 4677-4684

Martinez De Drets G, Arias A (1970) Metabolism of some polyols by *Rhizobium meliloti*. J Bact **103**: 97-103

Murashige T, Skoog F (1962) A revised medium for rapid growth and bioassays with tobacco tissue cultures. Physiol Plant **15**: 473-497

Pharr DM, Stoop JMH, Williamson JD, Studer-Feusi ME, Massel MO, Conkling MA (1995) The dual role of mannitol as osmoprotectant and photoassimilate in celery. J Am Soc Hort Sci (in press)

Richter DFE, Kirst GO (1987) D-mannitol dehydrogenase and D-mannitol-1-phosphate dehydrogenase in *Platymonas subcordiformis*: some characteristics and their role in osmotic adaptation. Planta **170**: 528-534

Schobert B (1977) Is there an osmotic regulatory mechanism in algae and higher plants? J Theor Biol **68**: 17-26

Smirnoff N, Cumbes QJ (1989) Hydroxyl radical scavenging activity of compatible solutes. Phytochemistry **28**: 1057-1060

Stoop JMH, Pharr DM (1992) Partial purification and characterization of mannitol:mannose 1-oxidoreductase from celeriac (*Apium graveolens* var. *rapaceum*) roots. Arch Biochem Biophys **298**: 612-619

Stoop JMH, Pharr DM (1993) Effect of different carbon sources on relative growth rate, internal carbohydrates, and mannitol 1-oxidoreductase activity in celery suspension cultures. Plant Physiol **103**: 1001-1008

Stoop JMH, Pharr DM (1994*a*) Growth substrate and nutrient salt environment alter mannitol to hexose partitioning in celery petioles. J Am Soc Hort Sci **119**: 237-242

Stoop JMH, Pharr DM (1994*b*) Mannitol metabolism in celery stressed by excess macronutrients. Plant Physiol **106**: 503-511

Stoop JMH, Williamson JD, Conkling MA, Pharr DM (1995) Purification of NAD-dependent mannitol dehydrogenase from celery suspension cultures. Plant Physiol (in press)

Tarczynski MC, Jensen RG and Bohnert HJ (1992) Expression of a bacterial mtlD gene in transgenic tobacco leads to production and accumulation of mannitol. Proc Natl Acad Sci USA **89**: 2600-2604

Tarczynski MC, Jensen RG, Bohnert HJ (1993) Stress protection of transgenic tobacco by production of the osmolyte mannitol. Science **259**: 508-510

Trip P, Krotkov G, Nelson CD (1964) Metabolism of mannitol in higher plants. Am J Bot **51**: 828-835.

Williamson JD, Stoop JMH, Massel MO, Conkling MA, Pharr DM (1995) Cloning and characterization of a mannitol dehydrogenase cDNA from plants; a potential role for the PR-protein ELI3. Proc Natl Acad Sci USA (in press)

Yalpani N, Raskin I (1993) Salicylic acid: a systemic signal in induced plant disease resistance. Trends Microbiol **1**: 88-92

Yamaguchi M (1993) Umbillefers: Carrots, celery and condiment herbs. *In* M. Yamaguchi, ed, World Vegetables. Principles, Production and Nutritive Values. Avi Publ Co, Wesport, CN, pp 246-248

Carbon Partitioning and Source-Sink Interactions in Plants, *Monica A. Madore* and *William J. Lucas*, eds, Copyright 1995, published by The American Society of Plant Physiologists

The Selection of Raffinose Family Oligosaccharides as Translocates in Higher Plants

Robert Turgeon

Section of Plant Biology, Division of Biological Sciences, Cornell University, Ithaca, NY 14853, USA

In a 1968 essay, Arnold wondered why sucrose serves as the translocate of higher plants. Since glucose is the preferred transport sugar in animals (though at much lower concentrations), he compared various physical characteristics of sucrose and glucose and found no compelling reason to favor the former on that basis. He then proposed the protected-derivative hypothesis: A good translocate should be nonreducing so that it will not react nonenzymatically with proteins and other compounds. Another element of Arnold's hypothesis is that the ideal translocate should be protected from enzymatic attack until it arrives at its destination. In this way, the flow of carbon in plants can be controlled by the presence of one or two key sucrose-hydrolyzing enzymes in appropriate sink tissues.

Arnold dealt only briefly with the "unusual" transport sugars, namely, those in the raffinose family: the tri-, tetra-, and penta-saccharides, raffinose, stachyose, and verbascose, respectively. These sugars are formed by the addition of D-galactose moieties to a sucrose molecule. The structure of these compounds is consistent with the protected-derivative hypothesis, and they have an additional metabolic constraint of needing an α-galactopyranosidase for hydrolysis. In this paper, I ask why raffinose oligosaccharides (RFO) are translocated in many species of higher plants (Arnold's characterization of them as unusual is incorrect—of the 515 species analyzed by Zimmermann and Zeigler (1975), 337 (65%) translocate detectable amounts of RFO.

In comparing glucose and sucrose, Arnold did not consider the osmotic characteristics of the two sugars far beyond the statement that the osmotic pressure generated per unit carbon of the former is approximately twice that of the latter. However, it is probable that translocation, as a pressure-driven system, requires a certain level of osmoticum to maintain optimal flow rates, and it is obvious that the larger the sugar, the more carbon it contains per unit of osmoticum. This might be of some importance for rapidly growing sink tissues such as cucurbit fruits.

PHLOEM LOADING

Recent discussions regarding the role of raffinose sugars in translocation have centered on their function in, and synthesis during, phloem loading. Members of the Cucurbitaceae have long been regarded as candidate species for symplasmic (through plasmodesmata) loading since the companion cells in the minor veins of these species are connected to surrounding bundle sheath cells by numerous plasmodesmata (Turgeon *et al.*, 1975; Schmitz *et al.*, 1987). The cucurbits also translocate considerable quantities of raffinose and stachyose.

The concept of symplasmic phloem loading has been quite controversial since it would seem, on first consideration, to violate the Second Law of Thermodynamics: Since transport through plasmodesmata is generally regarded as passive (Tucker *et al.*, 1989), and since there are no membranous structures enclosing the cytoplasmic sleeve upon which an active transport system could be situated (Ding *et al.*, 1992), it borders on the heretical to postulate that sugar could be moved through these organelles against a concentration gradient. In 1991, a model was presented that obviates these thermodynamic difficulties, at least for plants that translocate the raffinose sugars (Turgeon, 1991). According to this scheme, the synthesis of raffinose oligosaccharides is mechanistically linked to phloem loading (Fig. 1). Sucrose (or perhaps hexose) diffuses from the bundle sheath into companion cells through the plasmodesmata that connect the two cell types. Raffinose and stachyose are synthesized in the companion cells and this maintains the diffusion gradient. Raffinose and stachyose are not able to diffuse back into the mesophyll because they are too large to permeate the plasmodesmata. As a result, the concentration of sugar rises in the phloem. This 'trapping' of oligosaccharides in the sieve element-companion cell complex (SE-CCC) requires that the molecular size exclusion limit (SEL) of the numerous plasmodesmata between bundle sheath and intermediary cells be somewhat smaller than is common in plasmodesmata at other interfaces. The 'normal' SEL is approximately 800 to 1200 D, whereas the anhydrous mol wt of sucrose, raffinose, and stachyose are 342, 504, and 666, respectively.

Since the model was proposed, it has been shown that stachyose (Holthaus and Schmitz, 1991; Turgeon and Gowan, 1992) and the galactosyl donor galactinol (Beebe and Turgeon, 1992; Turgeon and Gowan, 1992) are indeed made in the companion (intermediary) cells of cucurbits and *Coleus blumei*. Measurements of the concentration of raffinose and stachyose have now been made in microdissected intermediary cells (E. Haritatos, F. Keller, and R. Turgeon, unpubl. data); they greatly exceed the concentrations of the same

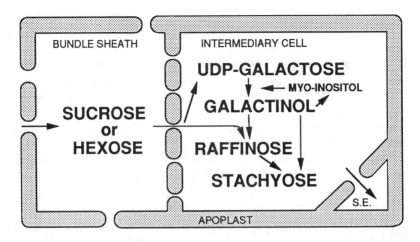

Figure 1. Symplasmic phloem loading model. Sucrose, or perhaps hexose, diffuses through the symplast from the mesophyll, via the bundles sheath, into the intermediary (companion) cells. Galactinol is used in the synthesis of raffinose and stachyose. These sugars enter the sieve element, but cannot leak back into the bundle sheath because the channels of the plasmodesmata are too narrow.

compounds in the mesophyll and are in the range expected of translocation sugars. Furthermore, it is now known that phloem loading, in at least some species that translocate raffinose and stachyose, is insensitive to *p*-chloromercuribenzenesulfonic acid (Weisberg *et al.*, 1988; Turgeon and Gowan, 1990; Flora and Madore, 1993; van Bel *et al.*, 1993), a potent inhibitor of phloem loading from the apoplasm. The plasmodesmata between the intermediary cells and bundle sheath are open to flux of dyes in the size range of sucrose, and transport of these dyes along a file of intermediary cells is faster than their exit from the cells (Turgeon and Hepler, 1989).

Another general prediction that follows from the polymer-trapping concept is that RFO-translocating species should have extensive symplasmic connection to the photosynthetic tissue. Indeed, such a correlation has been recognized for many years; it follows from a comparison of two large surveys of dicotyle-donous species, the analysis of phloem sap in woody plants by Zimmermann and Zeigler cited above (1975), and the equally broad survey of minor vein anatomy conducted by Gamalei over a period of many years (Gamalei, 1989, 1991). In his survey, Gamalei recognizes several types of companion cell. In the 'open' type (type 1) of minor vein phloem, the companion cells are con-nected to the surrounding mesophyll by numerous plasmodesmata. Closed (type 2) companion cells have very few such connections (there are no authen-ticated examples of species in which the minor vein phloem is completely isolated symplasmically). Gamalei recognizes three subdivisions of type 2 species; the most common of these are plants with smooth-walled companion cells (type 2a; frequently called 'ordinary' companion cells) and those with wall ingrowths (type 2b; transfer cells). Gamalei's type 1-2a plants fall between type 1 and type 2. To better compare the two surveys, we have converted the data of Zimmermann and Zeigler (1975) into quantitative form for each species and averaged the data for all species within a family. This averaging is justified on the grounds that the sugar concentration profiles for species within a family are usually quite uniform. In Figure 2, the averaged percentage RFO in the phloem exudate in each family is plotted against the companion cell type typical of that family according to Gamalei (1989). Although there are bound to be spurious data points from such a comparison (some of the families are represented by only a single species), it is clear that there is a correlation. Type 1 families translocate more RFO than type 1-2a or type 2 families.

To experimentally test the correlation between RFO synthesis and phloem anatomy, we studied randomly selected members of the Scrophulariaceae, which are known to vary in the amount of RFO synthesized (Turgeon *et al.*, 1993). Only those species with intermediary cells translocated high levels of RFO.

While the overall pattern observed in Figure 2 supports the concept that RFO synthesis is involved in symplasmic phloem loading, there is an obvious complication. Note the heterogeneity of type 1 families. While some translocate substantial quantities of RFO, others do not. Is this variability mirrored by differences in anatomy?

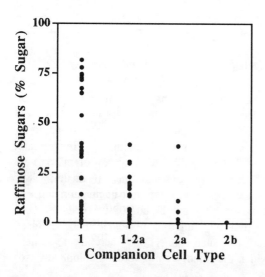

Figure 2. Type of companion cells found in different families, according to Gamalei (1991) plotted against the percentage of raffinose oligosaccharide in the translocate of the same families, according to Zimmermann and Zeigler (1975). Sugar concentrations were obtained by using the median values given by the authors and averaging data for all species analyzed in the family.

It should be noted that the anatomy of companion cells in the cucurbits is distinguished from that of typical 'apoplasmic loaders,' such as sugar beet or *Vicia faba*, by more than plasmodesmatal frequency. Several anatomical features set them apart. They are invariably positioned in the vein adjacent to the bundle sheath, the vacuoles are usually small and numerous, the plastids are rudimentary without well-developed granal thylakoids, the plasmodesmata linking them to bundle sheath cells are branched on both sides, there are more branches on the companion cell side, and, perhaps most notably, the plasmodesmata are especially narrow on the companion cell side. It may be that the narrow portions of the plasmodesmata are the size-exclusion filters that discriminate between the different sugars. These anatomical characteristics are not only common to the minor vein companion cells of cucurbits, but to those of some other families as well (Fisher, 1986; Flora and Madore, 1993; Turgeon *et al.*, 1993), and they make the cell type so recognizable that it is given a distinguishing name, the 'intermediary cell' (for discussion, see Turgeon *et al.*, 1993). The families known to have intermediary cells are shown in solid circles in Figure 3. Note that they are families that translocate more RFO than sucrose and in which the amount of stachyose in the exudate is greater than the amount of raffinose.

What about families that translocate only small amounts of RFO? How does the anatomy of the minor vein companion cells in these plants compare with that of intermediary cells? There are insufficient studies to make generalizations, but it is useful to consider the case of *Populus deltoides* (Salicaceae), studied by Russin and Evert (1985). Gamalei lists the Salicaceae

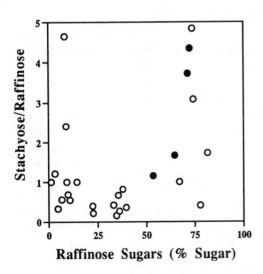

Figure 3. Percentage of raffinose oligosaccharide in the translocate in different families (as in Fig. 2) plotted as the ratio of stachyose to raffinose in the translocate. Solid circles denote families known to have true intermediary cells in the minor vein phloem.

as type 1 (1989). According to Zimmermann and Zeigler (1975), members of the Salicaceae translocate little RFO, and the amount of raffinose and stachyose is approximately the same, thus distinguishing the family from those known to have 'intermediary cells.' The companion cells of *P. deltoides* are similar to intermediary cells in a few intriguing ways, including the presence of many branched plasmodesmata joining them to the bundle sheath. However, it should be noted that the frequency of plasmodesmata is high at many interfaces in this species. Also, the plasmodesmata between bundle sheath cells and companion cells are more branched on the bundle sheath side, not the companion cell side, and the branches on both sides appear to be of equal width.

These considerations lead us to suggest that Gamalei's type 1 plants are heterogeneous and that the mechanism(s) of phloem loading may not be common to all type 1 species. This has important implications when considering the evolution of these structures and mechanisms. Gamalei (1991) has suggested that symplasmic loading (type 1 species) evolved first and that apoplasmic loading is a later evolutionary adaptation. I believe that we need to know more about type 1 species before such generalizations are made. At this point, it should be noted that there is anatomical evidence for the presence of more than one phloem-loading mechanism in a single species, even in a single vein. For example, in species with intermediary cells, the larger minor veins also contain 'ordinary' (type 2) companion cells. It is possible, therefore, that multiple forms of phloem loading were, and still are, exploited in ancestral dicots, and that further evolution has led to specialization of one form or the other. It is also conceivable that one, or both, forms of phloem loading have evolved more than once.

Raffinose Versus Stachyose

If the presence of RFO in the translocation stream of many species can be tentatively explained by the polymer trapping mechanism of phloem loading, another question remains: Why is stachyose, rather than raffinose, the predominant sugar in species that translocate a great deal of RFO (Fig. 3)? One possible explanation is that stachyose offers a compromise between necessary dimension and osmotic effectiveness, i.e. it is large enough to preclude leakage out of intermediary cells, yet small enough to be an effective osmoticum in the phloem. There are two lines of evidence in conflict with this suggestion. First, some species, such as *Catharanthus roseus*, translocate sucrose and a considerable amount of raffinose, but not stachyose. Second, if stachyose is the smallest sugar that can be efficiently trapped in intermediary cells, raffinose should be permeable to a certain extent and it should leak out of intermediary cells into the mesophyll. In contradiction to this, we find no detectable raffinose in the mesophyll of melon leaves.

Another, simpler, explanation for the prevalence of stachyose is that raffinose cannot be the major transport sugar because it has relatively limited solubility. While sucrose and stachyose are soluble at levels in excess of 1 M, the limit of raffinose solubility at physiological temperatures is in the 100- to 400-mM range (Fig. 4). According to the semiquantitative data of Zimmermann and Zeigler (1975), raffinose levels can be as high as 400 mM in exudate, but it is clear that at moderately low temperatures, the solubility of raffinose in water, or in an artificial phloem sap, is much less than this. Since the amount of sugar found in aphid stylet exudate exceeds 400 mM at least, this amount of osmoticum is probably required to drive translocation by mass flow. Obviously, raffinose could not serve as the sole transport sugar, and at relatively low physiological temperatures, it could only serve as a minor component.

The case has frequently been made that translocation of raffinose sugars is especially common in tropical trees and vines (van Bel and Gamalei, 1992). One wonders if it is on the basis of limited raffinose solubility, at least in part, that they have been selected against as transport compounds during the progressive extension of species into temperate habitats. The prevalence of stachyose in the translocation stream of many species might therefore be explained by the fact that raffinose is not soluble enough to be the major transport sugar, and stachyose, which is much more soluble, is the next sugar in the pathway. (Verbascose is seen in some species, but it is always a minor component of the translocate.)

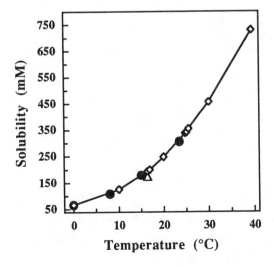

Figure 4. Solubility of raffinose plotted against temperature [◇, data from Hungerford and Nees (1934); ●, data from this study; Δ, in artificial phloem sap]. Artificial phloem sap contained 400 mM sucrose and salts commonly found in aphid exudate (Taiz and Zeiger, 1991).

CONCLUSIONS

Evolutionary adaptiveness of structures or compounds is seldom easy to understand; functions may be subtle. They may also be quite different from those we initially focus upon, our view polarized as it is by experimental bias. Furthermore, we should keep in mind that these functions may change over time and in various ecological settings. For now, the idea that raffinose and stachyose have been selected for on the basis of their usefulness in a molecular trapping mechanism serves as a practical working hypothesis. An important step in determining the true role(s) of RFO in translocation will be to study phloem loading in detail in select members of the more 'primitive' families of dicots.

ACKNOWLEDGMENTS

This research was supported by grants from the National Science Foundation (DCB-9104159) and the Department of Agriculture Competitive Grant Program (92-37306-7819).

LITERATURE CITED

Arnold WN (1968) The selection of sucrose as the translocate of higher plants. J Theoret Biol **21**: 13-20

Beebe DU, Turgeon R (1992) Localization of galactinol, raffinose, and stachyose synthesis in *Cucurbita pepo* leaves. Planta **188**: 354-361

Ding B, Turgeon R, Parthasarathy MV (1992) Substructure of freeze-substituted plasmodesmata. Protoplasma **169**: 28-41

Fisher DG (1986) Ultrastructure, plasmodesmata frequency, and solute concentration in green areas of variegated *Coleus blumei* Benth. leaves. Planta **169**: 141-152

Flora LL, Madore MA (1993) Stachyose and mannitol transport in olive (*Olea europaea* L.). Planta **189**: 484-490

Gamalei Y (1989) Structure and function of leaf minor veins in trees and herbs. A taxonomic review. Trees **3**: 96-110

Gamalei Y (1991) Phloem loading and its development related to plant evolution from trees to herbs. Trees **5**: 50-64

Holthaus U, Schmitz K (1991) Distribution and immunolocalization of stachyose synthase in *Cucumis melo* L. Planta **185**: 479-486

Hungerford EH, Nees AR (1934) Raffinose: preparation and properties. Indust Eng Chem **26**: 462-464

Russin WA, Evert RF (1985) Studies on the leaf of *Populus deltoides* (Salicaceae): ultrastructure, plasmodesmatal frequency, and solute concentrations. Am J Bot **72**: 1232-1247

Schmitz K, Cuypers, Moll M (1987) Pathway of assimilate transfer between mesophyll cells and minor veins in leaves of *Cucumis melo* L. Planta **171**: 19-29

Taiz L, Zeiger E (1991) Plant Physiology. Benjamin Cummings, New York, 155 pp

Tucker JE, Mauzerall D, Tucker EB (1989) Symplastic transport of carboxyfluorescein in staminal hairs of *Setcreasea purpurea* is diffusive and includes loss to the vacuole. Plant Physiol 90: 1143-1147

Turgeon R (1991) Symplastic phloem loading and the sink-source transition in leaves: a model. *In* J-L Bonnemain, S Delrot, WJ Lucas, J Dainty, eds, Recent Advances in Phloem Transport and Assimilate compartmentation. Ouest Editions, Nantes, France, pp 18-22

Turgeon R, Beebe DU, Gowan E (1993) The intermediary cell: minor vein anatomy and raffinose oligosaccharide synthesis in the Scrophulariaceae. Planta 191: 446-456

Turgeon R, Gowan E (1990) Phloem loading in *Coleus blumei* in the absence of carrier-mediated uptake of export sugar from the apoplast. Plant Physiol 94: 1244-1249

Turgeon R, Gowan E (1992) Sugar synthesis and phloem loading in *Coleus blumei* leaves. Planta 187: 388-394

Turgeon R, Hepler PK (1989) Symplastic continuity between mesophyll and companion cells in minor veins of mature *Cucurbita pepo* L. leaves. Planta 179: 24-31

Turgeon R, Webb JA, Evert RF (1975) Ultrastructure of minor veins in *Cucurbita pepo* leaves. Protoplasma 83: 217-232

van Bel AJE, Gamalei YV (1992) Ecophysiology of phloem loading in source leaves. Plant Cell Environ 15: 265-270

van Bel AJE, Ammerlaan A, van Dijk AA (1993) A three-step screening procedure to identify the mode of phloem loading in intact leaves: evidence for symplasmic and apoplasmic phloem loading associated with the type of companion cell. Planta 192: 31-39

Weisberg LA, Wimmers LE, Turgeon, R (1988) Photoassimilate-transport characteristics of nonchlorophyllous and green tissue in variegated leaves of *Coleus blumei*. Planta 175: 1-8

Zimmermann MH, Ziegler H (1975) List of sugars and sugar alcohols in sieve-tube exudates. *In* MH Zimmermann, JA Milburn, eds, Encyclopedia of Plant Physiology, New Series, Vol 1, Transport in Plants 1: Phloem Transport. Springer, New York, pp 480-503

Catabolism of Raffinose Family Oligosaccharides By Vegetative Sink Tissues

Monica A. Madore

*Department of Botany and Plant Sciences,
University of California, Riverside,
California 92521, USA*

Much of what is known concerning the synthesis and degradation of raffinose family oligosaccharides (RFO's) comes from early studies on seeds (Kandler and Hopf, 1980; Dey, 1990) where these sugars play key roles in storage (Dey, 1985) and desiccation tolerance (Koster and Leopold, 1988). It has only been in recent years that focus has been placed on the biosynthetic pathways of these sugars in source leaves. Significant inroads have been made in our understanding of the role of the biochemistry of these sugars in phloem loading and transport processes (Turgeon, this volume). However, our understanding of the catabolism of these sugars by vegetative tissues, particularly after phloem unloading, has not kept up with our knowledge of the reactions going on at the source end.

The importance of raffinose family oligosaccharides in plant carbohydrate metabolism is probably not yet fully appreciated. Although not all plant families use these compounds in phloem transport, the biochemical pathway leading to RFO formation is probably ubiquitous in the plant kingdom (Kandler and Hopf, 1980; Dey, 1990). For example, these sugars are frequently found as temporary storage metabolites in many plant organs (Dey, 1990). Storage RFOs may be delivered as such to the storage organ (Bachmann *et al.*, this volume) or may be derived from imported carbon and synthesized *de novo* within the storage organ (Dey, 1985). By whatever means the RFOs arise, the ability of vegetative tissues to import and store carbon in the form of RFOs also implies that the biochemical pathways for RFO degradation must also exist in these organs, if the carbon stored in this form is to be made available for sink growth and development.

STACHYOSE METABOLISM IN SINK TISSUES:
α-GALACTOSIDASE ACTIVITIES

For many years now it has been accepted that the primary means by which RFOs are degraded in sink tissues is via hydrolysis by α-galactosidase (Dey and Pridham, 1972; Kandler and Hopf, 1980; Dey, 1985, 1990). The general reactions for stachyose hydrolysis are as follows:

$$\text{Stachyose} \xrightarrow{\alpha\text{-galactosidase}} \text{Galactose} + \text{Raffinose}$$

$$\text{Raffinose} \xrightarrow{\alpha\text{-galactosidase}} \text{Galactose} + \text{Sucrose}$$

The sucrose moiety is then thought to be degraded by invertase or sucrose synthase, as in other plants. The galactose released by α-galactosidase activity is then phosphorylated by a galactokinase reaction. The sugar phosphate can then be converted to the nucleotide form, UDP-Gal, which can be interconverted to UDP-Glc by the action of UDP-Glc-4-epimerase. The sugar nucleotides can be used directly for synthesis of polysaccharides, or alternatively, UDP-Glc can be hydrolyzed via UDP-Glc-pyrophosphorylase to produce Glc-1-P, which can enter the general hexose-P respiratory pool.

A complete pathway for hydrolysis of stachyose to hexose-P has been demonstrated in the peduncle of cucumber (Gross and Pharr, 1982). In this tissue, operation of α-galactosidase, galactokinase, UDP-Gal pyrophosphorylase, UDP-Gal-4'-epimerase, UDP-Glc-pyrophosphorylase, and sucrose synthase activities were all detected, allowing for the conversion of stachyose, the normal transport form, to sucrose, the carbohydrate normally stored in the developing fruit (Shaffer et al., 1995).

However, there are a few problems which arise if the complete hydrolytic pathway is assigned solely to an α-galactosidase. Firstly, many of the known α-galactosidases have acidic pH optima (Dey and Pridham, 1972; Thomas and Webb, 1978), and show substrate specificity which is inversely proportional to substrate size. In general, the larger the galactoside, the less effective are the acidic α-galactosidases at performing the hydrolysis (Smart and Pharr, 1980), so that the acid forms of α-galactosidase are far more effective at cleaving melibiose (K_m = 3.0-3.5) than raffinose (K_m = 5.0-6.5 mM) or stachyose (K_m = 10-30 mM). This would indicate that the primary role of the acidic α-galactosidases is probably not the cleavage of imported stachyose.

Secondly, the acidic forms of α-galactosidase are widely distributed throughout the plant body, in both source and sink tissues (Thomas and Webb, 1978). Even cucurbit source leaves, which export large quantities of RFOs and which, therefore, would not be expected to hydrolyze stachyose in significant quantities, contain substantial levels of α-galactosidase activity. Multiple forms of the enzyme are also present in these source leaves (Thomas and Webb, 1977; Smart and Pharr, 1980). Of more significance, the total acidic α-galactosidase activity remains constant throughout the sink-source transition of the cucurbit leaf (Thomas and Webb, 1978). This again suggests that acidic α-galactosidase is not responsible for catabolism of imported stachyose in sink leaves.

These dilemmas were at least partially resolved by the discovery by Gaudreault and Webb (1982) of a new form of α-galactosidase in cucurbit leaves. This α-galactosidase differed from all those reported previously in that it had an alkaline pH optimum (Gaudreault and Webb, 1982), compatible with a cytoplasmic location for this enzyme. The enzyme also showed a high specificity (K_m = 4.5 mM) for stachyose (Gaudreault and Webb, 1982). The activity of this enzyme was six-fold greater in sink leaves than source leaves and showed a developmental decline in activity during the sink-source transition (Gaudreault and Webb, 1983; Pharr and Sox, 1984). Thus, both the specificity and the location of the alkaline α-galactosidase were entirely consistent with this enzyme having a primary role in hydrolysis of imported stachyose in sink leaves.

ALKALINE α-GALACTOSIDASE ACTIVITIES IN *PEPEROMIA CAMPTOTRICHA* L. SINK TISSUES

One possible short-term usage of RFOs occurs in certain plants which perform carbon dioxide fixation by the CAM pathway. In source leaves of *Xerosicyos danguyi* H. Humb, both mesophyll and minor vein pools of RFOs exist (Madore *et al.*, 1988). The mesophyll RFOs form a nontranslocated pool (Madore, 1992) which accumulates as a temporary storage reserve during the day, most likely in the mesophyll cell vacuoles. At night, this pool is completely degraded, presumably in part to support dark respiration and perhaps also to provide carbon skeletons for phosphoenolpyruvate (PEP) regeneration. The size of the mesophyll pool can be greatly increased when the plant is subjected to desiccation stress (M.A. Madore, unpubl. results). In these CAM plants, then, the mesophyll tissues act as a storage sink, and accumulate RFOs for night-time use. The mesophyll cells, therefore, must have both RFO biosynthetic enzymes to form these pools and also RFO-degrading enzymes to allow their nocturnal mobilization. The exact cellular location of these enzymes and their mechanisms for light/dark regulation are not yet understood.

In the genus *Peperomia* (family Piperaceae), RFOs are the primary exported form of carbohydrate (M.A. Madore, unpubl. results). Although both C_3 and CAM forms of *Peperomia* exist (Ting, 1985), it is only in the CAM forms that distinct mesophyll pools of RFOs are in evidence (M.A.

Madore, unpubl. results). Examination of the α-galactosidase activities in tissues of *Peperomia camptotricha* L., a CAM form (Ting, 1985), reveals that this species also possesses both acidic and alkaline forms of α-galactosidase (Fig. 1). The alkaline form is particularly evident in sink tissues such as young, developing leaves (Fig. 1A) and storage sinks such as stems (Fig. 1B). However, unlike the situation in cucurbit leaves (Gaudreault and Webb, 1983; Pharr and Sox, 1984), the alkaline α-galactosidase is also substantially active in mature leaves (Fig. 1C). This suggests that this α-galactosidase may also be involved in the night-time degradation of the pool of RFO's stored in the mesophyll "sink".

THE SUGAR CONTENT OF THE VEGETATIVE SINK TISSUES OF *PEPEROMIA CAMPTOTRICHA* L.

It is tempting to conclude, on the basis of its sink tissue distribution, that alkaline α-galactosidase activity satisfactorily accounts for RFO hydrolysis in sink tissues of *P. camptotricha*. However, if the sugar content of sink tissues is examined, a clear anomaly is seen. In young leaves (Fig. 2A) and stem tissues (Fig. 2B), the predominant sugars are not raffinose and sucrose, the products of the α-galactosidase reaction, but instead are galactinol and myoinositol. Although some raffinose and sucrose are seen, the sink sugar content seen is clearly not consistent with that expected if RFO hydrolysis is occurring entirely by the action of an α-galactosidase.

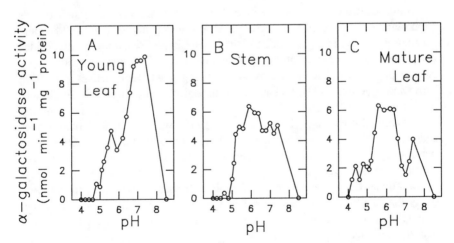

Figure 1. The effect of pH on α-galactosidase activity in young developing leaves **(A)**, stem storage tissues **(B)**, and mature source leaves **(C)** of *Peperomia camptotricha* L.

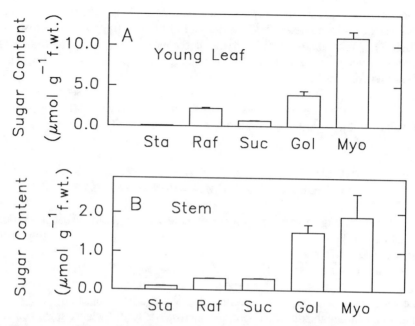

Figure 2. Soluble sugar contents of sink tissues of *P. camptotricha*. **A,** Young developing leaves. **B,** Stem storage tissues.

Significant quantities of galactinol have also been reported in sink tissues from other species, including cucumber sink leaves (Pharr and Sox, 1984) and nonphotosynthetic leaf tissues of *Coleus blumei* Benth. (Madore, 1990). Since galactinol (and the same can be said for myo-inositol) is not a major component of phloem exudates of stachyose-exporting plants (Mitchell *et al.*, 1992; Flora and Madore, 1993), its significant presence in sink tissues is unlikely to be due to import from the phloem. In addition, as in other the other sink tissues examined previously (Pharr and Sox, 1984; Madore, 1990), young leaves and stems of *P. camptotricha* also have negligible activities of galactinol synthase (M.A. Madore, unpubl. results). Therefore, *de novo* synthesis of galactinol from UDP-Gal and myo-inositol is also unlikely to explain the significant quantities of galactinol found in these tissues. Instead, it appears more likely that the presence of galactinol and myo-inositol in these sinks is somehow related, in some as yet unknown way, to the RFO degradation which is occurring in them.

The source leaf mesophyll tissues of *P. camptotricha* contain an appreciable pool of stachyose during the light period (Fig. 3A). However, during the subsequent dark period, this pool of stachyose disappears (Fig. 3B). In

P. camptotricha, the size-exclusion model proposed for phloem loading in other RFO-exporting plants (Turgeon, this volume) is also likely to hold, for *P. camptotricha* has companion cells of the intermediary cell type (M.A. Madore, unpubl. results). However, this means that the disappearance of stachyose from the mesophyll is unlikely to be a result of direct phloem loading of this stachyose, as the mesophyll-derived stachyose should be too large to permeate the intermediary cell plasmodesmata. Therefore, the disappearance of the mesophyll pool of stachyose must be a result of catabolism.

Although the mature leaf of *P. camptotricha* clearly possesses alkaline α-galactosidase activity, again it is unlikely that nocturnal RFO metabolism in

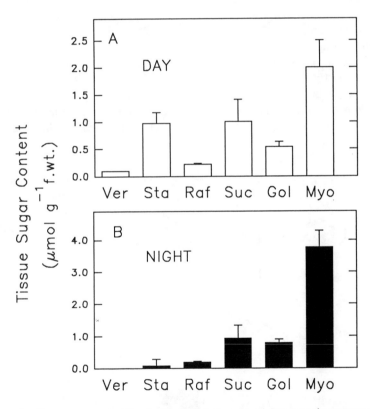

Figure 3. Sugar content of leaf mesophyll tissues of *Peperomia camptotricha* L. Mesophyll tissues, devoid of vascular tissues, were obtained by excising leaf discs and removing the abaxial portions, which consist entirely of meso-phyll cells, with a razor blade. **A,** Sugar content of tissues removed from leaves 10 h into the normal 16-h light period. **B,** Sugar content of tissues removed from leaves 6 h into the normal 8-h dark period.

mesophyll tissues can be accounted for entirely by the α-galactosidase reaction. The sugar content of the *P. camptotricha* leaf mesophyll at night (Fig. 3B) very closely reflects that seen in the young leaves and stems (Fig. 2). Again, galactinol and myo-inositol are present in substantial quantities, suggesting that the same unknown mechanism for RFO degradation which operates in the more conventional sink tissues may also be operative in the CAM mesophyll "storage sink."

GALACTINOL FORMATION IN SINK TISSUES
OF *PEPEROMIA CAMPTOTRICHA*

All of the sugar data obtained for *P. camptotricha* sink tissues strongly implicate the presence of high levels of galactinol with the catabolism of RFOs. Further evidence that this may be the case comes from studies on myo-inositol metabolism by stem tissues. As seen in Figure 4, crude extracts obtained from *P. camptotricha* stem tissues are capable of forming galactinol when incubated with myo-inositol. What is particularly interesting is that the rate of galactinol formation can be increased five-fold by addition of 10 mM raffinose. This indicates that raffinose can act as a galactosyl donor for galactinol formation from myo-inositol, and provides an alternative route for hydrolysis of raffinose in sink tissues. The products of this "raffinose

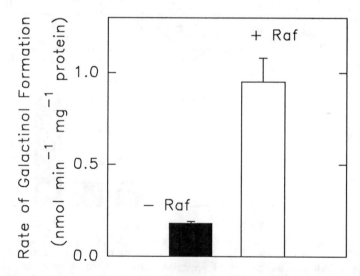

Figure 4. Galactinol formation from myo-inositol by crude extracts obtained from stem tissues of *P. camptotricha* in the absence (-Raf) or presence (+Raf) of 10 mM raffinose.

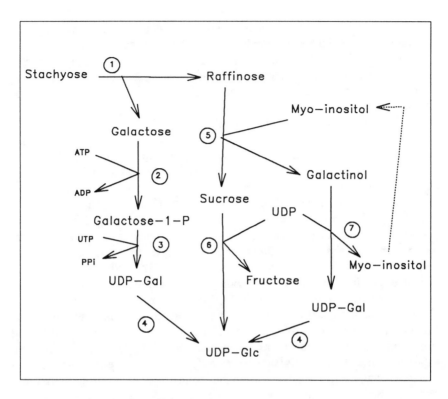

Figure 5. A hypothetical pathway for RFO metabolism in sink tissues. 1: Alkaline α-galactosidase; 2: Galactokinase; 3: Galactose-1-P Pyrophosphorylase; 4: UDP-Glc-4-epimerase; 5: "Raffinose Hydrolase"; 6: Sucrose Synthase; 7: "Galactinol Hydrolase."

hydrolase" reaction would be galactinol and sucrose, in agreement with the sugar content seen in the sink tissues.

STACHYOSE BREAKDOWN IN SINK TISSUES - A MODEL

From the data presented here, it would appear that both alkaline α-galactosidase and a yet uncharacterized "raffinose hydrolase" may be acting in concert to effect the hydrolysis of RFOs in *P. camptotricha* sink tissues. The alkaline α-galactosidase has been reported to hydrolyze stachyose (K_m = 4.5 mM) at a ten-fold higher rate than it does raffinose (K_m = 36.4 mM) (Gaudreault and Webb, 1983). Therefore, this enzyme is likely to be the one responsible for removal of the terminal galactose from the stachyose molecule, as indicated in Figure 5 (Reaction 1). The subsequent metabolism of galactose would occur, following phosphorylation by galactokinase (Reaction 2, Fig. 5) by the pathway previously reported by Gross and Pharr (1982), involving conversion to UDP-Gal by a pyrophosphorlyase step (Reaction 3, Fig. 5) and conversion to UDP-Glc (Reaction 4, Fig. 5). As can be seen in Figure 5, this hydrolytic pathway is energetically expensive, and requires the input of two ATP equivalents to convert the released galactose into the sugar nucleotide form.

From the data reported here, it is likely that further metabolism of the raffinose remaining after the cleavage of stachyose by α-galactosidase would then occur by the "raffinose hydrolase" reaction (Reaction 5, Fig. 5), and not by further α-galactosidase activity. This reaction would lead to the production of sucrose and galactinol, in agreement with the sugar content of the sink tissues. Sucrose would presumably be metabolized by the usual reactions (e.g. sucrose synthase, Reaction 6, Fig. 5).

The metabolism of galactinol, based on the high levels of myo-inositol seen in the sink tissues, most likely occurs by a reversal of the normal galactinol synthase (GSyn) reaction (Reaction 7, Fig. 5). Whether the enzyme involved is in fact GSyn, or another enzyme entirely (e.g., "Galactinol Hydrolase") still needs to be clarified. GSyn is known to be a fully reversible enzyme (Kandler and Hopf, 1980), but the mechanisms controlling the direction of its activity are not as yet known. Reversal of the GSyn reaction would result in the direct production of a sugar nucleotide, UDP-Gal, which could then be converted to UDP-Glc (Reaction 4, Fig. 5) for use in other polysaccharide syntheses, in a manner analogous to that operating during the sucrose synthase reaction in sinks.

The advantages of this proposed pathway, over the conventional hydrolysis by α-galactosidase, is two-fold. Firstly, as stated above, there is direct production of a sugar nucleotide, without need for ATP consumption. Secondly, myo-inositol, the acceptor molecule for the galactosyl residue of raffinose, is recycled, as indicated in Figure 5. A third benefit could arise if it is shown that the galactokinase used in Reaction 2 (Fig. 5) can utilize UTP as well as ATP to phosphorylate galactose released by the α-galactosidase reaction. If this proves to be the case, then the phosphorylation reaction will result in the generation of UDP, which is required in Reaction 7 (Fig. 5), the GSyn reversal reaction. This would allow a direct coupling of the α-galactosidase pathway reactions with those of the proposed raffinose hydrolase reaction pathway indicated in Figure 5.

ACKNOWLEDGMENTS

This work was supported in part by a National Science Foundation Grant (DCB-8901785). The author also thanks Michelle V. Gadush for providing excellent technical help and Dr. Irwin P. Ting for providing the plant material.

LITERATURE CITED

Bachmann M, Inan C, Keller F (1995) Raffinose Family Oligosaccharide Storage. *In* MA Madore, WJ Lucas, eds, Carbon Partitioning and Source-Sink Interactions in Plants. American Society of Plant Physiologists, Rockville MD, this volume

Dey PM (1985) D-galactose-containing oligosaccharides. *In* PM Dey, RA Dixon, eds, Biochemistry of Storage Carbohydrates in Green Plants. Academic Press, New York, pp 53-129

Dey PM (1990) Oligosaccharides. *In* PM Dey, JB Harborne, eds, Methods in Plant Biochemistry, Vol 2, Carbohydrates. Academic Press, New York, pp 189-218

Dey PM, Pridham JB (1972) Biochemistry of α-galactosidases. Adv Enzymol **36**: 91-130

Flora LL, Madore MA (1993) Stachyose and mannitol transport in olive (*Olea europeaea* L.). Planta **189**: 484-490

Gaudreault PR, Webb JA (1982) Alkaline α-galactosidase in leaves of *Cucurbita pepo*. Plant Sci Lett **24**: 281-288

Gaudreault PR, Webb JA (1983) Partial purification and properties of an alkaline α-galactosidase from mature leaves of *Cucurbita pepo*. Plant Physiol **71**: 662-668

Gross KC, Pharr DM (1982) A potential pathway for galactose metabolism in *Cucumis sativus* L., a stachyose transporting species. Plant Physiol **69**: 117-121

Kandler O, Hopf H (1980) Occurrence, metabolism and function of oligosaccharides. *In* J Preiss, ed, The Biochemistry of Plants: A Comprehensive Treatise, Vol 3, Carbohydrates: Structure and Function. Academic Press, New York, pp 189-218

Koster KL, Leopold AC (1988) Sugars and desiccation tolerance in seeds. Plant Physiol **88**: 829-832

Madore MA (1990) Carbohydrate metabolism in source and sink tissues of variegated leaves of *Coleus blumei* Benth. Plant Physiol **93**: 617-622

Madore MA (1992) Nocturnal stachyose metabolism in *Xerosicyos danguyi* H. Humb. Planta **187**: 537-541

Madore MA, Mitchell DE, Boyd CM (1988) Stachyose synthesis in source leaf tissues of the CAM plant *Xerosicyos danguyi* H. Humb. Plant Physiol **87**: 588-591

Mitchell DE, Gadus MV, Madore MA (1992) Patterns of assimilate production and translocation in muskmelon (*Cucumis melo* L.) I. Diurnal patterns. Plant Physiol **99**: 959-965

Pharr DM, Sox HN (1984) Changes in carbohydrate and enzyme levels during the sink to source transition of leaves of *Cucumis sativus* L., a stachyose translocator. Plant Sci Lett **35**: 187-193

Shaffer AA, Pharr DM, Madore MA (1995) Cucurbits. *In* E Zamski, AA Schaffer, eds, Photoassimilate Distribution in Plants and Crops: Source-Sink Relationships. Marcel Dekker Inc, New York (in press)

Smart EL, Pharr DM (1980) Characterization of α-galactosidase from cucumber leaves. Plant Physiol **66**: 731-734

Thomas B, Webb JA (1978) Distribution of α-galactosidase in *Cucurbita pepo*. Plant Physiol **62**: 713-717

Thomas BT, Webb JA (1977) Multiple forms of α-galactosidase in mature leaves of *Cucurbita pepo*. Phytochemistry **16**: 203-206

Ting IP (1985) Crassulacean acid metabolism. Annu Rev Plant Physiol **36**: 595-622

Turgeon R (1995) The Selection of Raffinose Family Oligosaccharides as Translocates in Higher Plants. *In* MA Madore, WJ Lucas, eds, Carbon Partitioning and Source-Sink Interactions in Plants. American Society of Plant Physiologists, Rockville MD, this volume

Raffinose Oligosaccharide Storage

Markus Bachmann, Canan Inan, and Felix Keller

*Institute of Plant Biology, University of Zurich, Zollikerstrasse 107,
CH-8008 Zurich, Switzerland (C.I., F.K.); and USDA-ARS, Plant
Science Research, 3127 Ligon Street, North Carolina State
University, Raleigh, NC 27695-7631, USA (M.B.)*

Storage carbohydrates have been arbitrarily defined as those which occur
at concentrations of at least 10 mg/g dry weight in a given tissue (Drew,
1984). Large quantity, however, is only one criterion for a carbohydrate to
function as a storage compound. Equally important is its ability to be
metabolically flexible and compatible. Metabolic flexibility is required to
guarantee efficient deposition when the supply of photosynthates exceeds
demand and remobilization when the physiological situation is reversed.
Compatibility is required because of the high carbohydrate concentrations
involved and the inherent danger to stress cells osmotically, damage membranes and organelles physically, and chemically inactivate enzymes. In this
article, we will show that, on these multiple criteria, raffinose oligosaccharides
[or raffinose family oligosaccharide(s), RFO] easily qualify as storage carbohydrates. Two case studies will form the basis of our discussion. We will
mainly consider two perennial labiates: (*i*) Japanese artichoke (*Stachys
sieboldii*), which overwinters with frost-hardy tubers and translocates and
stores predominantly stachyose; and (*ii*) common bugle (*Ajuga reptans*), which
overwinters with green leaves, translocates predominantly stachyose, and
stores large amounts of RFO of higher degree of polymerization (DP). For a
more complete picture of the role of RFO in carbon storage, the reader is
referred to a recent review (Keller and Pharr, 1995).

OCCURRENCE AND CONCENTRATIONS OF RFO

RFO [α-D-gal$_n$(1$\rightarrow$6)α-D-glc(1$\leftrightarrow$2)β-D-Fru] are one species of the large
family of α-galactosyl-sucrose oligosaccharides. They form a family of
oligomers with members of increasing DP of up to 15. The lower RFO mem-

bers all carry trivial names and are depicted in Figure 1. The RFO are the most widely occurring free oligosaccharides in the plant kingdom; raffinose is even thought to occur ubiquitously, similar to sucrose (Kandler and Hopf, 1982; Dey, 1990). The concentrations and DPs of the RFO found in plants vary greatly (Table I). With respect to concentrations, three groups may be distinguished: (*i*) the high RFO group with concentrations of 100 to 800 mg RFO/g dry weight mainly includes underground storage organs such as roots and tubers as well as leaves of frost-hardy perennial plants; (*ii*) the intermediate RFO group with RFO concentrations of 50 to 100 mg/g dry weight mainly includes seeds and needles; and (*iii*) the low RFO group with RFO concentrations below 50 mg/g dry weight mainly includes plants which transport RFO, but do not store them to any considerable degree. With respect to DP, some species preferentially accumulate a single RFO member, usually the tetrasaccharide stachyose (e.g. *Stachys, Hippuris, Salvia, Lupinus, Glycine*), although

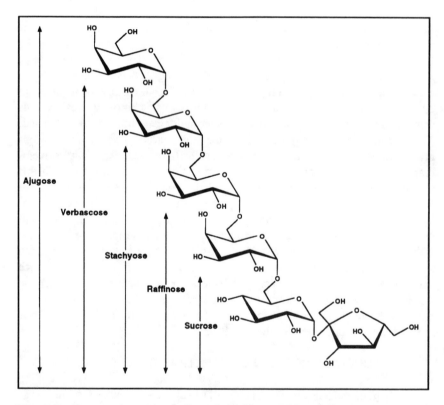

Figure 1. Structural representation of the lower RFO members up to ajugose (DP 6).

Table I. *Concentrations of Galactinol, Sucrose, and RFO in Selected RFO Plants and Organs*

For proper comparison, the concentrations are all given in mg/g dry weight. Plants are listed in decreasing order of total RFO concentrations. Our own results were obtained by HPLC-PAD (pulsed amperometric detection) analysis of desalted cryo saps or acetonitrile/water extracts separated on a CarboPac PA1 (Dionex, Sunnyvale, CA) or a BC-100-Ca (Benson Polymeric, Reno, NV) column [for details see Keller and Ludlow (1993); Bachmann *et al.* (1994)]. Gol, galactinol; Suc, sucrose; Raf, raffinose; Sta, stachyose; Ver, verbascose; DP >5, RFO with DP >5; total RFO, Raf and higher oligomers; n.a., not analyzed; n.d., not detected.

Plant Species and Organ		Plant Family	Harvest (month)	Carbohydrate							Reference
				Gol	Suc	Raf	Sta	Ver	DP >5	RFO Total	
A. High RFO group											
Stachys sieboldii	tuber	Lamiaceae	11	7	31	15	835	20	n.d.	870	This paper
Stachys palustris	tuber	Lamiaceae	11	4	13	108	690	26	n.d.	824	This paper
Ajuga reptans	leaf	Lamiaceae	4	10	12	15	32	59	436	542	This paper
	root		1	13	137	39	88	91	254	472	This paper
Glechoma hederacea	leaf	Lamiaceae	4	18	24	40	116	161	121	438	This paper
Hippuris vulgaris	basal stem	Hippuridaceae	--	n.a.	87	11	346	n.a.	n.a.	357	Janauer & Englmaier (1986)
Salvia officinalis	leaf	Lamiaceae	4	32	153	37	210	18	n.d.	265	This paper
Rosmarinus officinalis	leaf	Lamiaceae	11	59	19	100	77	23	n.d.	200	This paper
Verbascum phlomoides	root	Scrophulariaceae	3	3	11	5	32	32	39	108	This paper
	leaf		3	10	28	10	16	1	n.d.	27	This paper
B. Intermediate RFO group											
Lupinus albus	seed	Fabaceae	--	2	23	7	74	12	n.d.	93	Quemener & Brillouet (1983)
Picea excelsa	needle	Pinaceae	1	n.a.	78	62	3	n.d.	n.d.	65	Kandler & Hopf (1982)
Pisum sativum	seed	Fabaceae	--	n.d.	23	6	20	31	n.d.	57	Quemener & Brillouet (1983)
Glycine max	seed	Fabaceae	--	n.d.	68	5	43	3	n.d.	51	Quemener & Brillouet (1983)
C. Low RFO group											
Cucurbita maxima	leaf	Cucurbitaceae	8	4	13	3	9	1	n.d.	13	This paper
Ocimum basilicum	leaf	Lamiaceae	8	6	1	3	6	1	n.d.	10	This paper
Coleus blumei	leaf	Lamiaceae	4	4	5	2	4	1	n.d.	7	This paper

217

a preferential accumulation of raffinose (e.g. in *Rosmarinus* and *Picea*) or verbascose (e.g. in *Pisum*) has been observed. High concentrations of raffinose are often accompanied by high concentrations of higher DP RFO. Alternatively, a whole series of RFO may accumulate collectively (e.g. in *Ajuga, Glechoma, Verbascum*).

The plants listed in Table I are only a minute selection of the wide variety of RFO plants found in nature. For a more complete list, the reader is referred to reviews (Kandler and Hopf, 1982; Dey, 1990). The RFO concentrations shown in Table I are momentary values taken at one particular developmental stage and environmental condition. It has to be kept in mind that they usually vary greatly with development, environmental conditions, and genetic variety.

SYNTHESIS AND STORAGE OF STACHYOSE

The biosynthetic pathway of the RFO of at least up to DP 4 (stachyose) is well established. It proceeds by a sequential three-step action of α-galactoside transferases according to:

(1) UDP-Gal + *myo*-inositol → galactinol + UDP (galactinol synthase, GSyn, EC 2.4.1.123)

(2) galactinol + sucrose → raffinose + *myo*-inositol [raffinose synthase (RS) EC 2.4.1.82]

(3) galactinol + raffinose → stachyose + *myo*-inositol (stachyose synthase, STS, EC 2.4.1.67).

Research has mainly focused on galactinol synthase (GSyn) and stachyose synthase (STS) in cucurbit leaves although, historically, the isolation and demonstration of these two enzymes was first performed with leguminous seeds (Kandler and Hopf, 1984). Recently, GSyn and STS were purified to near homogeneity and polyclonal antibodies exist (Holthaus and Schmitz, 1991*a, b*; Smith *et al.*, 1991; Beebe and Turgeon, 1992). Kinetically, GSyn, RS, and STS are fairly similar showing pH optima in the neutral range and K_m values in the lower millimolar range. GSyn stands out to be the only enzyme whose activity is strictly dependent on divalent cations, notably Mn^{2+}. These enzyme characteristics would favor a cytosolic subcellular location. This has been demonstrated to be so for GSyn in tubers of *Stachys sieboldii* (Keller, 1992*a*), and GSyn, RS, and STS in leaves of *Ajuga reptans* (M. Bachmann and F. Keller, unpubl. results).

Preferential accumulation of stachyose has been observed in storage organs as diverse as tubers, stems, leaves, and seeds in a variety of plant species (Table I). It may constitute up to 80% of the dry weight of a storage organ. Such high concentrations of a soluble carbohydrate may only be accommodated in the large central vacuole which often makes up between 80 to 90% of the volume of a storage cell. The vacuolar location of stachyose was clearly demonstrated in tubers of Japanese artichoke, *Stachys sieboldii*, by comparing the stachyose content of pith parenchyma protoplasts with that of vacuoles isolated from them (Keller and Matile, 1985). A decade later, this result was confirmed using a similar approach (Niland and Schmitz, 1995).

What are the main processes which lead to the accumulation and storage of stachyose in *Stachys* tuber vacuoles? There is increasing evidence that the following sequence of events is operative: (*i*) stachyose synthesis in leaves; (*ii*) stachyose translocation in the phloem along the path petiole → stem → stolon → tuber; (*iii*) symplasmic stachyose phloem unloading in developing tubers; (*iv*) active stachyose uptake into vacuoles; and (*v*) stachyose storage in dormant tubers. When leaves were photosynthetically labeled with $^{14}CO_2$, radioactive stachyose was readily formed, in addition to sucrose and raffinose (Niland and Schmitz, 1995; M. Bachmann, C. Inan, and F. Keller, unpubl. results). We recently analyzed the carbohydrates present in the phloem sap of *Stachys* using an EDTA exudation method recently developed by M. Bachmann and F. Keller (unpubl. results). More than 60% of the carbohydrates of source leaf phloem sap consisted of stachyose; raffinose (15%), sucrose (5%), and verbascose (5%) were only minor components. The major carbohydrate of the phloem sap of stolons was again stachyose (50%), followed by raffinose (20%), sucrose (10%), and verbascose (5%). These results strongly support the notion that tubers are primarily supplied by stachyose from source leaves via the phloem.

Evidence that stachyose phloem unloading in the tubers is symplasmic and no (or only little) stachyose *de novo* synthesis occurs during stachyose accumulation includes the findings that: (*i*) the activities of the enzymes involved in stachyose synthesis (i.e. GSyn, RS, and STS) are low even in developing tubers (Keller, 1992*a*, and unpubl. results); (*ii*) stachyose and sucrose are only taken up very slowly by isolated tuber parenchyma protoplasts; (*iii*) invertase and α-galactosidase activities are low in the apoplasm; and (*iv*) the different cell types of the tubers (from phloem to pith storage parenchyma) are interconnected with abundant plasmodesmata (Niland and Schmitz, 1995).

The decisive step for stachyose accumulation in the vacuole, therefore, has to be its transport across the tonoplast. This was anticipated to be an active process because compartmentation studies had shown that the concentration of stachyose was much higher in the vacuole than the cytosol [180 versus 0 mM (Keller and Matile, 1985); 138 versus 0 mM (Niland and Schmitz, 1995)]. Transport studies with isolated vacuoles (Keller, 1992*b*; Niland and Schmitz, 1995) and tonoplast vesicles (Greutert and Keller, 1993) clearly established that an active stachyose carrier is situated on the tonoplast of *Stachys* tuber vacuoles and operates most probably by an H^+-antiport mechanism. The stachyose carrier could be fueled by Mg·ATP and pyrophosphate, showed saturation kinetics (K_m for stachyose around 50 mM), and was strongly inhibited by sugars which contained a terminal fructosyl residue.

SYNTHESIS AND STORAGE OF HIGHER RFO

In Table I, examples of three plants are given which accumulate large amounts of higher DP RFO in addition to stachyose. These are *Ajuga reptans* (roots and leaves), *Glechoma hederacea* (leaves), and *Verbascum phlomoides* (roots). Common features of these plants are their perennial nature and ability to survive freezing winter conditions. They might, therefore, ideally combine carbon storage and frost hardiness using one and the same type of carbohydrate, the RFO, similarly to fructans which exert this dual purpose in many temperate grasses (Housley and Pollock, 1993). In an extensive study, we recently looked into the role of RFO in the life cycle of *Ajuga reptans*, a frost-hardy, perennial labiate which is known for its vigor of growth and competence for survival, even under quite adverse conditions (Bachmann *et al.*, 1994; M. Bachmann and F. Keller, unpubl. results). We demonstrated that, in field-grown *Ajuga* plants, the RFO are the most predominant components throughout the whole year. RFO content was lowest in summer (75 mg/g fresh weight) and highest in autumn and winter (up to 200 mg/g fresh weight). The DP of the RFO increased similarly, from about 6 to 9 (summer) up to 15 (winter). This cold-season increase of RFO could also be obtained when warm-grown (25°C) *Ajuga* plants were subjected to cold treatment in a growth chamber (10/3°C day/night). Depending on the time of the year and the physiological status of the warm-grown plants, we can now routinely achieve a four- to ten-fold increase of RFO leaf concentration in 2 to 3 weeks by this type of cold treatment. The DP of the RFO also increases, similarly to field-grown plants.

We have used this experimental RFO induction system to answer the two main questions of: (*i*) how the RFO biosynthetic pathway is changed to allow RFO accumulation and chain elongation (Bachmann *et al.*, 1994); and (*ii*) how the RFO accumulation is compartmentalized on the inter- and intracellular level (M. Bachmann and F. Keller, unpubl. results).

Cold treatment did not affect the activities of the sucrose biosynthetic enzyme sucrose-phosphate synthase (SPS) or of the galactosyl transferases RS and STS. Initial results indicated that the activity of the first unique enzyme of the RFO pathway, GSyn, increased during cold treatment. Unfortunately, we have not been able to repeat this finding consistently for reasons which are not clear at the moment. One enzyme, however, which always responded to cold treatment with increased activity (6 to 15-fold) was a novel RFO chain elongation enzyme GGT (galactan:galactan galactosyltransferase). This galactinol-independent galactosyltransferase was shown to produce, in desalted crude enzyme extracts, from two molecules of RFO the next higher and lower DP of RFO according to:

$$RFO_n + RFO_m \leftrightarrow RFO_{n-1} + RFO_{m+1}.$$

The pH optimum of the reaction was between 4.5 and 5. Raffinose, stachyose, and verbascose could all serve as substrates, but stachyose showed the highest rate of synthesis at 40 mM substrate concentration. We are currently in the process of purifying GGT. A two-step procedure involving ammonium sulphate precipitation and Con A affinity chromatography has resulted in a 14- to 18-fold purification of GGT. When this purified preparation was incubated, RFO chain elongation was clearly observed. Figure 2 shows that after a 3-h incubation, verbascose (DP 5) was the main product, in addition to some ajugose (DP 6) and DP 7 RFO. It is also apparent that some α-galactosidase activity has remained in the preparations, as indicated by an increase of galactose and sucrose. Whether this hydrolytic activity is due to insufficient purification or an intrinsic property of GGT is currently not known. GGT action under the experimental conditions chosen, however, is clearly not a general feature of plant α-galactosidases. When desalted crude enzyme extracts of *Stachys* tubers, which showed high α-galactosidase activity (Keller and Matile, 1985), and a commercial coffee bean α-galactosidase preparation (Sigma) were tested with 40 mM raffinose and stachyose as substrates, only hydrolytic, but no GGT, activity was detected.

Having obtained preliminary evidence for GGT being a key enzyme for RFO accumulation in *Ajuga* leaves, we were also interested to know more about the inter- and intracellular compartmentation of the RFO metabolism and possible mechanisms involved in the accumulation of such large amounts of RFO. We compared cold-acclimated leaves with mesophyll protoplasts and vacuoles isolated from them. The results will be presented in a forthcoming paper (M. Bachmann and F. Keller, unpubl. results) and will only be briefly summarized here. The mesophyll was clearly shown to be the predominant site of RFO synthesis. Mesophyll protoplasts were capable of forming ^{14}C-RFO upon *in situ* and *in vitro* $^{14}CO_2$-photosynthesis. All major enzymes involved in the synthesis of high DP RFO (SPS, GSyn, RS, STS, and GGT) were found in mesophyll protoplasts. Some of the leaf STS activity was also found outside the mesophyll, and is most likely located in the intermediary cells of the phloem, possibly involved in the symplasmic phloem loading process of stachyose. The mesophyll vacuoles were shown to be the main stores for accumulated higher RFO (DP ≥ 4). Mesophyll GSyn and STS were mainly extravacuolar, probably cytosolic; GGT was exclusively vacuolar. Taken together, these results indicate that the sequence of events leading to the accumulation of storage RFO in *Ajuga* leaves ies: (*i*) the classical RFO synthesis up to stachyose in the cytosol (involving SPS, GSyn, RS, and STS); (*ii*)

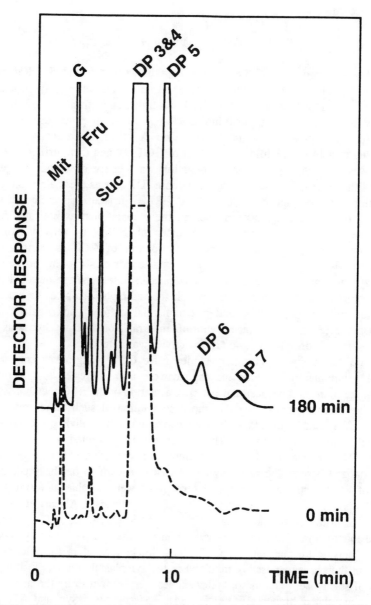

Figure 2. GGT activity of a partially purified enzyme preparation from cold-acclimated *Ajuga reptans* leaves. Reactions were performed with 40 mM stachyose at pH 5 and 30°C. Carbohydrates were analyzed by HPLC-PAD on a CarboPac PA1 column (Bachmann *et al.*, 1994). Mit, Mannitol (internal standard); G, glucose and galactose; DP, DP of RFO.

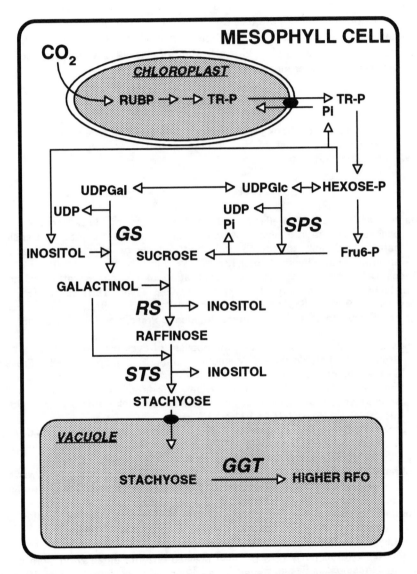

Figure 3. Tentative scheme depicting the subcellular compartmentation of storage RFO and their metabolism in a mesophyll cell of cold-acclimated *Ajuga reptans*.

transport of stachyose into the vacuole; and (*iii*) RFO chain elongation by GGT in the vacuole. These processes are summarized in Figure 3.

This paper was written with a strong focus on the role of RFO in carbon storage; hence, the emphasis on the large central vacuole of tuber parenchyma cells for stachyose storage and of leaf mesophyll cells for RFO chain elongation and storage. For a more balanced view on the compartmentation of RFO metabolism in plants, however, the importance of the intermediary cells of minor veins in synthesis and phloem loading of stachyose would also need to be considered (for a recent review, see Grusak *et al.*, 1995).

ACKNOWLEDGMENTS

We would like to thank Helen Greutert and Sandra Parpan for their valuable contributions. Most of the authors' research was supported by the Swiss National Foundation.

LITERATURE CITED

Bachmann M, Matile P, Keller F (1994) Metabolism of the raffinose family oligosaccharides in leaves of *Ajuga reptans* L. Cold acclimation, translocation, and sink to source transition: discovery of chain elongation enzyme. Plant Physiol **105**: 1335-1345

Beebe DU, Turgeon R (1992) Localization of galactinol, raffinose, and stachyose synthesis in *Cucurbita pepo* leaves. Planta **188**: 354-361

Dey PM (1990) Oligosaccharides. *In* PM Dey, ed, Methods in Plant Biochemistry, Vol 2, Carbohydrates. Academic Press, San Diego, London, pp 189-218

Drew EA (1984) Physiology and metabolism of cyclitols. *In* DH Lewis, ed, Storage Carbohydrates in Vascular Plants. Cambridge Univ Press, Cambridge, pp 133-155

Greutert H, Keller F (1993) Further evidence for stachyose and sucrose/H$^+$ antiporters on the tonoplast of Japanese artichoke (*Stachys sieboldii*) tubers. Plant Physiol **101**: 1317-1322

Grusak MA, Beebe DU, Turgeon R (1995) Phloem loading. *In* E Zamski, AA Schaffer, eds, Photoassimilate Distribution in Plants and Crops: Source-Sink Relationships. Marcel Dekker, New York (in press)

Holthaus U, Schmitz K (1991*a*) Stachyose synthesis in mature leaves of *Cucumis melo*. Purification and characterization of stachyose synthase (EC 2.4.1.67). Planta **184**: 525-531

Holthaus U, Schmitz K (1991*b*) Distribution and immunolocalization of stachyose synthase in *Cucumis melo* L. Planta **185**: 479-486

Housley TL, Pollock CJ (1993) The metabolism of fructan in higher plants. *In* NJ Chatterton, M Suzuki, eds, Science and Technology of Fructans. CRC Press, Boca Raton, FL, pp 192-225

Janauer GA, Englmaier P (1986) The effects of emersion on soluble carbohydrate accumulation in *Hippuris vulgaris* L. Aquat Bot **24**: 241-248

Kandler O, Hopf H (1982) Oligosaccharides based on sucrose (sucrosyl oligosaccharides). *In* FA Loewus, W Tanner, eds, Encyclopedia of Plant Physiology, New Series, Vol 13A, Plant Carbohydrates I, Intracellular Carbohydrates. Springer-Verlag, Berlin, Heidelberg, New York, pp 348-383

Kandler O, Hopf H (1984) Biosynthesis of oligosaccharides in vascular plants. *In* DH Lewis, ed, Storage Carbohydrates in Vascular Plants. Cambridge Univ Press, Cambridge, pp 115-131

Keller F (1992*a*) Galactinol synthase is an extravacuolar enzyme in tubers of Japanese artichoke (*Stachys sieboldii*). Plant Physiol **99:** 1251-1253

Keller F (1992*b*) Transport of stachyose and sucrose by vacuoles of Japanese artichoke (*Stachys sieboldii*) tubers. Plant Physiol **98:** 442-445

Keller F, Ludlow MM (1993) Carbohydrate metabolism in drought-stressed leaves of pigeonpea (*Cajanus cajan*). J Exp Bot **44:** 1351-1359

Keller F, Matile P (1985) The role of the vacuole in storage and mobilization of stachyose in tubers of *Stachys sieboldii*. J Plant Physiol **119:** 369-380

Keller F, Pharr DM (1995) Metabolism of carbohydrates in sinks and sources: galactosyl-sucrose oligosaccharides. *In* E Zamski, AA Schaffer, eds, Photoassimilate Distribution in Plants and Crops: Source-Sink Relationships. Marcel Dekker, Inc, New York (in press)

Niland S, Schmitz K (1995) Sugar transport into storage tubers of *Stachys sieboldii* Miq. Evidence for symplastic unloading and stachyose uptake into storage vacuoles by an H^+-antiport mechanism. Bot Acta **7:** (in press)

Quemener B, Brillouet JM (1983) Ciceritol, a pinitol digalactoside from seeds of chickpea, lentil and white lupin. Phytochemistry **22:** 1745-1751

Smith PT, Kuo TM, Crawford CG (1991) Purification and characterization of galactinol synthase from mature zucchini squash leaves. Plant Physiol **96:** 693-698

Carbon Partitioning and Source-Sink Interactions in Plants, *Monica A. Madore* and *William J. Lucas*, eds, Copyright 1995, published by The American Society of Plant Physiologists

Regulation of Carbon Metabolism in Roots

Hans Lambers and Owen Atkin

Department of Plant Ecology and Evolutionary Biology,
Utrecht University, Sorbonnelaan 16,
3584 CA Utrecht, The Netherlands

Depending on the potential growth rate of the species and on the nutrient supply, herbaceous plants invest 17 to 35% of their daily produced photosynthates in root growth (Table I). Root respiration requires 8 (fast-growing) to 19% (slow-growing herbs) of the plant's carbon budget at an optimum nutrient supply, and 38 (slow-growing) to 52% (fast-growing) at a limiting nitrogen supply. Carbon losses due to root exudation into the rhizosphere may also be of major importance, e.g. when phosphate is scarcely available (Dinkelaker *et al.*, 1989; Hoffland *et al.*, 1989). Therefore, these results demonstrate that roots, and in particular their respiration, are a major sink for the products of photosynthesis (Table I).

The increased significance of root growth and respiration as a portion of the plant's carbon budget when nutrients are in short supply, raises the question: how is the increased carbon allocation to roots brought about? A major question also includes the significance of the nonphosphorylating alternative respiratory path and the manner in which its activity is regulated. It is the aim of this contribution to first provide a general background of carbon import into, and respiratory metabolism in roots. Based on this background, the question of the significance of the alternative path will be tackled.

CARBON IMPORT INTO ROOTS

The mechanism of phloem unloading in roots has only been studied in detail for a very limited number of species, e.g. *Pisum sativum* (Dick and ap Rees, 1975) and *Zea mays* (Giaquinta *et al.*, 1983). Based on these studies, it is widely believed that in roots, sucrose is transported from the phloem to other root cells via symplasmic diffusion. Recently, Bret-Harte and Silk (1994) calculated that the mass flow of sucrose through plasmodesmata may be

Table I. *Utilization of Photosynthates in Plants, as Dependent on the Nutrient Supply*

Values marked * pertain to inherently slow-growing species; ? indicates that there is no information on the costs of these processes under nutrient limitation. [Based on data in Van der Werf *et al.* (1994).]

Item	Use of Photosynthates (% Amount Fixed in Photosynthesis)	
	Optimum Supply	Limiting Supply
Root growth	17 - 18*	33* - 35
Root respiration	8 - 19*	38* - 52
- growth	3.5 - 4.6*	6* - 9
- maintenance	0.6 - 2.6*	?
- ion transport	4 - 3*	?
Exudation	<5	<23

insufficient to meet the carbon demands of a growing root tip. They conclude that either the structure and functioning of plasmodesmata differs from currently held views, or that additional sucrose transport pathways exist. Whether there are additional pathways or not, it is most likely that the phloem in roots is unloaded without the use of respiratory energy. Evidence for this contention comes from the observation that the concentration of carbohydrates in roots rises when ATP production is restricted by hypoxia and, more recently, from the absence of any effect of respiratory inhibitors and uncouplers on short-term carbon import into roots while exogenous addition of sucrose reduces carbon import (Farrar and Minchin, 1991).

It is rather disconcerting that our current understanding of carbon transport to growing root tips is based on such a limited number of species and that no attention has been given to species which transport carbohydrates other than sucrose. This is most remarkable, in view of the observation that the mechanisms of the loading of carbohydrates into the phloem differ between species, partly related to the major transport compound in the phloem (Van Bel and Visser, 1994). Care, therefore, has to be taken when extrapolating data for one species to the entire plant kingdom. Further study of this process in other species is warranted.

Assuming that carbohydrates do enter the sink cells in the roots via symplasmic diffusion, it would seem that roots can exert little control over the rate of carbon import into the roots. Indeed, metabolic inhibitors added to one half of a split-root system have no effect on the import of [11]C (Farrar and Minchin,

1991). This is in contrast to some other sinks, e.g. developing fruits, in which the water potential in the apoplasm, which is largely determined by sucrose on its way from the phloem to the embryo cells, is a major factor controlling phloem unloading (Wolswinkel and Ammerlaan, 1986). In roots, a decrease in the water potential in the apoplasm of part of the root system also enhances carbon import to and respiration in that part of the root system exposed to the low water potential. However, this is only a transient effect and not an aspect of the regulation of carbon import into roots (Williams *et al.*, 1991).

It appears that the only way roots might determine the rate of phloem import is by their rate of structural growth, storage, respiration, and exudation. However, as pointed out below, current evidence indicates that the rate of sucrose import controls the rates of growth and respiration, rather than being controlled by them. It appears that roots are a poor sink, to which only those assimilates are exported which are left over by sinks which have a capacity to exert control over the rate of phloem unloading. This model has been advocated for several decades (e.g. Brouwer, 1983). However, is there experimental evidence to support this model? The following section suggests that there is.

CARBON ALLOCATION TO ROOTS AS DEPENDENT ON RESOURCE SUPPLY

Nagel *et al.* (1994) compared the growth, photosynthesis, water relations, and pattern of carbon allocation of ABA-deficient mutants with wild-type *Lycopersicon esculentum*. The mutant has a greater stomatal conductance, a reduced hydraulic conductance of the roots, and a decreased water potential in the leaves. It incorporates less carbon into leaf biomass and shows a proportionally greater allocation of carbon to the roots. Very similar results were obtained with a number of GA-deficient tomato mutants (O.W. Nagel, unpubl. data). The mutants show reduced leaf and stem elongation, because the GA concentration is too low to support normal leaf and stem growth. Consequently, more carbon is left for translocation to the roots. Thus, when leaf sink strength is reduced via hormonal control, more carbon is allocated to the roots.

At a low water potential in the root environment, relatively more carbon is invested in roots (Creelman *et al.*, 1990). It is very likely that this is controlled in a somewhat similar manner as in the ABA-deficient plants. That is, the low water potential does not sustain leaf growth at the rate of control plants, albeit not because of the low water potential per se, but because of the accumulation of ABA. ABA strongly inhibits leaf growth, while root growth is affected considerably less (Saab *et al.*, 1990). As long as photosynthesis is inhibited less at a low water potential than leaf growth is, more carbon is available for translocation to the roots. The control in plants grown at a low nitrogen supply is likely to be more complicated. The reduced nitrogen supply is possibly the cause of reduced cytokinin export to the leaves (Kuiper *et al.*, 1989). Due to the lower cytokinin import into leaves, protein synthesis and growth in the leaves is less. Since photosynthesis declines less than leaf growth, more carbon is available for root growth. The roots may either grow at the same rate as those of control plants, or their growth may be increased.

It is concluded that current evidence indicates that roots have very little direct control over the rate of carbon export from the leaves. If they do exert control, it is in an indirect manner, via their control of leaf growth which depends on the supply of cytokinins and water from the roots (Van der Werf, 1995). This lack of control over carbon import might well require a respiratory system which not only functions to generate ATP, but also allows the oxidation of sucrose to proceed with little ATP production.

RESPIRATION AND ITS CONTROL BY
CARBOHYDRATES AND ADENYLATES

When plants are grown under conditions of a low-light intensity and a short day, their roots tend to show a diel fluctuation in the level of soluble sugars and respiration (CO_2 production and O_2 consumption; Lambers *et al.*, 1995). At higher light intensity and longer days, such a diurnal pattern disappears. A similar correlation of respiration with the carbohydrate level has been found for several other tissues, and later investigations have revealed that this is, in part, based on a causal relationship (Lambers, 1985). Root respiration is also regulated by adenylates, which control both the rate of electron transport and that of glycolysis. This control by adenylates often coincides with regulation by the availability of substrate (Fig. 1; Lambers *et al.*, 1995).

In short-term experiments, increased substrate levels are thought to predominantly increase the activity of the alternative path, rather than that of the cytochrome path. This may not be so after prolonged exposure to increased exogenous or endogenous sucrose levels, which affect the respiratory capacity. The change in respiratory capacity is a relatively slow response (several hours), compared to the fast responses where the existing respiratory capacity is used to a greater extent. However, it is likely to be of significance in the plant's response to environmental factors. The protein pattern of the roots of plants is affected within 24 h after altering their carbohydrate supply (Williams *et al.*, 1992). Mitochondria isolated from such roots show changes in respiratory properties. Sucrose feeding to roots also modifies the activity of several respiratory enzymes, particularly sucrose synthase (Paul and Stitt, 1993), likely due to regulation of gene expression by carbohydrate levels.

It is concluded that root respiration is controlled both by adenylates and by the substrate supply. The substrate supply affects respiration both directly and

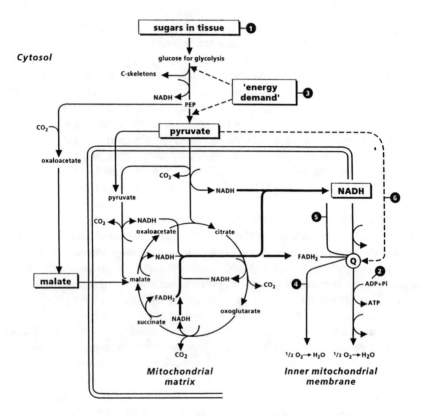

Figure 1. A simplified scheme of respiration and its points of control. Controlling factors include the level of carbohydrates, both as a substrate and as a factor controlling expression of genes involved in respiratory metabolism (1). Adenylate control plays a role in most roots (2, 3); adenylates may exert control on electron transport via a constraint on the rate of oxidative phosphorylation (2), on glycolysis, via modulation of the activity of phosphofructokinase and pyruvate kinase ['energy demand' (3)], or a combination of both. When the input of electrons into the respiratory chain exceeds that which can be accepted by the cytochrome path, a greater fraction of ubiquinone (Q) tends to become reduced, but the alternative path then becomes engaged (4), so that the fraction of reduced Q remains rather constant. There is increasing evidence that the nonphosphorylating rotenone-insensitive bypass (5) operates only when the concentration of NADH is very high. Pyruvate affects the affinity of the alternative oxidase for ubiquinol, provided the oxidase is in its high-activity ('reduced') state (6); other organic acids have similar effects.

indirectly, via an effect on gene expression leading to a modified capacity of the respiratory apparatus.

THE REGULATION OF THE ALTERNATIVE PATH

One of the major substrates for plant mitochondria *in vivo* is malate, produced in the cytosol (Bryce and ap Rees, 1985). Thus, in plant cells, malate is a major end-product of glycolysis, which is at variance with the situation in mammalian cells, where pyruvate is the predominant glycolytic end-product. Malate tends to be oxidized at a far greater rate by isolated plant mitochondria than pyruvate is, due to a more rapid uptake of this substrate. The malate is oxidized partly via malic enzyme and partly via malate dehydrogenase. *In vivo*, pyruvate is subsequently oxidized via pyruvate dehydrogenase, producing acetyl-CoA, which reacts with oxaloacetate to form citrate, which is then oxidized in the TCA cycle, so that malate is regenerated. In isolated mitochondria, the oxidation of malate tends not to continue beyond the formation of pyruvate and/or oxaloacetate.

Electrons originating from the oxidation of malate and other TCA-cycle intermediates, are first donated to ubiquinone (Q) and then transferred to O_2 via the cytochrome path or the alternative path. The existence of two mitochondrial respiratory pathways, both transporting electrons to O_2, raises the question as to how the diversion of electrons between these paths is regulated. This is particularly relevant, since transport of electrons from Q via the cytochrome path is coupled to proton extrusion, while transport via the alternative path is not.

Bahr and Bonner (1973) were the first to conclude that simple competition for electrons between the alternative pathway and the cytochrome pathway cannot explain the experimental data obtained with isolated mitochondria. This conclusion has been corroborated using tissue slices (Theologis and Laties, 1978) and intact roots (e.g. De Visser and Blacquière, 1984; Bingham and Farrar, 1987). These authors demonstrated that respiration is not inhibited by a low concentration of KCN in the absence of an inhibitor of the alternative path (e.g. SHAM). At a slightly higher KCN concentration, respiration decreases steadily, until the cytochrome path is fully inhibited. In the presence of SHAM, even a low KCN concentration reduces respiration. Apparently, KCN does not inhibit the total respiration as long as electrons can be redirected through the alternative path. Upon saturation of the alternative path, a further increase of the KCN concentration inhibits respiration. In the presence of SHAM, no such redirection to the alternative path is possible, so that respiration is inhibited also at a low KCN concentration. The titration data showed that, once the alternative path has been filled with electrons, KCN inhibits to the same extent in the presence as in the absence of SHAM. This has led to the conclusion that the alternative path functions as an 'overflow.' Further evidence supporting this contention has come from experiments in which respiration is titrated with SHAM in the absence and presence of a concentration of KCN which fully blocks the cytochrome path. It was concluded that electrons cannot be redirected from the alternative path to the cytochrome path, while they can readily be redirected from the cytochrome path to the alternative path.

On the basis of the evidence presented above, until a year ago, the widely held view was that the alternative path acts as an 'overflow,' never 'shares' electrons with the cytochrome path, and only becomes engaged when the cytochrome path is inhibited or saturated with electrons. This manner of partitioning of electrons between the two electron transport pathways can be explained by the differential response of the cytochrome path and the alternative path to their common substrate, reduced ubiquinone (Q_r). In isolated mitochondria, the activity of the cytochrome path increases linearly with the fraction of ubiquinone that is in its reduced state (Q_r/Q_t). In contrast, the alternative path shows no appreciable activity until Q_r/Q_t is at least 30 to 40%, after which the activity increases very rapidly (Dry et al., 1989; Fig. 2).

Quite recently, the view that the alternative path invariably never 'shares' electrons with the cytochrome path had to be modified substantially. Though the overflow concept may still be valid for some species and tissues, it cannot be generalized, as evidenced by titration experiments with intact roots. Titrating root respiration of several Poa species with KCN in the absence and presence of SHAM showed that the activity of the cytochrome path increases upon inhibition of the alternative path and that in roots of these species, the alternative pathway shares electrons from Q_r with the cytochrome path (Atkin et al., submitted).

How can we account for this sharing of electrons between the two electron transport pathways, in view of their response to Q_r/Q_t? Probably, when the two respiratory pathways share electrons, the curve describing the activity of the alternative path as a function of Q_r/Q_t has shifted to the left (Fig. 2). Such a shift is brought about by a reversible allosteric effect of organic acids, e.g. pyruvate (Millar et al., 1993; Day et al., 1994), which is most noticeable when the alternative oxidase is in its high-activity ('reduced') state (Umbach and Siedow, 1993; Umbach et al., 1994). It is not known how the interconversion of the 'reduced' and the 'oxidized' configuration is brought about. It is likely that it is enzymatically catalyzed and that the conversion to the reduced configuration is favored under conditions where the NADH/NAD ratio tends to be high.

Organic acids are likely to accumulate when their rate of production is not matched by their oxidation in the mitochondria. The allosteric effect of organic acids, most pronounced when the alternative oxidase has been 'reduced,' suggests that the ability of the alternative path to accept electrons from Q_r is greatly enhanced when the substrate supply to the mitochondria is large compared to the need for ATP production. That is, also when the alter

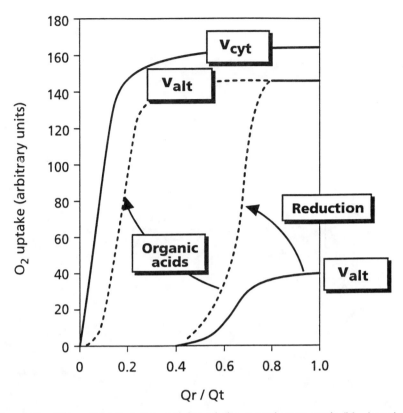

Figure 2. Dependence of the activity of the cytochrome path (V_{cyt}) and of the alternative path (V_{alt}) on the fraction of ubiquinone that is in its reduced state (Q_r/Q_t). When the alternative oxidase is in its 'reduced' state (high-activity configuration), it has a greater capacity to accept electrons. The alternative oxidase can also be affected allosterically by organic acids, which not only increase its affinity for Q_r, but also enhance its capacity. The increase in affinity is most pronounced when the oxidase is in its 'reduced' configuration. [Based on information in Dry *et al.* (1989), Umbach *et al* (1994), and Day *et al.* (1994).]

native path does share electrons with the cytochrome pathway, the alternative path still functions as an 'energy overflow,' be it in a far more sophisticated manner than originally proposed (Fig. 3). Although many aspects still have to be investigated, we can now envisage how the capacity of the alternative path to transport electrons at a certain Q_r/Q_t can be increased rapidly (Fig. 2). However, there must also be control mechanisms to decrease the activity of the alternative path again. If not, once the alternative oxidase has been reduced and its affinity for Q_r/Q_t has been increased, considerably less ATP will be

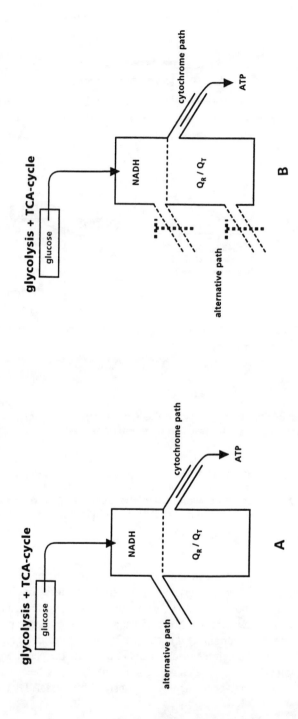

Figure 3. The alternative path as an 'energy overflow.' In (A), the alternative path does not function until the cytochrome path is saturated. In (B), the cytochrome path is not saturated, but an increased input of electrons, due to rapid oxidation of substrate in glycolysis and TCA cycle, enhances the capacity to transport electrons to O_2 via the alternative path. Reduced ubiquinone (Q_r) is the substrate common to both pathways. It is likely that Q_r/Q_t is maintained at a constant level. For further explanation, see text. [Model (A) is based on the model originally presented in Lambers and Steingröver (1978).]

produced. This leads to an increased activity of glycolysis and greater production of organic acids, which enhance the ability of the alternative path to accept electrons even more. In other words, there must be mechanisms to prevent the system to run into a 'respiratory crisis.' At the present, we have no idea how these mechanisms function.

The manner in which electrons are partitioned between the two respiratory pathways has a major impact on the interpretation of the effects of inhibitors. If there is no competition of the alternative path with the cytochrome pathway, inhibition by SHAM equals the activity of the alternative path (cf. Møller *et al.*, 1988). However, if the alternative path shares electrons with the cytochrome pathway, the SHAM inhibition is less than the activity of the alternative path (Atkin *et al.*, submitted). Although further work is needed, the main point is very clear—the contribution of the alternative path in root respiration may be far greater than one might conclude from the effect of SHAM on respiration. It is very likely that the alternative path plays a major, and until now vastly under-rated, role in roots of many, if not all species.

The alternative path appears to be a major aspect of the regulation of respiration in higher plants. But what exactly is regulated by this nonphosphorylating path? Reduced ubiquinone (Q_r) is the substrate common to both pathways. Recently, Wagner and coworkers (A.M. Wagner, pers. commun.) have demonstrated that Q_r/Q_t is maintained remarkably constant in plant cells, even upon addition of an uncoupler which greatly enhances respiration. This suggests that Q_r/Q_t is regulated by the alternative oxidase. If the ratio tends to increase, the alternative path may be brought into a configuration to restore the original ratio; if it tends to drop below a set point, the activity of the alternative path may be reduced, to restore Q_r/Q_t. The significance of the tight regulation of Q_r/Q_t, as speculated here, is likely that in this way, the formation of potentially damaging radicals in mitochondria is avoided (Purvis and Shewfelt, 1993).

CONCLUSION

Roots are a major sink for carbon, particularly when nutrients are in short supply. A major portion of the carbon translocated to the roots is used in respiration. Part of the respiration proceeds via the nonphosphorylating, alternative respiratory pathway.

In roots of some species, the alternative path is possibly engaged only when the cytochrome path is virtually saturated. In roots of many other species the alternative path shares electrons with the cytochrome path. In those species which show very little inhibition by an inhibitor of the alternative path, the contribution of the nonphosphorylating pathway in the carbon metabolism of roots may have been greatly underestimated.

The alternative path is also likely to function as an intricately controlled 'overflow' in roots in which electrons are shared between the cytochrome and alternative path, possibly regulating the fraction of ubiquinone that is in its reduced state.

ACKNOWLEDGMENTS

We wish to thank Jan-Kees van Amerongen for his constructive criticism.

LITERATURE CITED

Atkin OK, Villar R, Lambers H (1995) Competition for electrons between the cytochrome and the alternative pathways in intact roots of several plant species. Its implications for the ATP yield *in vivo*. Plant Physiol (submitted)

Bahr JT, Bonner WD Jr (1973) Cyanide-insensitive respiration. II. Control of the alternative pathway. J Biol Chem **248**: 3446-3450

Bingham IJ, Farrar JF (1987) Respiration of barley roots: Assessment of the activity of the alternative path using SHAM. Physiol Plant **70**: 491-498

Bret-Harte M, Silk WK (1994) Nonvascular, symplasmic diffusion of sucrose cannot satisfy the carbon demands of growth in the primary root tip of *Zea mays* L. Plant Physiol **105**: 19-33

Brouwer R (1983) Functional equilibrium: sense or nonsense? Neth J Agric Sci 31: 335-348

Bryce JH, ap Rees T (1985) Rapid decarboxylation of the products of dark fixation of CO_2 in roots of *Pisum* and *Plantago*. Phytochemistry **24**: 1635-1638

Creelman RA, Mason HS, Bensen RJ, Boyer JS, Mullet JE (1990) Water deficit and abscisic acid cause differential inhibition of shoot versus root growth in soybean seedlings. Analysis of growth, sugar accumulation, and gene expression. Plant Physiol **92**: 205-214

Day DA, Millar AH, Wiskich JT, Whelan, J (1994) Regulation of alternative oxidase activity by pyruvate in soybean mitochondria. Plant Physiol **106**: 1421-1427

De Visser R, Blacquire T (1984) Inhibition and stimulation of root respiration in *Pisum* and *Plantago* by hydroxamate. Its consequences for the assessment of alternative path activity. Plant Physiol **75**: 813-817

Dick PS, ap Rees T (1975) The pathway of sugar transport in roots of *Pisum sativum*. J Exp Bot **26**: 305-314

Dinkelaker B, Römheld V, Marschner H (1989) Citric acid excretion and precipitation of calcium citrate in the rhizosphere of white lupin. Plant Cell Environ **12**: 285-292

Dry IB, Moore AL, Day DA, Wiskich JT (1989) Regulation of alternative pathway activity in plant mitochondria. Non-linear relationship between electron flux and the redox poise of the quinone pool. Arch Biochem Biophys **273**: 148-157

Farrar JF, Minchin PEH (1991) Carbon partitioning in split root systems of barley: relation to metabolism. J Exp Bot **42**: 1261-1269

Giaquinta RT, Lin W, Sadler NL, Franceschi VR (1983) Pathway of phloem unloading of sucrose in corn roots. Plant Physiol **72**: 362-367

Hoffland E, Findenegg GR, Nelemans JA (1989) Solubilization of rock phosphate by rape. II. Local root exudation of organic acids as a response to P-starvation. Plant Soil **113**: 161-165

Kuiper D, Kuiper PJC, Lambers H, Schuit JT, Staal M (1989) Cytokinin contents in relation to mineral nutrition and benzyladenine addition in *Plantago major* ssp. *pleiosperma*. Physiol Plant **75**: 511-517

Lambers H (1985) Respiration in intact plants and tissues: Its regulation and dependance on environmental factors, metabolism and invaded organisms. *In* R Douce and DA Day, eds, Encyclopedia of Plant Physiology, New Series. Springer-Verlag, Berlin, pp 418-473

Lambers H, Steingröver E (1978) Growth respiration of a flood-tolerant and a flood-intolerant *Senecio* species: Correlation between calculated and experimental values. Physiol Plant **43**: 219-224

Lambers H, Atkin OK, Scheurwater I (1995) Respiratory patterns in roots in relation to their functioning. *In* Y Waisel, A Eshel, U Kafkaki, eds, Plant Roots: The Hidden Half. Marcel Dekker, Inck New York (in press)

Millar AH, Wiskich JT, Whelan J, Day DA (1993) Organic acid activation of the alternative oxidase of plant mitochondria. FEBS Lett **329**: 259-262

Møller IM, Berczi A, van der Plas LHW, Lambers H (1988) Measurement of the activity and capacity of the alternative pathway in intact plant tissues: Identification of problems and possible solutions. Physiol Plant **72**: 642-649

Nagel OW, Konings H, Lambers (1994) Growth rate, plant development and water relations of the ABA-deficient tomato mutant *sitiens*. Physiol Plant **92**: 102-108

Paul MJ, Stitt M (1993) Effects of nitrogen and phosphorus deficiencies on levels of carbohydrates, respiratory enzymes and metabolites in seedlings of tobacco and their response to exogenous sucrose. Plant Cell Environ **16**: 1047-1057

Purvis AC, Shewfelt RL (1993) Does the alternative pathway ameliorate chilling injury in sensitive plant tissues? Physiol Plant **88**: 712-718

Saab IN, Sharp RE, Pritchard J, Voetberg GS (1990) Increased endogenous abscisic acid maintains primary root growth and inhibits shoot growth of maize seedlings at low water potentials. Plant Physiol **93**: 1329-1336

Theologis A, Laties GG (1978) Relative contribution of cytochrome-mediated and cyanide-resistant electron transport in fresh and aged potato slices. Plant Physiol **62**: 232-237

Umbach AL, Siedow JN (1993) Covalent and noncovalent dimers of the cyanide-resistant alternative oxidase protein in higher plant mitochondria and their relationship to enzyme activity. Plant Physiol **103**: 845-854

Umbach AL, Wiskich JT, Siedow JN (1994) Regulation of alternative oxidase kinetics by pyruvate and intermolecular disulfide bond redox status in soybean mitochondria. FEBS Lett **348**: 181-184

Van Bel AJE, Visser AJ (1994) Phloem transport, carbon and nitrogen allocation, and interspecific differences in relative growth rate. *In* J Roy, E Garnier, eds, A Whole-Plant Perspective on Carbon-Nitrogen Interactions. SPB Academic Publ, The Hauge, pp 171-197

Van der Werf A (1995) Growth analysis and photoassimilate partitioning. *In* E Zamski, AA Schaffer, eds, Photoassimilate distribution in plants and crops: source-sink relationships. Marcel Dekker, Inc, New York (in press)

Van der Werf A, Poorter H, Lambers H (1994) Respiration as dependent on a species' inherent growth rate and on the nitrogen supply to the plant. *In* J Roy, E Garnier, eds, A Whole-Plant Perspective on Carbon-Nitrogen Interactions. SPB Academic Publ, The Hague, pp 91-110

Williams JHH, Minchin PEH, Farrar JF (1991) Carbon partitioning in split root systems of barley: the effect of osmotica. New Phytol **42:** 453-460

Williams JHH, Winters AL, Farrar JF (1992) Sucrose: a novel plant growth regulator. *In* H Lambers, LHW Van der Plas, eds, Plant Respiration. Molecular, Biochemical and Physiological Aspects. SPB Academic Publ, The Hague, pp 463-469

Wolswinkel P, Van Ammerlaan A (1986) Turgor-sensitive transport in developing seeds of legumes: the role of the stage of development and the use of excised vs. attached seed coats. Plant Cell Environ **9:** 133-140

Carbon Partitioning and Source-Sink Interactions in Plants, *Monica A. Madore* and *William J. Lucas*, eds, Copyright 1995, published by The American Society of Plant Physiologists

Genetic Aspects of Sucrose-Metabolizing Enzymes in Developing Maize Seed

Prem S. Chourey, Wan-Hsing Cheng,
Earl W. Taliercio, and Kyung H. Im

*USDA-ARS (P.S.C.; E.W.T.) and University of Florida,
Program in Plant Molecular and Cellular Biology
(P.S.C.; W-H.C.), Department of Plant Pathology
(P.S.C.; K.H.I), Gainesville, FL 32611-0680, USA*

Sucrose, the ubiquitous source of carbon in most higher plants, is also the principal and preferred form of photosynthate for transport to various sink tissues. Sucrose is also increasingly recognized as a major player in metabolic regulatory signaling processes in gene expression, and ultimately in determining development and differentiation in plants. In developing seed, the development of endosperm is intimately dependent upon the metabolic utilization of sucrose, initially in the cell division processes, and later in its use in numerous assimilatory activities and storage as starch.

There have been several anatomical, as well as physiological, studies aimed at elucidating the cellular path of sucrose from pedicel (maternal tissue at the base of the seed) to developing endosperm or cotyledon of various crop plants. In wheat, there is clear evidence that sucrose enters the endosperm without prior hydrolysis (Patrick *et al.*, 1991; Wang and Fisher, 1994). However, the results in maize have remained controversial (Miller and Chourey, 1992, and references therein). Briefly, the early data strongly suggest that sucrose hydrolysis occurs prior to its entrance into the endosperm (Shannon *et al.*, 1986 and references therein). The more recent studies (Felker, 1992; Shannon *et al.*, 1993) indicate that a substantial portion of sucrose enters the endosperm without the invertase-mediated hydrolysis. Although these data show that the pedicellar sucrose enters the endosperm, how this transfer occurs, especially if there is a lack of symplastic continuity between the pedicel and the endosperm, is unknown. We speculate that several forces, including passive efflux of sucrose, pedicel cell turgor, and a sucrose carrier protein, may be involved. In this report, we focus on gene expression aspects of invertases, sucrose-phosphate synthase (SPS), and the two isozymes of sucrose synthase (SS), particularly in the lower part of the developing endosperm which is predominantly comprised of transfer cells and a few layers of long and elongated cells.

MATERIALS AND METHODS

Enzyme Extraction and Assay

Immature kernels at various developmental stages were harvested, quick-frozen in liquid N_2, and stored at -80°C until used in assays. At the time of extraction, each endosperm was cut into two parts. The lower part was represented by approximately the 1/4 to 1/3 of the endosperm adjoining the base, and the remainder of the tissue (the central and the crown region) was treated as the upper endosperm. Enzyme activity assays for invertase and SS were as described by Miller and Chourey (1992) and Chourey (1981), respectively. For the SPS enzyme, extraction and assay ("V_{max} assay") were as previously described by Weiner et al. (1992). Western and Northern blot analyses were done as previously described (Chourey and Taliercio, 1994). A kernel-specific cell wall (CW) invertase clone was isolated recently (P.S. Chourey, E.W. Taliercio, S. Shanker, and J. Choi, unpubl. data) from a 14-d-after-pollination (DAP) kernel cDNA library using a full-length CW invertase clone from maize cell suspension culture (Shanker et al., 1995).

RESULTS

Figures 1a and 1b show SDS Western blots representing CW-specific invertase polypeptides in kernel extracts of various genotypes. The blots were cross-reacted with polyclonal antibody against carrot CW invertases. A single polypeptide, approximately 67 kD in size, was detected in extracts from only the lower part of the $Mn1$ kernels (50 μg protein/ lane), and no protein band was seen in the $mn1$ mutant, at levels as high as 150 μg protein/lane. Furthermore, the results presented in Figure 1b show that the intensity of the protein band in various genotypes was gene-dose dependent on the number of $Mn1$ gene copies in the triploid endosperm.

Figure 1c represents a Northern blot showing total RNA from various samples probed with a kernel-specific CW invertase clone. The most abundant level of the approximately 2.2-kb transcript was detected in the RNA from the lower part of the $Mn1$ endosperm (lane 2). There was no detectable hybridization in similar samples from $mn1$ endosperm or the upper endosperm of the $Mn1$ genotype.

Figures 2a, 2b, and 2c represent SDS Western blots and Northern blots showing SS1 and SS2 polypeptides and the corresponding RNA transcripts in various samples, as indicated in the figure. The detection of polypeptides was based on the use of isozyme-specific monoclonal antibodies, and the RNA

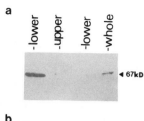

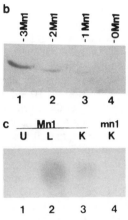

Figure 1. SDS Western blots (a and b) and a Northern blot (c) showing CW invertase-specific polypeptides and RNA transcripts in samples as indicated. **a,** Each lane represents 50 μg of protein present in crude extracts of lower and upper parts of *Mn*1 (1-2) and *mn*1 lower endosperm (3) and *Mn*1 whole kernel. **b,** Each lane represents 50 μg of protein present in crude extracts of (1) Mn1 Mn1 Mn1, (2) Mn1 Mn1 mn1, (3) Mn1 mn1 mn1, and (4) mn1 mn1 mn1 genotypes. **c,** Each lane represents 10 μg of total RNA from upper (U), lower (L), and whole kernels (K) of *Mn1* (1-3) and *mn1* (4).

transcripts were visualized using Sh1 and Sus1 cDNA probes (Chourey and Taliercio, 1994). At the protein level, the SS2 protein was detected in both the upper and lower parts of the endosperm; however, the SS1 protein was seen in only the upper part of the endosperm (Fig. 2a). At the RNA level, although the SS2 transcripts were detected in both the upper and lower parts of the endosperm, the SS1 transcripts were at much higher steady-state levels in the upper part relative to the lower part of the endosperm (Fig. 2c). Previous data concerning the SS enzyme activity show that the *sh*1 mutant, lacking the SS1 protein, has only approximately 5% level of SS activity as compared to the normal *Sh*1 endosperm (Chourey, 1981). Based on the Western blot shown in Figure 2a and the previous enzyme data, it appears that the entire *Sh*1-encoded SS activity is localized in the upper part of the endosperm.

Similar studies were also conducted for the SPS protein and RNA transcripts in upper and lower parts of the 22-DAP endosperm by SDS Western and Northern blot analyses, respectively (data not shown). At both RNA and protein levels, SPS expression was detectable in only the lower part of the kernel (E.W. Taliercio, K.H. Im, and P.S. Chourey, unpubl. data). SPS enzyme activity, in lower and upper parts was 61.0 ± 8.3 and 17.0 ± 3.4 nM suc synthesized/mg protein/min, respectively. In terms of grams fresh weight (FW), the SPS activity in lower and upper part of the endosperm was 55.0 ± 5.1 and 13.0 ± 3.1 μM suc/g FW/h, respectively. Although there is a significant level of SPS activity in the upper parts of the endosperm, albeit at

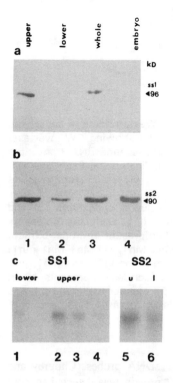

Figure 2. SDS Western blots (a and b) and Northern blot (c) showing sucrose synthase (SS)-specific polypeptides and RNA transcripts in 22 DAP kernels. **a, b,** Each lane represents (a) 1.0 and (b) 10 μg of protein in crude extracts of endosperm and embryo samples. The blot was cross-reacted with maize (a) SS1 and (b) SS2-specific monoclonal antibodies. **c,** Poly-(A+) RNA in (1) lower part of the endosperm, 1.0 μg, (2-4) upper endosperm: 0.50, 0.25, and 0.10 μg, respectively, (5-6) 10 μg total RNA from upper and lower endosperm, respectively. Nytran membranes were hybridized with Sh1 (1-4) and Sus1 cDNA inserts.

much lower levels than in the basal part, it was undetectable by Western blot analyses. It is probable that the enzyme activity assay was slightly more sensitive than the Western blot tests.

DISCUSSION

It is now reasonable to conclude that a large proportion of photoassimilated sucrose enters the developing maize endosperm without prior hydrolysis (Felker, 1992; Shannon et al., 1993). Thus, sucrose cleavage reactions in the endosperm cells have a potential to determine the sink strength of a developing kernel. The role of invertase is of significant importance as it is entirely localized in the basal endosperm (Doehlert and Felker, 1987; Miller and Chourey, 1992; Fig. 1) and is developmentally the earliest enzyme with the highest specific activity levels in the endosperm (W.H. Cheng and P.S. Chourey, unpubl. data). Consistent with these biochemical data are the genetic data which show that invertase-deficient *mn*1 seed mutant is associated with a loss of nearly 80% of the seed weight at maturity (Miller and Chourey, 1992). Despite such a pivotal role, gene-dose-enzyme data on invertase activity clearly indicate that a large proportion of enzyme activity is dispensable without any detectable change in seed size or phenotype (Miller and Chourey, 1992; Cheng and Chourey, 1994).

Because the *Mn*1 locus and invertase activity have such a profound effect on normal seed development, it is pertinent to ask if there is a genetic relationship between the *Mn*1 locus and invertase activity. One of our two proposed hypotheses (Miller and Chourey, 1992) is that *Mn*1 locus is the structural gene for invertase activity in the kernel. Our recent biochemical and molecular genetic studies, including a good gene-dose relationship between the number of *Mn*1 gene copies in the endosperm and the levels of CW invertase activity (Cheng and Chourey, 1994), as well as the levels of CW invertase polypeptide (Fig. 1b), have further strengthened the structural gene hypothesis.

Based on the specific detection of the SS2 isozyme and the SPS enzyme in the basal endosperm (Chen and Chourey, 1989; Fig. 2), we suggest that the two enzymes might be engaged in the resynthesis of sucrose from the hexoses present in abundant levels in this part of the endosperm (Doehlert and Kuo, 1990). The data on up regulation of the *Sus*1 gene by glucose in isolated rice embryos (Karrer and Rodriguez, 1992; Thomas *et al.*, this volume) and in excised maize roots (Koch *et al.*, 1992) are consistent with such an interpretation. The SPS is a major enzyme of sucrose synthesis in photosynthetic tissues (see review; Huber *et al.*, 1993); therefore, it is likely that it performs a similar function in nonphotosynthetic tissues. However, it is unknown why there is sucrose inversion and resynthesis in the same part of the endosperm. One possibility is that it might be related to a futile cycle to attain strict regulatory controls in the sink tissue.

Genetic data clearly indicate that the loss of the *Sh*1-encoded SS1 isozyme in the *sh*1 mutant is associated with a slight reduction in starch content and early CW degeneration (Chourey *et al.*, 1991, and references therein). Additional data on the possible role of the *Sh*1 gene in cellulose biosynthesis are from the molecular studies which show that inhibition of cellulose biosynthesis in maize protoplasts blocks *Sh*1 promoter activity (Maas *et al.*, 1990). In addition, Maas *et al.* have demonstrated that the *Sh*1 promoter is repressed by high concentration of sucrose. We believe these data on metabolic regulation of the *Sh*1 in transient transformation studies (Maas *et al.*, 1990) provide a possible basis for explaining our observations on the lack of *Sh*1 expression in basal endosperm which is known to have the highest concentration of sucrose in a developing endosperm (Doehlert and Kuo, 1990).

ACKNOWLEDGMENTS

This work was supported in part by U.S. Department of Agriculture NRICGP Grant 92-001919. We are grateful to Drs. Arnd Sturm (FMI, Basel, Switzerland) and Toni Voelker (Calgene Inc., Davis, CA) for sharing antibodies against carrot CW invertase, and maize SPS cDNA clone and antibodies, respectively, and to Fred Felker (USDA, ARS, Peoria, IL) for critical reading of the manuscript. This was a cooperative investigation of the U.S. Department of Agriculture, Agricultural Research Service and the Institute of Food and Agricultural Sciences, University of Florida (Agricultural Experiment Journal Series No. R-04417).

LITERATURE CITED

Chen YC, Chourey PS (1989) Spatial and temporal expression of the two sucrose synthase genes in maize. Theor Appl Genet **78**: 553-559

Cheng WH, Chourey PS (1994) A rate-limiting role of invertase in seed development in maize. Plant Physiol **105**: 165

Chourey PS (1981) Genetic control of sucrose synthase in maize endosperm. Mol Gen Genet **184**: 372-376

Chourey PS, Chen YC, Miller ME (1991) Early cell degeneration in developing endosperm is unique to the *shrunken1* mutation in maize. Maydica **36**: 141-146

Chourey PS, Taliercio EW (1994) Epistatic interaction and functional compensation between the two tissue and cell-specific sucrose synthase genes in maize. Proc Natl Acad Sci, USA **91**: 7917-7921

Doehlert DC, Felker FC (1987) Characterization and distribution of invertase activity in developing maize (*Zea mays*) kernels. Physiol Plant **70**: 51-57

Doehlert DC, Kuo TM (1990) Sugar metabolism in developing kernels of starch deficient endosperm mutants of maize. Plant Physiol **92**: 990-994

Felker FC (1992) Participation of cob tissue in the uptake of medium components by maize kernels cultured *in vitro*. J Plant Physiol **139**: 647-652

Huber SC, Huber JL, Pharr M (1993) Assimilate partitioning and utilization in source and sink tissues. Intl Crop Sci I: 789-796

Karrer EK, Rodriquez RL (1992) Metabolic regulation of rice α-amylase and sucrose synthase gene *in planta*. Plant J **2**: 517-523

Koch KE, Nolte KD, Duke ER, McCarty DR, Avigne WT (1992) Sugar levels modulate differential expression of maize sucrose synthase genes. Plant Cell **4**: 59-69

Maas C, Schaal S, Werr W (1990) A feed back control element near the transcription start site of the maize *shrunken* gene determines promoter activity. EMBO J **9**: 3447-3452

Miller ME, Chourey PS (1992) The maize invertase-deficient *miniature1* seed mutation is associated with aberrant pedicel and endosperm development. Plant Cell **4**: 297-305

Patrick JW, Offler CE, Wang HL, Wang X-D, Jin SP, Zhang WC, Ugalde TD, Jenner CF, Wang N, Fisher DB, Felker FC, Thomas PA, Crawford CG (1991) Assimilate transport in developing cereal grain. *In* Recent Advances in Phloem Transport and Assimilate Compartmentation. Ouest Editions, Presses Academiques, Nantes, France, pp 223-243

Shanker S, Salazar RW, Taliercio EW, Chourey PS (1995) Cloning and characterization of full length cDNA encoding cell-wall invertase from maize (*Zea mays* L). Plant Physiol (in press)

Shannon JC, Knievel DP, Chourey PS, Liu S-Y, Liu KC (1993) Carbohydrate metabolism in the pedicel and endosperm of miniature maize kernels. Plant Physiol **102**: 42

Shannon JC, Porter GA, Knievel DP (1986) Phloem unloading and transfer of sugars into developing corn endosperm. *In* J Cronshaw, WJ Lucas, R. T. Giaquinta, eds, Phloem Transport. Allan R Liss, Inc, New York, 265-277

Thomas BR, Terashima M, Katoh S, Rodriguez RL (1995) Metabolic regulation of source/sink relations in cereal seedlings. *In* MA Madore and WJ Lucas, eds, Carbon Partitioning and Source/Sink interactions in Plants. Amer Soc Plant Physiol, Rockville, MD, this volume

Wang N, Fisher DB (1994) Monitoring phloem unloading and post-phloem transport by microperfusion of attached wheat grains. Plant Physiol **104**: 7-16

Weiner H, McMichael RW, Huber SC (1992) Identification of factors regulating the phosphorylation status of sucrose-phosphate synthase *in vivo*. Plant Physiol **99**: 1435-1442

Carbon Partitioning and Source-Sink Interactions in Plants, *Monica A. Madore* and *William J. Lucas*, eds, Copyright 1995, published by The American Society of Plant Physiologists

Plant Responses to Sugar Accumulation in Transgenic Tobacco Plants

Uwe Sonnewald, Ingo Wilke, and Karin Herbers

Institut für Pflanzengenetik und Kulturpflanzenforschung, Corrensstrasse 3, 06466 Gatersleben, Germany

Photosynthetic energy conversion leads to the final products sucrose and starch in leaves. Intermediates are formed during this process and utilized in other biosynthetic pathways. Several molecular approaches have been used to manipulate the synthesis and distribution of assimilates in transgenic plants (summarized in Sonnewald and Willmitzer, 1992; Sonnewald et al., 1994). Either classical mutants or antisense technology have been used to study the *in vivo* function of endogenous plant enzymes involved in the Calvin cycle (Rodermel et al., 1988; Hudson et al., 1992; Koßmann et al., 1994), starch synthesis (Caspar et al., 1985; Jones et al., 1986; Lin et al., 1988; Müller-Röber et al., 1992), sucrose synthesis (Neuhaus et al., 1989; Sharkey et al., 1992), and sugar transport (Riesmeier et al., 1993, 1994; Barnes et al., 1994). An alternative approach was to express foreign genes encoding novel enzymatic activities and/or enzymes with altered regulatory properties (von Schaewen et al., 1990; Worrell et al., 1991; Sonnewald, 1992; Stark et al., 1992; Burrell et al., 1994). This approach has successfully been used to alter metabolite concentrations in transgenic plants, and the influence of these manipulations on whole plant development has been studied.

Two independent approaches leading to sugar accumulation in source leaves have been described: (*i*) expression of a chimeric yeast *suc2* gene encoding cell wall invertase (von Schaewen et al., 1990; Sonnewald et al., 1991); and (*ii*) expression of a chimeric *E. coli ppa* gene encoding cytosolic inorganic pyrophosphatase (Jelitto et al., 1992; Sonnewald, 1992). The rationale of those experiments was that the invertase should hydrolyze sucrose within the cell wall leading to the inhibition of sucrose export and that the cytosolic inorganic pyrophosphatase should decrease the cytosolic pyrophosphate content and thereby stimulate sucrose synthesis. The enzymes PPi:Fru-6-P 1-phosphotransferase and the UDP-Glc pyrophosphorylase work near equilibrium. Consequently, a decrease in PPi should avoid the reaction leading to glycolysis and increase sucrose synthesis. Indeed, plants expressing the *E. coli ppa*-gene showed an increase in UDP-Glc and sucrose content and a decrease in hexosephosphates and PPi content (Jelitto *et al.*, 1992).

Unexpectedly, however the plants showed stunted growth, chlorophyll loss, and a reduced root formation, suggesting that in addition to increased sucrose synthesis in leaf mesophyll cells, the export of photoassimilates had been affected.

Expression of a chimeric yeast *suc2* gene, encoding a cell wall invertase, in transgenic tobacco plants was one of the first examples demonstrating the potential use of heterologous genes to alter sink-source relations (von Schaewen *et al.*, 1990). In subsequent studies, the coding region of the yeast *suc2* gene has been fused to a variety of different promoter and targeting sequences, and the consequences of elevated invertase activities in different cells, organs, and subcellular compartments have been studied (Sonnewald *et al.*, 1991; Lerchl *et al.*, in press). Constitutive expression of cell wall invertase in transgenic tobacco plants leads to accumulation of carbohydrates, inhibition of photosynthesis, and stimulation of respiration in source leaves (von Schaewen *et al.*, 1990). Inhibition of photosynthesis was accompanied by a decrease of Calvin cycle enzymes (Stitt *et al.*, 1990). The decrease of Calvin cycle enzymes is thought to be the consequence of metabolic repression of photosynthetic genes, also found in other experimental systems (summarized in Sheen, 1994). In addition to the biochemical changes, reduced root formation, stunted growth, and necrotic lesions on source leaves were observed. Ultrastructural analysis of these plants revealed that the development of secondary plasmodesmata was arrested (Ding *et al.*, 1993). Stunted growth and reduced root formation found in those plants might be explained by the inhibition of sucrose export from source leaves to sink tissues, but the reason for the formation of necrotic regions within source leaves remains completely unknown.

A common mechanism of sugar sensing in the repression of photosynthetic and the activation of stress-related genes has already been discussed (Jang and Sheen, 1994). A number of studies have been pursued to investigate the effect of increased endogenous sugar levels on photosynthetic and defense-related genes (Johnson and Ryan, 1990; Sheen, 1990; Kim *et al.*, 1991; Krapp *et al.*, 1991, 1993; Tsukaya *et al.*, 1991; Goldschmidt and Huber, 1992).

The aim of the presented work was to investigate the phenotypical changes induced in sugar-accumulating transgenic plants in more detail. Sugar-modulated gene expression and a possible pre-conditioned alarm state of the transgenic plants were analyzed. Furthermore, transgenic plants were used as a tool to isolate sugar-responsive genes by means of subtractive cDNA cloning.

RESULTS AND DISCUSSION

Accumulation of Soluble Sugars Leads to Increased Cell Turgor and Induces Cell Enlargement in Pyrophosphatase-Expressing Plants

Previous results have shown that transgenic tobacco plants expressing the *E. coli ppa* gene (ppa-1) or a chimeric yeast *suc2* gene coding for either cell wall invertase (cwInv) or vacuolar invertase (vacInv) accumulate high amounts of soluble sugars. To determine whether this increase in soluble sugars would lead to increased turgor pressure, the water and osmotic potential of source leaves from ppa-1, vacInv, cwInv, and control plants were measured, and the resulting turgor pressure calculated. As shown in Table I, the water potential of ppa-1 leaves was not significantly altered, whereas the water potential of vacInv and cwInv leaves became more negative as compared to control leaves harvested from untransformed tobacco plants. The osmotic potential decreased in ppa-1 (38%), vacInv (17%), and cwInv (36%) leaves as compared to wild-type leaves. Calculation of the turgor pressure revealed an approximately nine-fold increase in source leaves of ppa-1 plants.

Assuming that increasing turgor pressure would lead to cell enlargement, leaf cross sections of ppa-1 and control plants were prepared. Following glutaraldehyde fixation and ethanol dehydration, leaf discs were embedded in LR-White resin, and thin sections were investigated by light microscopy as described by Sonnewald *et al.* (1989). A dramatic increase in mesophyll cell size of ppa-1 leaves was observed which resulted in a leaf thickness of 0.41 mm $\pm$ 0.014 (n=17) in comparison to wild-type leaves which were half as thick (0.26 mm $\pm$ 0.004; n=17) (see Fig. 1).

Table I. *Water Relation Parameters Measured in Source Leaves of Wild-Type and Transgenic Tobacco Plants*

Fully expanded leaves were harvested in light. The results are given in bar as mean $\pm$ SD (n = 6). The water potential of leaf discs was measured in a C52 sample chamber using a HR-33T dew point microvoltmeter (Wescor). The osmotic potential was determined in a vapor pressure osmometer (Wescor model 5500).

Plant	Water Potential	Osmotic Potential	Turgor Pressure
Control	-10.1 $\pm$ 0.3	-10.5 $\pm$ 0.3	0.4
ppa-1	-11.0 $\pm$ 0.4	-14.5 $\pm$ 0.6	3.5
vacInv	-12.6 $\pm$ 0.6	-12.8 $\pm$ 0.7	0.3
cwInv	-13.4 $\pm$ 1.1	-14.3 $\pm$ 1.5	0.9

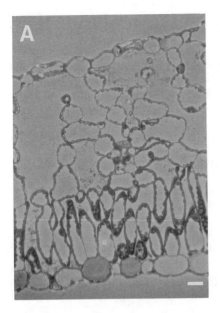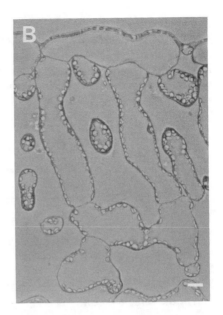

Figure 1. Leaf cross section of wild-type (A) and ppa-1 (B) plants. Bar = 12.5 µm.

Alteration of Cell Wall Polymers in Response to Elevated Turgor Pressure

Cell enlargement is assumed to be dependent on the extensibility of the cell wall and the turgor pressure (Dale, 1988, and references cited therein). GA_3-induced cell expansion in a suspension culture of spinach is paralleled by the secretion of pectins into the medium (Fry, 1980). A similar increase of soluble pectins was found when growth of pea stems was induced by auxin (Terry and Jones, 1981). From these data, it was speculated that pectins could switch from a bound form in which they contribute to the structural coherence of the cell wall to a soluble form in which they play no structural role, leading to changes in wall extensibility. Support for this hypothesis comes from experiments in which tobacco cells were adapted to saline and PEG stress (Iraki *et al.*, 1989; McCann *et al.*, 1994). In those experiments, cell expansion and secretion of uronic acid were inhibited.

To investigate whether the observed cell enlargement of ppa-1 mesophyll cells was accompanied by alteration in cell wall polymers, the cellulose, uronic acid, and pectin content of cell walls from source leaves was analyzed. As shown in Table II, the cellulose content slightly decreased in ppa-1 plants. In contrast, the uronic acid and pectin content increased by 14 and 43%, respectively, as compared to control plants. Since cell enlargement was found to be

Table II. *Cell Wall Polymers of ppa-1 And Control Plants*

Cell walls were isolated from source leaves and the cellulose, uronic acid, and pectin content determined. Results are the mean of three independent cell wall preparations ± SE (mg/g dry wt). Purification, fractionation, and sugar determination of cell walls was done according to Fry (1980).

Compound	Control	ppa-1
Cellulose	136.0 ± 1.15	123.0 ± 2.6
Uronic acid	0.167 ± 0.014	0.19 ± 0.016
Pectin	13.7 ± 0.9	19.6 ± 1.0

associated with increasing amounts of soluble pectins; the amount of water-soluble pectins was determined as well. As compared to control plants a four-fold increase of soluble pectins was observed in source leaves of ppa-1 plants. Pectin determination in the extracellular fluid confirmed the cell wall localization of the soluble pectin fraction.

Isolation of cDNAs Induced in Sugar-Accumulating Tobacco Plants

To elucidate the molecular changes associated with increased turgor pressure and cell enlargement in tobacco, a subtractive library enriched for transcripts present in ppa-1 transgenic plants was prepared (K. Herbers, G. Mönke, R. Badur, and U. Sonnewald, submitted). The subtractive library was successively hybridized to radioactively-labeled cDNA prepared from mRNA of wild-type and ppa-1 plants. Twelve differentially hybridizing clones were purified and sequenced. By sequence homologies, six cDNA clones could be identified, while the remaining six had no homologous sequences in the databanks (Table III). One of the six unknown cDNAs displayed features similar to pathogenesis-related proteins. It was strongly inducible by salicylic acid and accumulated in infected and, to a lower degree, uninfected leaves of wild-type tobacco plants that had been treated with potato virus Y (K. Herbers, G. Mönke, R. Badur, and U. Sonnewald, submitted).

Expression analysis of all cDNA clones in ppa-1 plants showed that the corresponding steady-state mRNA levels increased from sink to source leaves which are characterized by increasing sugar levels in the same order (Sonnewald, 1992). Much weaker hybridization signals were detected in source leaves of wild-type plants.

The expression analysis of the cDNAs encoding pathogenesis-related (PR)-proteins was extended to vacInv and cwInv plants in order to investigate whether their induction was a common feature in sugar-accumulating plants. Even higher levels of the transcripts under study accumulated in the invertase-expressing plants.

Table III. *cDNA Clones Isolated by Differential Hybridization of a Subtractive Library Enriched for Transcripts from Sugar-Accumulating Transgenic Tobacco Plants (ppa-1)*

Isolated Clone	Function	Reference
1	PR-1b	Cornelissen *et al.* (1986)
2	PR-Q	Payne *et al.* (1990)
3	SAR8.2	Ward *et al.* (1991)
4	ACC-oxidase	Holdsworth *et al.* (1987)
5	Calmodulin-like protein	Bartling, EMBL data library, X68054
6	ribosomal L19 protein	Kumabe *et al.* (1992)
7	novel PR protein	K. Herbers, G. Mönke, R. Badur, and U. Sonnewald (submitted)
8-12	unknown	

In *Dictyostelium*, it has been reported that the ribosomal protein L19 has calmodulin-binding activity (Sonnemann *et al.*, 1991), and a calmodulin antagonist was found to inhibit protein synthesis, suggesting that calmodulins might play a role in the latter process (Kumar *et al.*, 1991). Thus, our current model of why the ribosomal protein L19 and the calmodulin-like protein accumulate in the transgenic plants is that they are involved in the adaptation of protein synthesis in plant cells that prevail in a different physiological state due to continuous confrontation with high levels of photoassimilates.

PR-proteins, on the other hand, are known to be induced under a number of stress conditions like viral infection, pathogen invasion, injury, UV light, ozone, chemical treatment, salicylic acid, ethylene, and other plant hormones (reviewed in Ohashi and Ohshima, 1992). Osmotin, a protein which belongs to group 5 of PR-proteins, had first been found to be induced in cultured tobacco cells osmotically adapted to high salt conditions (Singh *et al.*, 1987, 1989). However, by floating leaves of wild-type tobacco plants on sorbitol, which is a nonpenetrating solute, only little induction of the PR-protein transcripts was observed while there was a massive induction if leaves were floated on sucrose (K. Herbers, G. Mönke, R. Badur, and U. Sonnewald, submitted). The latter situation is similar to the physiological state of the vacInv and cwInv tobacco plants, where the osmotic and water potential values were determined to be more negative than in wild-type plants (Table I). The question arises as to how the induction of the PR-protein mRNAs is mediated and whether the transduction mechanism/s might be common in all physiological situations where plants accumulate photoassimilates in their cells. Jang and Sheen (1994) hypothesized a common mechanism of sugar sensing in the repression of photosynthetic genes and the activation of stress-related/PR genes as other defense-related genes, such as proteinase inhibitor II and chalcone synthase, had been reported to be sugar-inducible (Johnson and Ryan, 1990; Kim et al., 1991, Tsukaya et al., 1991). This is in accordance with data on the ppa-1 and the invertase-expressing plants which were found to possess reduced photosynthetic electron-transport capacity (Stitt et al., 1990; R. Zrenner and U. Sonnewald, unpubl. data) and reduced expression of rbcS transcript (Krapp et al., 1993). However, other mechanisms for the induction of PR-proteins in response to sugars cannot be ruled out at the moment. For instance, the accumulation of the mRNA coding for ACC-oxidase in the sugar-accumulating plants might indicate a role of ethylene in the induction process. This is supported by the finding that carbohydrates stimulate ethylene production in tobacco leaf discs (Philosoph-Hadas et al., 1985).

Preconditioned Alarm State of Sugar-Accumulating Transgenic Plants

We were interested to see whether the isolated cDNAs would represent just part of a general induction process of the complete set of acidic PR-proteins. To this end, proteins from the intercellular washing fluid were isolated from wild-type and the invertase-expressing transgenic tobacco plants and separated by one-dimensional denaturing PAGE as described in Herbers et al. (1995) (Fig. 2). As PR-proteins are induced by a number of pathogens, including potato virus Y (PVY; Kassanis et al., 1974), wild-type tobacco plants were infected with this virus. PR-proteins accumulated in all leaves that were infected with PVY (Fig. 2, control-inf, lanes 1-3). PR-proteins were also induced in the intercellular fluids of vacInv and cwInv plants in contrast to nontransgenic control plants, and as expected, they were more abundant in mature source (lanes 2) than in younger leaves (lanes 3). Hardly any induction could be observed in primary leaves (lanes 1).

The synergistic induction of all acidic PR-proteins inducible by PVY encouraged us to study other defense-related responses in the transgenic tobacco plants, i.e. (i) phytoalexins; (ii) fluorescent phenolic compounds; (iii) induction of peroxidases; (iv) callose production; and (v) salicylic acid levels and resistance characteristics in the transgenic plants. Tobacco suspension cells respond to treatment with elicitors with the synthesis of sesquiterpenoids, primarily the phytoalexin capsidiol (Chappell et al., 1987). Central to capsidiol biosynthesis is the induction of a sesquiterpene cyclase [5-epi-aristolochene synthase (EAS) (Facchini and Chappell, 1992)]. We found that EAS was strongly induced in the transgenic vacInv and cwInv plants (K. Herbers, P. Meuwly, J-P Métraux, and U. Sonnewald, in prep.). These plants were also strongly fluorescent under UV light indicating the occurrence of induced soluble and cell-wall-bound phenolic compounds. The presence of peroxidase activities was visualized after electrophoretic separation of protein extracts from leaves using guaiacol as the substrate (Coll et al., 1993). Furthermore,

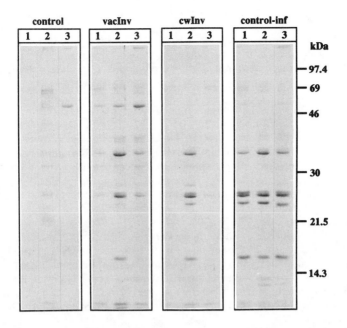

Figure 2. Accumulation of PR-proteins in transgenic tobacco plants expressing vacuolar (vacInv) and apoplastic (cwInv) yeast-derived invertase.

the amounts of salicylic acid and callose were found to be elevated (K. Herbers, P. Meuwly, J-P Métraux, and U. Sonnewald, in prep.).

Taken together, these biochemical data pointed to a possible pre-conditioned alarm state of the transgenic tobacco plants. To test this hypothesis, the plants were challenged with PVY, and spreading and accumulation of the virus was followed throughout the plant. In ppa-1 plants, a reduced local accumulation and retarded spreading to systemic leaves of PVY was observed, while the final titer of PVY in these leaves was comparable to wild type (K. Herbers, G. Mönke, R. Badur, and U. Sonnewald, submitted). In contrast, invertase-expressing tobacco plants showed a reduced local and systemic accumulation of PVY throughout the experiment (K. Herbers, P. Meuwly, J-P Métraux, and U. Sonnewald, in prep.).

ACKNOWLEDGMENTS

We would like to thank Heike Deppner, Andrea Knospe, and Christiane Prüßner for excellent technical assistance and Birgit Schäfer and Heike Ernst for the photographic work. We are also indebted to Hellmuth Fromme and his colleagues for taking care of the greenhouse plants. This work was funded by the Deutsche Forschungsgemeinschaft (Grant: So 300/2-1).

LITERATURE CITED

Barnes SA, Knight JS, Gray JC (1994) Alteration of the amount of the chloroplast phosphate translocator in transgenic tobacco affects the distribution of assimilate between starch and sugar. Plant Physiol **106**: 1123-1129

Burrell MM, Mooney PJ, Blundy M, Carter D, Wilson F, Green J, Blundy KS, ap Rees T (1994) Genetic manipulation of 6-phosphofructokinase in potato tubers. Planta **194**: 95-101

Caspar T, Huber SC, Somerville C (1985) Alterations in growth, photosynthesis, and respiration in a starchless mutant of *Arabidopsis thaliana* (L.) deficient in chloroplast phosphoglucomutase activity. Plant Physiol **79**: 11-17

Chappell J, Nable R, Fleming P, Andersen RA, Burton HR (1987) Accumulation of capsidiol in tobacco cell cultures treated with fungal elicitor. Phytochemistry **26**: 2259-2260

Coll PM, Tabernero C, Santamaria R, Perez P (1993) Characterization and structural analysis of the laccase I gene from the newly isolated lignolytic Basidomycete PM1 (CECT 2971). Appl Environ Microbiol **59**: 4129-4135

Cornelissen BJC, van Huijsduijnen RAMH, van Loon LC, Bol FJ (1986) Molecular characterization of messenger RNAs for pathogenesis-related proteins 1a, 1b and 1c, induced by TMV infection of tobacco. EMBO J **5**: 37-40

Dale JE (1988) The control of leaf expansion. Annu Rev Plant Physiol Plant Mol Biol **39**: 267-295

Ding B, Haudenshield JS, Willmitzer L, Lucas WJ (1993) Development of secondary plasmodesmata is arrested in tobacco expressing a yeast derived invertase gene. Plant J **4**: 179-189

Facchini PJ, Chappell J (1992) Gene family for an elicitor-induced sesquiterpene cyclase in tobacco. Proc Natl Acad Sci USA **89**: 11088-11092

Fry SC (1980) Gibberellin-controlled pectinic acid and protein secretion in growing cells. Phytochemistry **19**: 735-740

Goldschmidt EE, Huber SC (1992) Regulation of photosynthesis by end-product accumulation in leaves storing starch, sucrose and hexose sugars. Plant Physiol **99**: 1443-1448

Herbers K, Wilke I, Sonnewald U (1995) A thermostable xylanase from *Clostridium thermocellum* expressed at high levels in the apoplast of transgenic tobacco plants has no detrimental effect on the plants. BioTechnology (in press)

Holdsworth MJ, Bird CR, Ray J, Schuch W, Grierson D (1987) Structure and expression of an ethylene-related mRNA from tomato. Nucl Acids Res **15**: 731-739

Hudson GS, Evans JR, von Caemmerer S, Arvidsson YBC, Andrews TJ (1992) Reduction of ribulose-1,5-bisphosphate carboxylase/oxygenase content by "antisense" RNA reduces photosynthesis in transgenic tobacco plants. Plant Physiol **98**: 294-302

Iraki NM, Bressan RA, Carpita NC (1989) Extracellular polysaccharides and proteins of tobacco cell cultures and changes in composition associated with growth-limiting adaptation to water and saline stress. Plant Physiol **91**: 54-61

Jang JC, Sheen J (1994) Sugar sensing in higher plants. Plant Cell **6**: 1665-1679

Jelitto T, Sonnewald U, Willmitzer L, Hajirezaei M, Stitt M (1992) Inorganic pyrophosphate content and metabolites in potato and tobacco plants expressing *E. coli* pyrophosphatase in their cytosol. Planta **188**: 238-244

Johnson R, Ryan CA (1990) Wound-inducible potato inhibitor II genes: Enhancement of expression by sucrose. Plant Mol Biol **14**: 527-536

Jones TW, Gottlieb LD, Pichersky E (1986) Reduced enzyme activity and starch level in an induced mutant of chloroplast phosphoglucose isomerase. Plant Physiol **81**: 367-371

Kassanis B, Gianinazzi S, White RF (1974) A possible explanation of the resistance of virus-infected tobacco plants to second infection. J Gen Virol **23**: 11-16

Kim SR, Costa MA, An G (1991) Sugar response element enhances wound response of potato proteinase inhibitor II promoter in transgenic tobacco. Plant Mol Biol **17**: 973-983

Koßmann J, Sonnewald U, Willmitzer L (1994) Reduction of chloroplastic fructose-1,6-bisphosphatase in transgenic potato plants impairs photosynthesis and plant growth. Plant J **6**: 637-650

Krapp A, Quick WP, Stitt M (1991) Ribulose-1,5-bisphosphate carboxylase/oxygenase, other photosynthetic enzymes and chlorophyll decrease when glucose is supplied to mature spinach leaves via the transpiration stream. Planta **186**: 58-69

Krapp A, Hofmann B, Schäfer C, Stitt M (1993) Regulation of the expression of rbcS and other photosynthetic genes by carbohydrates: a mechanism for the 'sink regulation' of photosynthesis? Plant J **3**: 817-828

Kumabe T, Schma Y, Yamamoto T (1992) Human cDNAs encoding elongation factor 1g and the ribosomal protein RL19. Nucl Acid Res **20**: 2598-2598

Kumar RV, Panniers R, Wolfman A, Henshaw EC (1991) Inhibition of protein synthesis by antagonists of calmodulin in Ehrlich ascites tumor cells. Eur J Biochem **195**: 313-319

Lerchl J, Geigenberger P, Stitt M, Sonnewald U Impaired photoassimilate partitioning caused by phloem-specific pyrophosphate removal can be complemented by a phloem-specific cytosolic yeast-derived invertase in transgenic plants. Plant Cell (in press)

Lin T-P, Caspar T, Somerville C, Preiss J (1988) A starch deficient mutant of *Arabidopsis thaliana* with low ADPglucose pyrophosphorylase activity lacks one of the subunits of the enzyme. Plant Physiol **88**: 1175-1181

McCann MC, Shi J, Roberts K, Carpita NC (1994) Changes in pectin structure and localization during the growth of unadapted and NaCl-adapted tobacco cells. Plant J **5**: 773-785

Müller-Röber B, Sonnewald U, Willmitzer L (1992) Inhibition of the ADP-glu-cose pyrophosphorylase in transgenic potatoes leads to sugar-storing tubers and influences tuber formation and expression of tuber storage protein genes. EMBO J **11**: 1229-1238

Neuhaus HE, Kruckeberg AL, Feil R, Stitt M (1989) Reduced-activity mutants of phosphoglucose isomerase in the cytosol and chloroplast of *Clarkia xanthiana*. Planta **178**: 110-122

Ohashi Y, Ohshima M (1992) Stress-induced expression of genes for pathogenesis-related proteins in plants. Plant Cell Physiol **33**: 819-826

Payne G, Ahl P, Moyer M, Harper A, Beck J, Meins F Jr, Ryals J (1990) Isolation of complementary DNA clones encoding pathogenesis-related proteins P and Q, two acidic chitinases from tobacco. Proc Natl Acad Sci USA **87**: 98-102

Philosoph-Hadas S, Meir S, Aharoni N (1985) Carbohydrates stimulate ethylene production in tobacco leaf discs. II. Sites of stimulation in the ethylene biosynthesis pathway. Plant Physiol **78**: 139-143

Riesmeier J, Flügge UI, Schulz B, Heineke D, Heldt HW, Willmitzer L, Frommer WB (1993) Antisense repression of the chloroplast triose phosphate translocator affects carbon partitioning in transgenic potato plants. Proc Natl Acad Sci USA **90**: 6160-6164

Riesmeier JW, Frommer WB, Willmitzer L (1994) Evidence for an essential role of the sucrose transporter in phloem loading and assimilate partitioning. EMBO J **13**: 1-7

Rodermel SR, Abbott MS, Bogorad (1988) Nuclear-organelle interactions: nuclear antisense gene inhibits ribulose bisphosphate carboxylase enzyme levels in transformed tobacco plants. Cell **55**: 673-681

Sharkey TD, Savitch LV, Vanderveer PJ, Micallef BJ (1992) Carbon partitioning in a *Flaveria linearis* mutant with reduced cytosolic fructose bisphosphatase. Plant Physiol **100**: 210-215

Sheen J (1990) Metabolic repression of transcription in higher plants. Plant Cell **2**: 1027-1038

Sheen J (1994) Feedback control of gene expression. Photosyn Res **39**: 427-438

Singh NK, Bracker CA, Hasegawa PM, Handa AK, Buckel S, Hermodson MA, Pfankoch E, Regnier FE, Bressan RA (1987) Characterization of osmotin. Thaumatin-like protein associated with osmotic adaptation in plant cells. Plant Physiol **85**: 529-536

Singh NK, Nelson DE, Kuhn D, Hasegawa PM, Bressan RA (1989) Molecular cloning of osmotin and regulation of its expression by ABA and adaptation to low water potential. Plant Physiol **90**: 1096-1101

Sonnemann J, Bäuerle A, Winkler T, Mutzel R (1991) A ribosomal calmodulin-binding protein from *Dictyostelium*. J Biol Chem **266**: 23091-23096

Sonnewald U (1992) Expression of *E. coli* inorganic pyrophosphatase in transgenic plants alters photoassimilate partitioning. Plant J **2**: 571-581

Sonnewald U, Brauer M, von Schaewen A, Stitt M, Willmitzer L (1991) Transgenic tobacco plants expressing yeast-derived invertase in either the cytosol, vacuole or apoplast: a powerful tool for studying sucrose metabolism and sink/source interactions. Plant J **1**: 95-106

Sonnewald U, Lerchl L, Zrenner R, Frommer W (1994) Manipulation of sink-source relations in transgenic plants. Plant Cell Environ **17**: 649-658

Sonnewald U, Studer D, Rocha-Sosa M, Willmitzer L (1989) Immunocytochemical localization of patatin, the major glycoprotein in potato (*Solanum tuberosum* L.) tubers. Planta **178**: 176-183

Sonnewald U, Willmitzer L (1992) Molecular approaches to sink-source interactions. Plant Physiol **99**: 1267-1270

Stark DM, Timmermann KP, Barry GF, Preiss J, Kishore GM (1992) Regulation of the amount of starch in plant tissues by ADP-glucose pyrophosphorylase. Science **258**: 287-292

Stitt M, von Schaewen A, Willmitzer L (1990) "Sink" regulation of photosynthetic metabolism in transgenic tobacco plants expressing yeast invertase in their cell wall involves a decrease of Calvin cycle enzymes and an increase of glycolytic enzymes. Planta **183**: 40-50

Terry ME, Jones RL (1981) Soluble cell wall polysaccharides released from pea stems by centrifugation. Plant Physiol **68**: 531-537

Tsukaya H, Oshima T, Naito S, Chino M, Komeda Y (1991) Sugar-dependent expression of the CHS-A gene for chalcone synthase from petunia in transgenic *Arabidopsis*. Plant Physiol **97**: 1414-1421

von Schaewen A, Stitt M, Schmidt R, Sonnewald U, Willmitzer L (1990) Expression of a yeast-derived invertase in the cell wall of tobacco and *Arabidopsis* plants leads to accumulation of carbohydrate and inhibition of photosynthesis and strongly influences growth and phenotype of transgenic tobacco plants. EMBO J **9**: 3033-3044

Ward ER, Uknes SJ, Williams SC, Dincher SS, Wiederhold DL, Alexander DC, Ahl-Goy P, Métraux J-P, Ryals A (1991) Coordinate gene activity in response to agents that induce systemic acquired resistance. Plant Cell **3**: 1085-1094

Worrell AC, Bruneau JM, Summerfelt K, Boersig K, Voelker TA (1991) Expression of a maize sucrose phosphate synthase in tomato alters leaf carbohydrate partitioning. Plant Cell **3**: 1121-1130

The Regulation of Carbon Partitioning in Plants

David T. Dennis and Stephen D. Blakeley

Department of Biology, Queens University, Kingston, Ontario K7L 3N6, Canada

Ten years ago, it appeared that we had made considerable progress in determining the mechanisms by which carbon is allocated to different metabolic pathways in plants. Our predictions about the future were, however, far from correct. We seem to know less now than we did 10 years ago or, to be more accurate, there was much more to know than we anticipated. This realization has resulted from the advent and use of molecular genetics which has allowed us to modify plants in ways that were inconceivable a decade ago. We now realize that plant metabolism is extremely complex and is fundamentally different from the more comprehensively studied animal and bacterial systems. The ability to manipulate enzyme levels in transgenic plants and the inherent complexity of plant metabolism have profound implications for the future of plant biotechnology and we can, realistically, only expect to manipulate the central pathways of metabolism through a thorough understanding of the knowledge we have acquired in the last decade. It is our intention to illustrate the ways in which the perceptions of the plant science community as a whole have changed in the last decade through a recapitulation of our own work on the glycolytic pathway.

Plant glycolysis, the primary pathway of carbon metabolism (Fig. 1), has several unique features (Blakeley and Dennis, 1993). Firstly, there is the compartmentation of this pathway between the cytosol and the plastid, and we are only beginning to understand the complexity of the controls regulating the flux of glycolytic intermediates across the plastid envelope. In some tissues, the transfer of carbon occurs at the level of triose phosphates, whereas in others, hexose phosphates are transported (Tyson and ap Rees, 1988; Hill and Smith, 1991; Neuhaus *et al.*, 1993; Tetlow *et al.*, 1994). These differences have significant implications for the overall partitioning of carbon intermediates.

Secondly, carbon in the hexose phosphate pool can be utilized for sucrose or starch synthesis or be catabolized via glycolysis. The regulation of utiliza

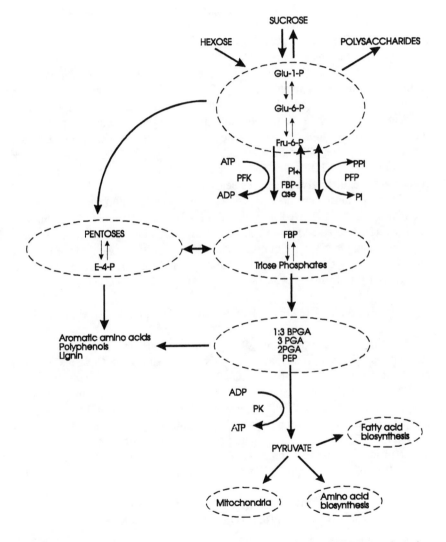

Figure 1. Diagrammatic representation of the major pathways of carbon metabolism in plants.

tion of metabolites from this pool is, therefore, central in determining the distribution of carbon between the various end-products. Another exit from this pool that is often neglected is the synthesis of cell walls, which is probably the major route of carbon flow in developing tissues. Carbon entering glycolysis from the hexose phosphate pool provides intermediates for production of fatty acids, terpenes, amino acids, and nucleic acids, and flux to these pathways will also vary considerably at different stages of development. For example, the flux of carbon through the shikimate pathway to lignins and polyphenols via aromatic amino acids may, at times, consume as much as 20% of the total photosynthate (DH Turpin, pers. commun.).

Thirdly, phosphoenolpyruvate (PEP) has a central role in plant metabolism (Fig. 1). Not only is this compound an intermediate of glycolysis, as the substrate for pyruvate kinase (PK), but it is also the precursor for the synthesis of aromatic and other amino acids. PEP is in equilibrium with other C_3 acids and the triose phosphates which are transported into the plastid via the phosphate translocator, and it appears that in some tissues, PEP itself can use this transporter (Borchert *et al.*, 1993). Finally, PEP is a feedback inhibitor of the ATP-dependent phosphofructokinase (PFK) and, therefore, functions to regulate glycolysis (see below).

Fourthly, most biosynthetic pathways in plants occur in plastids. Plastid glycolysis has been viewed as a means of supplying carbon for biosynthetic reactions (Dennis and Miernyk, 1982). However, biosynthetic pathways also require an abundant supply of cofactors, and glycolysis may be sequestered in plastids to satisfy this requirement without having to involve shuttle systems to import cofactors from the cytosol (Dennis and Blakeley, 1993).

THE REGULATION OF CARBON FLOW IN PLANT GLYCOLYSIS

Considering the above, it is not surprising that the regulation of glycolysis in plants is different from that in animals. PEP and other C_3 acids are at a metabolic crossroads, and these metabolites are the principal inhibitors of the PFK. Therefore, plant glycolysis is regulated from bottom to top by 3-phosphoglycerate (3PGA) and PEP. Consequently, PEP utilization by the various competing pathways must be precisely controlled by the plant (Dennis and Greyson, 1987). In contrast, animal glycolysis is regulated from the top down by the product of the PFK reaction, Fru-1,6-bisP, which regulates the utilization of PEP by activating PK. Plant PKs are not regulated by this compound.

THE ATP AND PPi-DEPENDENT PHOSPHOFRUCTOKINASES IN PLANTS

Plant PFK has regulatory properties similar to those described for the enzyme from other sources, but they are not so pronounced (Dennis and

Greyson, 1987). In plants, there are plastid and cytosolic isozymes of PFK and, surprisingly, the most pronounced regulatory properties are found in the plastid form (Garland and Dennis, 1980). In fact, the cytosolic enzyme shows only minimal regulation and less than might be expected from an enzyme so important in the flow of carbon to so many biosynthetic pathways. Most studies on this enzyme have failed to consider the presence of isozymes of PFK, and because of this, many types of regulation have been described (reviewed by Dennis and Greyson, 1987). Little has been added to our knowledge of this enzyme since 1987 because our attention was diverted by the discovery of a second enzyme in plants that catalyzes this step of glycolysis.

Since the mid-1980s, much of our attention has been focused on the PPi-dependent phosphofructokinase (PFP). The enzyme is found in all plants (Carnal and Black, 1983; Stitt, 1990), and there was great excitement and much speculation when it was found that PFP was activated by low levels of Fru-2,6-bisP (Sabularse and Anderson, 1981), a potent activator of animal glycolysis. There followed a plethora of paper biochemistry attempting to incorporate PFP into a central role in plant metabolism. The most persuasive was a role for this enzyme in the breakdown of sucrose, where it was suggested that PFP might provide a source of PPi and UDP for the newly accepted pathway of sucrose breakdown via sucrose synthase and UDP-glucose (UDPG) pyrophosphorylase (Black et al., 1987; ap Rees, 1988). It was also suggested that PFP might function to stabilize the concentration of pyrophosphate (ap Rees, 1988). Up until this point, plant biologists had accepted the dogma of other biochemists that PPi was broken down rapidly to drive biosynthetic reactions in the direction of synthesis. However, PPi is present at relatively high and stable concentrations in the plant cytosol (Smyth and Black, 1984; ap Rees et al., 1985).

Because PFP activity is higher in young tissues and declines in more mature parts of the plant (Smyth et al., 1984), it was thought that PFP might provide a bypass to PFK at times of high metabolic flux in biosynthetically active tissues (Dennis and Greyson, 1987). Alternatively, it was suggested that PFP may be a stress enzyme (Black et al., 1987). For example, PFP was proposed to be involved in the relief of stress during phosphate deficiency since there was a correlation between the level of PFP and the presence and absence of phosphate in the growth media of Brassica nigra cell suspension cultures (Theodorou and Plaxton, 1992).

It became more difficult to invoke a simple role for PFP as we gained more knowledge of the structure and properties of the enzyme. PFP is, in most plants, composed of two immunologically unrelated subunits (Kruger and Dennis, 1987). Furthermore, the amount of α- and β-subunit varies in different plant tissues (Botha and Botha, 1991) and, in some cases, correlates with phosphate status of the tissue (Theodorou and Plaxton, 1992).

The sequence of cDNA clones for the α- and β-subunits of PFP indicates that the β-subunit is catalytic, since it has putative binding sites for Fru-6-P and PPi. Recently, PFP from the intestinal anaerobe *Giardia lamblia* has been shown to have only one subunit which is similar to the β- rather than the α-subunit of plant PFP (Rozario *et al.*, 1995). The α-subunit has structural features that would render the Fru-6-P binding site catalytically inactive. Hence, this subunit may bind the activator Fru-2,6-bisP. Both subunits of PFP are expressed in most tissues (Carlisle *et al.*, 1990), but there can also be differential expression of the two genes (Blakeley *et al.*, 1992). The differential expression of the subunits, both of which are required to produce an enzyme with significant activity, is difficult to explain.

It has been suggested that the α-subunit of PFP was derived from the β-subunit by a recent gene duplication (Carlisle *et al.*, 1990). However, the genes for the two subunits are complex and different with the α- and β-genes containing 19 and 16 exons, respectively (Todd *et al.*, 1995). Furthermore, only two introns can be aligned. A phylogenetic analysis of the coding sequences of these genes was consistent with an ancient divergence and again suggested that the β-subunit of plant PFP is more closely related to PFK. Hence, the genes for both subunits of PFP have been retained through evolution suggesting that this enzyme does play a significant role in plant metabolism.

Stitt and his coworkers have used cDNA clones to reduce PFP activity in tobacco and potato to almost zero (Hajirezaei *et al.*, 1994, Paul *et al.*, 1995). Although there was a marked reduction of 3PGA and PEP in these plants, suggesting that the enzyme functioned in the glycolytic direction, there was little effect on growth or morphology. Considering the importance of PEP and 3PGA in plant metabolism, it is surprising that the reduced level of these intermediates had so little effect. Furthermore, few differences were seen when these plants were placed under stress. We must conclude that PFP does not play an *essential* role in metabolism. PFP has perhaps been retained during evolution because the presence of the enzyme confers some relatively obscure advantage to the plant. Conditions requiring this advantage for survival may only be found in the more stressful environment experienced by plants in nature and may not be easy to duplicate under laboratory conditions.

PYRUVATE KINASE

In animals, PK is controlled by the activity of PFK since Fru-1,6-bisP is a powerful activator of the enzyme. The animal enzyme is also controlled by phosphorylation/dephosphorylation. Considering the central role of PEP as an intermediate in carbon allocation in plants, and because PEP inhibits PFK, it was predicted that plant PK would be a regulatory enzyme. In fact, PK shows little or no control in tissues that should regulate PEP utilization (Duggleby and Dennis, 1973; Ireland *et al.*, 1980).

In contrast, PK from the green alga, *Selenastrum minutum*, does show regulatory kinetics (Lin *et al.*, 1989), but these are directed towards the control of the flow of carbon to amino acids rather than for use in energy metabolism. Recently, Plaxton and his co-workers have shown that cytosolic PKs from various plant tissues have a variety of regulatory properties with some resembling the algal enzyme (Podesta and Plaxton, 1994). Hence, there may be tissue-specific isozymes of PK which may have distinct properties related to the metabolic activities of that tissue.

Cytosolic PK (PK_c) has now been cloned from a number of plants and this has demonstrated the absence of the regulatory and phosphorylation sites found in other PKs (Blakeley *et al.*, 1990). The gene for the cytosolic enzyme from potato has also been cloned (Cole *et al.*, 1992). It has three introns, in contrast to the 11 found in the animal gene, and they are located at different places. Several variants of the gene have been found which is consistent with the possibility of tissue-specific isozymes, and two distinct cDNA clones have been isolated from a canola seed indicating that more than one gene for PK_c can be expressed in this tissue (S.D. Blakeley and D.T. Dennis, unpubl. data).

When tobacco was transformed with a modified PK_c clone, several transformants were isolated in which the level of PK_c had been reduced to zero (Gottlob-McHugh *et al.*, 1992). Surprisingly, these plants appear to grow normally, although it has now been found that the root-to-shoot ratio is reduced. This indicates that plants can overcome the loss of PK_c with little effect on growth and development.

The regulation of PEP levels is complicated in plants by the presence of plastid isozymes of PK. In some tissues, PEP can traverse the plastid envelope and the plastid form of PK may play a role in the regulation of carbon flow and ATP generation in these organelles (Borchert *et al.*, 1993). Plastid PK has kinetic properties quite different from the cytosolic isozyme (Ireland *et al.*, 1980). It is also considerably less stable. The purified plastid enzyme appears to be composed of nonidentical polypeptides (Plaxton *et al.*, 1990), although they can be separated to some extent by ion exchange chromatography suggesting that they may not be obligate subunits (see below).

cDNA clones for two isozymes of plastid pyruvate kinase (PK_pA and PK_pG) have been isolated from tobacco, castor, and *Brassica* (Blakeley *et al.*, 1991, 1995). These two forms are distinct, with the derived amino acid sequences being about 40% identical. A phylogenetic analysis of PK_c, PK_pA, and PK_pG has demonstrated that these different forms of PK have been retained by plants throughout evolution (J Hattori, B Baum, SG Gottlob-McHugh, SD Blakeley, DT Dennis, and BL Miki, submitted). Antibodies and NH_2-terminal sequencing have identified the two polypeptides found in the purified enzyme from castor endosperm as being the products of PK_pA and

PK$_p$G. The kinetics of the two forms are different. PK$_p$A, associated with PK$_p$G, is the most active form with a pH optimum of 8.0, similar to that of other plastid PKs (F.B. Negm, pers. commun.). In contrast, PK$_p$G alone has a much lower specific activity and a pH optimum closer to 7.0, similar to PK$_c$. The presence of multiple forms of PK$_p$, *in vivo*, may allow plants to regulate flux through plastid glycolysis under different metabolic conditions.

The genes for PK$_p$A and PK$_p$G are differentially expressed in castor and tobacco (Blakeley *et al.*, 1995), and PK$_p$G is the only protein found in chloroplasts where it is located exclusively in the stroma of the organelle. In contrast, both PK$_p$A and PK$_p$G are found in leucoplasts from developing castor endosperm (J Wan, SD Blakeley, DT Dennis, and K Ko, submitted). PK$_p$G is also located in the stroma of the leucoplast, whereas PK$_p$A can be found both in the stroma and, in small amounts, attached to the outer membrane of the envelope. *In vitro*-translated PK$_p$G will import readily into the stroma of both leucoplasts and chloroplasts in a process that requires 1 mM ATP (J Wan, SD Blakeley, DT Dennis, and K Ko, submitted). The import of PK$_p$G is, therefore, typical of other plastid proteins. In contrast, PK$_p$A will not import into either organelle at 1 mM ATP and is only imported into the stroma of leucoplasts at ATP concentrations above 2 mM. The requirement for higher than normal levels of ATP is governed by a domain between the transit peptide and the region encoding PK, and this domain will impart similar import properties, *in vitro*, to other, heterologous, proteins (J Wan, SD Blakeley, DT Dennis, and K Ko, submitted).

These results suggest that PK$_p$G is a constitutive plastid protein, present in all forms of this organelle, whereas PK$_p$A may only be transported into leucoplasts when the cytosolic ATP concentration rises. This would enhance the capacity of the leucoplast to generate internal ATP for biosynthetic purposes when ATP levels in the cytosol are high.

CONCLUSIONS

Although the last 10 years have seen major advances in our understanding of the allocation of carbon to the various plant metabolic pathways, many of the concepts we held in 1985 have proven to be inadequate. We are left with the disappointing conclusion that, despite our efforts, we have little understanding the nature of the controls regulating, for example, the flux of carbon through glycolysis. The cytosolic ATP-dependent phosphofructokinase does not have the pronounced regulatory properties that we might have expected. Furthermore, the near removal of PFP activity, the other enzyme that might influence flux, has little effect in transgenic plants. We have found that the level of metabolites that were thought to be of major regulatory significance can be changed with little effect. We have multiple forms of glycolytic enzymes such as pyruvate kinase and now know that the cytosolic form can be removed with little effect. Clearly, there is still a lot to be learned and 10 years from now, we will undoubtedly look back and be surprised at our present naivety. It is clear that plants have a great deal of flexibility built into their metabolism and can endure more abuse from the environment and plant biochemists than we ever expected.

LITERATURE CITED

ap Rees T (1988) Hexose phosphate metabolism by non-photosynthetic tissues of higher plants. *In* J Preiss, ed, Biochemistry of Plants, Vol 14. Academic Press, New York, pp 1-33

ap Rees T, Morrell S, Edwards J, Wilson PM, Green JH (1985) Pyrophosphate and the glycolysis of sucrose in higher plants. *In* J Preiss RL Heath, eds, Regulation of Carbon Partitioning in Photosynthetic Tissues. American Society of Plant Physiologists, Rockville, MD, pp 76-92

Black CC, Mustardy L, Sung SS, Kormanic PP, Xu W-P, Paz N (1987) Regulation and roles for alternative pathways of hexose metabolism in plants. Physiol Plant **69:** 387-394

Blakeley SD, Crews SAL, Todd JF, Dennis DT (1992) Expression of the genes for the α- and β-subunits of pyrophosphate-dependent phosphofructokinase in germinating and developing seeds from *Ricinus communis.* Plant Physiol **99:** 1245-1250

Blakeley SD, Dennis DT (1993) Molecular approaches to the manipulation of carbon allocation in plants. Can J Bot **71:** 765-778

Blakeley SD, Gottlob-McHugh SG, Crews SAL, Ko K, Miki BL, Dennis DT (1995) Molecular characterisation of plastid pyruvate kinase from castor and tobacco. Plant Mol Biol (in press)

Blakeley SD, Plaxton WC, Dennis DT (1990) Cloning and characterization of a cDNA for the cytosolic isozyme of plant pyruvate kinase: the relationship between the plant and non-plant enzyme. Plant Mol Biol **15:** 665-669

Blakeley SD, Plaxton WC, Dennis DT (1991) Relationship between the subunits of leucoplast pyruvate kinase from *Ricinus communis* and a comparison with the enzyme from other sources. Plant Physiol **96:** 1283-1288

Borchert S, Harborth J, Schunemann D, Hofericher P, Heldt HW (1993) Studies of the enzyme capacities and transport properties of pea root plastids. Plant Physiol **101:** 303-312

Botha A-M, Botha FC (1991) Pyrophosphate dependent phosphofructokinase of *Citrullus lanatus:* molecular forms and expression of subunits. Plant Physiol **96:** 1185-1192

Carlisle SA, Blakeley SD, Hemmingsen SM, Trevanion SJ, Hiyoshi T, Kruger NJ, Dennis DT (1990) Pyrophosphate-dependent phosphofructokinase: conservation of protein sequence between the alpha and beta subunits and with the ATP-dependent phosphofructokinase. J Biol Chem **265:** 18366-18371

Carnal NW, Black CC (1983) Phosphofructokinase activities in photosynthetic organisms. Plant Physiol **71:** 150-155

Cole KP, Blakeley SD, Dennis DT (1992) Structure of the gene encoding potato cytosolic pyruvate kinase. Gene **122**: 255-261

Dennis DT, Blakeley, SD (1993) Carbon Partitioning in developing oilseeds. *In* P Shewry, ed, Seed Storage Compounds. Oxford University Press, Oxford, UK, pp 262-276

Dennis DT, Greyson MF (1987) Fructose 6-phosphate metabolism in plants. Physiol Plant **69**: 395-404

Dennis DT, Miernyk, JA (1982) Compartmentation of non-photosynthetic carbohydrate metabolism. Annu Rev Plant Physiol **33**: 27-50

Duggleby RG Dennis DT (1973) Pyruvate kinase a possible regulatory enzyme in higher plants. Plant Physiol **52**: 312-317

Garland WJ, Dennis DT (1980) Plastid and cytosolic phosphofructokinases from the developing endosperm *Ricinus communis*. II. Comparison of the kinetics and regulatory properties of the isoenzymes. Arch Biochem Biophys **204**: 310-317

Gottlob-McHugh SG, Sangwan RS, Blakeley SD, Vanlerberghe G, Ko K, Plaxton WC, Turpin DH, Miki BL, Dennis DT (1992) Normal growth of tobacco in the absence of cytosolic pyruvate kinase. Plant Physiol. **100**: 820-825

Hajirezaei M, Sonnewald U, Viola R, Carlisle SA, Dennis DT, Stitt M (1994) Transgenic potato plants with strongly decreased expression of pyrophosphate: fructose 6-phosphate phosphotransferase show no visible phenotype and only minor changes in tuber metabolism. Planta **192**: 16-30

Hill LM, Smith AM (1991) Evidence that glucose 6-phosphate is imported as the substrate for starch synthesis by the plastids of developing pea embryos. Planta **185**: 91-96

Ireland RJ, DeLuca V, Dennis DT (1980) Characterisation and kinetics of isoenzymes of pyruvate kinase from developing castor bean endosperm. Plant Physiol **56**: 1188-1193

Kruger NJ, Dennis DT (1987) Molecular properties of pyrophosphate:fructose 6-phosphate phosphotransferase from potato tubers. Arch Biochem Biophys **56**: 273-279

Lin M, Turpin DH, Plaxton WC (1989) Pyruvate kinase isozymes from the green alga *Selenastrum minutum*. Kinetic and regulatory properties. Arch Biochem Biophys **269**: 228-238

Neuhaus HE, Henrichs G, Scheibe R (1993) Purification of highly intact plastids from various heterotropic plant tissues: analysis of enzymatic equipment and precursor dependency for starch biosynthesis. Biochem J **296**: 395-401

Paul M, Sonnewald U, Dennis DT, Stitt M (1995) Transgenic tobacco plants with strongly decreased expression of pyrophosphate: fructose 6-phosphate 1-phosphotransferase do not differ significantly from wild type in photosynthate partitioning, plant growth or their ability to cope with limiting phosphate, limiting nitrogen and suboptimal temperatures. Plant Cell Environ (in press)

Plaxton WC, Dennis DT, Knowles VL (1990) Purification of leucoplast pyruvate kinase from developing castor bean endosperm. Plant Physiol **94**: 1528-1534

Podesta FE, Plaxton WC (1994) Regulation of cytosolic carbon metabolism in germinating *Ricinus communis* cotyledons. II. Properties of phospho-*enol*pyruvate carboxylase and cytosolic pyruvate kinase associated with the regulation of glycolysis and nitrogen assimilation. Planta **194**: 381-387

Rozario C, Smith MW, Muller M (1995) Primary sequence of a putative inorganic pyrophosphate linked phosphofructokinase of *Giardia lambia.* Biochim Biophys Acta (in press)

Sabularse DC, Anderson RL (1981) D-Fructose 2,6-bisphosphate: a naturally occurring activator for inorganic pyrophosphate:fructose 6-phosphate in plants. Biochem Biophys Res Commun **103**: 848-854

Smyth DA, Black CC (1984) Measurement of pyrophosphate content in plant tissues. Plant Physiol **75**: 862-864

Smyth DA, Wu M-X, Black CC (1984) Phosphofructokinase and fructose 2,6- bisphosphatase activities in developing corn seedlings (*Zea mays* L.). Plant Sci Lett **33**: 61-70

Stitt M (1990) Fructose 2,6-bisphosphate as a regulatory molecule in plants. Annu Rev Plant Physiol Plant Mol Biol **41**: 153-158

Tetlow IJ, Blisset KJ, Emes MJ (1994) Starch synthesis and carbohydrate oxidation in amyloplasts from developing wheat endosperm. Planta **194**: 454-460

Theodorou ME, Plaxton WC (1992) Metabolic adaptations of plant respiration to nutritional phosphate deprivation. Plant Physiol **101**: 334-339

Todd J, Blakeley SD, Dennis DT (1995) Structure of the genes for the alpha and beta subunits of pyrophosphate dependent phosphofructokinase from castor. Gene (in press)

Tyson RH, ap Rees T (1988) Starch synthesis by isolated amyloplasts from wheat endosperm. Planta **175**: 33-38

Growth of Spinach Under Salinity Induces a Decrease in the Activity and Activation State of Sucrose-Phosphate Synthase and an Increase in the Activity of ADP-Glucose Pyrophosphorylase

M. D. Adcock, S. Moscatello, and A. Battistelli

Instituto per l'Agroselvicoltura, CNR, Via Marconi 2,
05010 Porano (TR), Italy

Permanent address: Robert Hill Institute and
Department of Animal and Plant Sciences, The University of
Sheffield, Sheffield S10 2UQ, UK

Five-week-old spinach plants were irrigated with water containing 100 mM NaCl for 3 d, 200 mM for a further 3 d, and 30 mM for the following 3 weeks prior to measurement of: (*i*) gas exchange at ambient CO_2 concentration; (*ii*) light- and CO_2-saturated O_2 evolution; (*iii*) diurnal changes in the leaf content of sucrose and starch; (*iv*) the activities of Rubisco, stromal fructose bisphosphatase (FBPase), and ADP-Glc pyrophosphorylase (ADP-Glc PPase); (*v*) the activity and the activation state of sucrose phosphate synthase (SPS); and (*vi*) the content of phosphorylated intermediates of the Calvin cycle and of the sucrose synthesis pathway, in leaves of salt-treated and control plants. The metabolite and enzyme measurements were carried out on leaves that exhibited similar rates of O_2 evolution for at least 30 min.

Salt treatment strongly decreased stomatal conductance, photosynthesis, and growth. Salt-treated plants accumulated much less carbohydrate between 0900 HR and 1800 HR than did the control plants. The maximum photosynthetic capacity, evaluated as light- and CO_2-saturated O_2 evolution, was unaffected by growth under salt conditions. Rubisco and stromal FBPase activities were similar in treated and control plants. The maximum activity of SPS (V_{max}), measured under saturating substrates and without inorganic phosphate, was reduced by 22% in salt-grown plants with respect to control plants. The activation state of SPS, evaluated as the ratio between V_{max} and the activity measured with limiting substrates in the presence of Pi, was severely reduced in salt-grown leaves. The amounts of Glu-6-P and Fru-6-P, and their ratio, did not change significantly, while UDP-Glc was about three times higher in the control plants than in the salt-grown plants.

SPS represents a key control point in photosynthetic sucrose synthesis in spinach leaves. A decrease in the activity and activation state of SPS should lead to a decrease in sucrose synthesis capacity unless the concentration of substrates and activators can overcome this limitation. Our data on phosphorylated metabolites indicate that this was not the case, since the amounts of Fru-6-P and Glu-6-P were similar in the two treatments and that of UDP-Glc was markedly lower in salt-stressed plants.

From these results, we infer that the capability of salt-stressed leaves to synthesize sucrose was severely limited. This should have limited photosynthesis, particularly at high assimilation rates, due to the limited Pi recycling capability of the cytoplasm. However, the O_2 evolution data, the activities of Rubisco and FBPase, and the amounts of metabolites did not show any evidence of a limitation of maximum photosynthetic capacity.

Starch synthesis represents an alternative sink-to-sucrose synthesis for photosynthetic products. In the short term, a decrease in sucrose synthesis would stimulation starch synthesis via metabolic control of ADP-Glc PPase to allow for optimal end-product synthesis and phosphate recycling in photosynthetic cells without any change in the amount of enzyme proteins. However, our data do not provide evidence of such metabolic activation of starch synthesis. Instead, measurements of the maximum activity of ADP-Glc PPase, made under optimal conditions, indicated that salt-grown plants had a significantly higher ADP-Glc PPase activity than in the control plants. This should also allow an increase of carbon partitioning toward starch, in the presence of a limited sucrose synthesis capability. The fact that salt-grown plants accumulated much less starch than the control plants could be due to the low assimilation rates of these plants, and does not contradict the data on the activities of SPS and ADP-Glc PPase.

The V_{max} of SPS and the ADP-Glc PPase activity, as measured here, represents a reasonable estimate of the amount of SPS and ADP-Glc PPase protein in spinach leaves. We can, therefore, conclude that during the period of salt irrigation, the amount of SPS protein was selectively reduced, and the amount of ADP-Glc PPase protein was increased, while maintaining key enzymes of the Calvin cycle unaffected.

Although the metabolic and the physiological effects of the modifications of SPS and ADP-Glc PPase activities are still unclear, these results represent the first evidence of a specific and coordinated regulation of sucrose and starch synthesis capacity in leaves in response to long-term stimuli, which appears to involve the control of amounts of enzyme protein.

The Movement Protein of Tobacco Mosaic Virus Influences Carbon Partitioning in Transgenic Tobacco Plants

Suchandra Balachandran, Richard J. Hull, Shmuel Wolf, Yoash Vaadia, and William J. Lucas

Section of Plant Biology, University of California, Davis, CA 95616, USA (S.B.; W.J.L.); Department of Plant Sciences, University of Rhode Island, Kingston, RI 02881, USA (R.J.H.); Department of Botany (S.W.) and Department of Vegetable Crops (Y.V.), The Hebrew University of Jerusalem, Rohovot 76-100, Israel

Transgenic tobacco plants expressing the movement protein of tobacco mosaic virus (TMV-MP) show a reduction in biomass partitioning to roots, suggesting that this protein influences the integrated physiology of these plants. In these transgenic plants, the size exclusion limit (SEL) of plasmodesmata between the mesophyll and bundle sheath cells of mature leaves is increased from 800 D to 9.4 kD. In contrast to the expectation that this increase in SEL will increase symplasmic transport of photosynthetic assimilates, translocation of the assimilates from the mature leaves was decreased during the day in transgenic plants which express the viral MP. This suggests that the TMV-MP, in addition to its role in viral trafficking during infection, also alters carbohydrate metabolism and biomass partitioning within the plant.

Using reciprocal graft experiments between control and TMV-MP-expressing plants, we showed that the expression of MP in leaf tissues is sufficient to alter biomass partitioning within the plant. When TMV-MP was expressed only in the phloem tissue, biomass partitioning, as reflected by root-to-shoot ratios, was comparable to that of vector control plants. This further established that the TMV-MP exerts its influence over biomass partitioning from the mesophyll tissue. Transgenic plants that express the mutant forms of the TMV-MP were investigated to determine possible domains in the MP that are responsible for the alteration in carbon allocation. Transgenic tobacco plants that express a deletion mutant form of the MP which contains a deletion of 93 amino acids at the C-terminus (that resides in the SEL domain), exhibited comparable growth characteristics and root-to-shoot ratios to those plants which express the wild-type MP. Also, another deletion mutant line in which 116 amino acids deleted from the C-terminus that spans the whole domain responsible for the increase in SEL, showed comparable biomass partitioning characteristics to that of plants expressing the wild-type MP. These experiments provide unequivocal evidence that the ability of this MP to alter carbon allocation was independent of its effects on plasmodesmal SEL. Transgenic tobacco plants that express a mutant form of MP that has a 10 amino acid deletion at the C-terminus, had no effect on root-to-shoot ratio and were comparable to vector control plants, suggesting a role for this region to influence biomass partitioning.

Further studies on effects of water and nitrogen stress factors and light on biomass partitioning in transgenic plants expressing the TMV-MP will be presented. We propose that the TMV-MP interferes with a signal trafficking pathway via plasmodesmata that may be involved in the integration of carbon allocation between sink tissues. The mechanism(s) through which TMV-MP could mediate its effects on carbon partitioning will be discussed.

Raffinose Oligosaccharides in the Intermediary Cells of *Cucumis melo*

Edith Haritatos, Felix Keller, and Robert Turgeon

Section of Plant Biology, Cornell University, Ithaca, NY 14850, USA (E.H.; R.T.); and Institute of Plant Biology, University of Zurich, Zollikerstrasse 107, CH-8008 Zurich, Switzerland (F.K.)

Raffinose and stachyose are translocated in many species, especially tropical trees and vines. The presence of these sugars adds additional complexities to studies of carbohydrate synthesis, phloem loading, carbon partitioning, and sink-source interactions. It is known that raffinose, stachyose, and galactinol are synthesized in intermediary cells (specialized companion cells) of the minor vein phloem. In order to better understand the role of these sugars, and the regulation of their synthesis and transport, we have measured the concentrations of each of the components of the raffinose oligosaccharide synthetic pathway in mesophyll and intermediary cells in the leaves of melon. To do this, we first developed a method for determining sugar concentrations in microdissected tissues. This methodology can easily be applied to other systems, such as leaves of other species, reproductive tissues, etc. Melon (*Cucumis melo* cv Hale's Best Jumbo) leaves are snap frozen and lyophilized. Mesophyll is removed from lyophilized leaves by a gentle abrasion technique, and sugar and chlorophyll are extracted. The sugar is quantified by HPLC using a pulsed amperometric detector, and chlorophyll is measured fluorometrically. Once the veins are exposed, the blind endings of areoles are sampled. Blind endings are the most anatomically simple of the minor veins in melon; they have the fewest cell types, consisting, in most cases, of intermediary cell(s), sieve element(s), and a tracheary element. Lengths of the blind endings are measured, and blind endings are then removed with a fine needle, pooled, and extracted. There is a certain amount of mesophyll which remains attached to the blind endings. However, since there are no chloroplasts in the veins, the amount of mesophyll contamination in the vein sample can be determined from the amount of chlorophyll. The mesophyll sugar contribution is then subtracted from the vein sample to determine the amount of sugar in the veins. Intermediary cell volumes are calculated by multiplying the total lengths of the veins in the sample by cross-sectional areas of intermediary cells and associated sieve elements, as determined by morphometric analysis. Since intermediary cells contain a large number of small acidic vacuoles, subcellular volumes are calculated and used to evaluate hypothetical compartmentation schemes. Sugar concentrations in mesophyll cells are determined by the same approach. Using this methodology, we have shown that the additive concentration of sugars in the intermediary cells of minor veins is similar to the concentration of sucrose found in the phloem of apoplastic-loading species. Raffinose and stachyose concentrations are high in the intermediary cells, and hexose concentrations are near zero. Sucrose levels appear to be higher in the intermediary cells than in the mesophyll, but further evidence indicates that sucrose may be sequestered in the vacuoles of the intermediary cells. Considering the equilibrium constants for raffinose and stachyose synthesis, and the concentrations of raffinose and stachyose in intermediary cells, calculations indicate that the sucrose concentration in the cytosol of intermediary cells may be approximately the same as the sucrose concentration measured in the mesophyll. These calculations are consistent with symplastic transport of sucrose from the mesophyll to the phloem.

The Evidence of Two Peptide Isoforms and Two cDNA of Sucrose Synthase in Tomato Plant: Expression in Different Tissues

Binh Nguyen Quoc, Raphael Anguenot,
Hyacinthe N'tchobo, and Serge Yelle

*Centre de Recherche en Horticulture, Faculté des
Sciences de l'Agriculture et de l'Altimentation, Université
Laval, Québec, Canada G1K 7P4*

Photoassimilates produced in the source leaf are translocated toward different utilization sink or accumulation sink organs. A better understanding of the metabolic reactions involved in source/sink relationships in higher plants might allow for an increase in the translocation of carbohydrates toward economically important organs. In higher plants, sucrose usually constitutes the major energy source translocated to developing organs via the phloem. Because of its central role in plant physiology, several studies on sucrose-metabolism enzymes have been conducted. Among those enzymes, sucrose synthase (SS; EC 2.4.1.13), which catalyzes either sucrose cleavage or sucrose synthesis, is a key enzyme.

In monocotyledonous plants, the physiological functions of SS are directed by two distinct isoforms acting in specific organs. In maize, for instance, a first form, SS1 (96 kD), is mainly associated with starch synthesis in the seed, while a second form, SS2 (90 kD), is closely associated with developing organs. Contrary to monocots, the existence in dicotyledonous plants of more than one SS form has been reported only in *Arabidopsis*. Global SS activity into tomato plants was explained so far by the presence of a single 90-kD isoform. The use of a partially purified antibody and appropriate electrophoretic conditions allowed the identification of two tomato SS isoforms, SST1 (100 kD) and SST2 (88 kD), immunologically related to maize SS1 and SS2. The SST2 peptide was easily detected in all organs analyzed, particularly those actively growing (young fruit, young leaf and stem). In accordance with previous results showing the presence of SS2 in growing tissues of maize kernels, such observations suggest the importance of SST2 in the growth processes involved in tomato plant development. In contrast, the SST1 peptide was detected in fruit, cotyledon, and leaf extracts, but not in stem or root extracts. Indicating a role for SST1 possibly associated to specific organs, the occurrence of a single SS form in the latter two organs also shows the importance of studying extracts from several tissues when assessing the role of different SS isoforms.

In tomato, only one SS gene was cloned and sequenced. However, we recently confirmed the presence of a second isoform of SS by cloning and characterizing a partial tomato cDNA encoding a SS peptide different than the previous one. Sequence analysis shows that the encoded region has a high homology (92%) with the already cloned SS, while the noncoded region is completely different (40% homology).

NAD-Dependent Mannitol Dehydrogenase in Plants

Johan M. H. Stoop, John D. Williamson,
Mark A. Conkling, and Mason Pharr

*Department of Horticultural Science, North Carolina
State University, Raleigh, NC 27695-7609, USA*

The acyclic polyol mannitol occurs in a wide variety of plants including many important agronomic crops and horticultural plants. In plants, mannitol can serve as a storage compound, hydroxyl scavenger, and/or compatible solute protecting plants from a variety of stresses. In celery (*Apium graveolens* L.), mannitol is a major phloem translocated photoassimilate that is utilized specifically in sink tissues. In 1992, we discovered an NAD-dependent mannitol dehydrogenase (MTD), which is a 1-oxidoreductase that oxidizes mannitol to mannose, in sink tissues of celery and celeriac. This poster reports the purification of this enzyme from celery suspension cultures to homogeneity. A highly efficient and simple purification protocol was developed involving PEG fractionation, DEAE-anion exchange chromatography, and NAD-affinity chromatography using gradient elution. Native molecular mass of the purified MTD was determined by Matrix-Assisted Laser Desorption Ionization Mass Spectroscopy (MALDI) to be 40.35 kD. SDS-PAGE together with MALDI analysis, indicated that the MTD was monomeric. Polyclonal antibodies against MTD were raised in rabbits. Immunotitration studies using this antiserum showed total inhibition of activity of the purified MTD. MTD activity was also observed in parsley (*Petroselinum crispum* L.) which is closely related to celery. The celery MTD antiserum was cross reactive with a 40-kD protein in extracts from parsley sink tissues, indicating that the MTD is not specific to celery and is present and enzymatically active in other plant tissues. The importance of this enzyme in carbon partitioning and controlling mannitol pools in plants will be discussed.

Spectral Quality Effects on Growth and Carbohydrate Metabolism in Wheat

Monica M. Sanwo, Neil C. Yorio, and Christopher S. Brown

Plant Space Biology Laboratory, Mail Code DYN-3, Kennedy Space Center, FL 32899, USA (M.M.S.); and Dynamac Corporation (N.C.Y.; C.S.B.)

Light emitting diodes (LEDs) are a potential light source for growing plants in space flight systems because of their superior safety and reliability, small mass and volume, electrical efficiency, and longevity. Prior to their acceptance for use in space flight hardware for plant research, the influence of narrow-spectrum LEDs on plant growth and metabolism must be determined. Biomass accumulation and yield, seed viability, and carbohydrate metabolism in leaves and seeds of wheat (*Triticum aestivum* L. cv Superdwarf) grown under red LEDs (peak emission 660 nm) were compared to plants grown under daylight fluorescent (white) light, red LEDs + 1% blue fluorescent light, and red LEDs + 10% blue fluorescent light. Seed development was delayed in the wheat plants grown under the red LED and red LED + 1% blue light, requiring 84 d to produce mature seeds, while plants grown under daylight fluorescent light produced mature seeds after 70 d, and plants grown under red LED + 10% blue light produced mature seeds after 77 d. Viable seeds (90% germination rates) were produced in all plants regardless of the light treatment. Plants were taller and had longer flag leaves when grown under red LEDs or red LEDs + 1% blue light compared to those grown with 10% blue light or under daylight fluorescent. Total dry matter, head dry matter, and seed dry matter were similar in the plants grown under the four light regimes, and there were no differences in the starch, protein, or soluble sugar content of the seeds. Starch levels were 4 times greater and sucrose levels 2.5 times greater in leaves of plants grown under the red LEDs compared to daylight fluorescent. The activity of sucrose phosphate synthase (SPS), a regulatory enzyme of sucrose synthesis, was 2.5 times lower in leaves grown under the red LEDs compared to daylight fluorescent. These results indicate that wheat can be successfully grown under red LEDs, but that there are differences in carbohydrate concentration and metabolism in photosynthetic tissue.

Photosynthetic Carbon Metabolism and Translocation in Wild-Type and Starch-Deficient Mutant *Nicotiana sylvestris* L.

Donald R. Geiger, Wen-Jang Shieh, and Xiao-Min Yu

*Department of Biology, University of Dayton,
Dayton, OH 45469-2320, USA*

A high rate of daytime export of assimilated carbon from leaves of a starch-deficient mutant tobacco, *Nicotiana sylvestris* L., was found to be a key factor that enabled shoots to grow at rates comparable to those in wild-type plants under a 14-h light period. Much of the newly fixed carbon that would be used for starch synthesis in leaves of wild-type plants was used instead for sucrose synthesis in the mutant. As a result, export doubled and accumulation of sucrose and hexoses increased markedly during the day in leaves of the mutant plants. The increased rate of export to sink leaves appeared to be responsible for the increase in the proportion of their growth that occurred during the day compared to wild-type plants. Daytime growth of source leaves also increased, presumably as a result of the increased accumulation of recently assimilated soluble carbon in the leaves. Even though starch accumulation did not occur in the leaves of mutant plants, nearly all the sugar that accumulated during the day was exported in the period of deceasing irradiance at the end of the diurnal light period. Changes in carbon allocation that occurred in leaves of wild-type and mutant plants near the end of the light period appeared to result from endogenous diurnal regulation associated with the day-night transition.

Quantifying Source, Sink, and Transport/Competition Limitations in Peach

T. M. DeJong and Y. L. Grossman

Department of Pomology, University of California, Davis, CA 95616, USA

Crop load on trees of early- and late-maturing peach cultivars ('Spring Lady' and 'Cal Red,' respectively) were adjusted on April 1, 1 month after bloom, to a range of values between approximately 50 and 700 fruits per tree. 'Spring Lady' fruits were harvested from replicate trees on May 2 and May 21 (fruit maturity). 'Cal Red' fruits were harvested from replicate trees on May 20, June 26, and July 31 (fruit maturity). The relationships between crop dry weight per tree and fruit number were determined for each harvest date, then used to calculate the maximum relative growth rate of fruits on lightly cropped trees and the potential fruit sink demand on trees with varying crop loads during each harvest interval. The total crop dry weight on heavily cropped trees was used to estimate source supply for each interval. Source, sink, and transport/competition limitations on fruit growth were calculated for various crop loads and harvest intervals. The results indicate that source limitations are important at higher crop loads throughout the fruit growth period on the early-maturing cultivar and during the early and late growth periods on the late-maturing cultivar. Sink limitations are important during the middle growth period of the late-maturing cultivar. Transport/competition limitations are more important during early stages of fruit growth than during the period of final fruit swell.

Tissue and Cell Level Expression of Sucrose Phosphate Synthase in Relation to Sucrose Biosynthesis in Maize Leaves

Wan-Hsing Cheng, Kyung H. Im, and Prem S. Chourey

University of Florida (W-H.C; K.H.I.; P.S.C.)
and USDA-ARS (P.S.C.), Gainesville, FL, USA

We describe two forms of sucrose phosphate synthase (SP) proteins based on cell-specific immunolocalization in bundle sheath (BS) and mesophyll (M) cells, in young (sucrose-sink) and mature (sucrose-source) leaves in maize. Developmentally, the earliest detection of the SPS protein was predominantly in the BS cells in young green leaves, and in greening leaves after the light treatment to dark-grown etiolated seedlings which showed otherwise undetectable levels of SPS protein. The Northern blot analyses on RNAs from etiolated and greening leaves indicate that SPS induction was at the level of transcription or at transcript stability. In contrast to young leaves, the mature leaves showed near equal levels of SPS signal in both BS and M cells. Day treatments of 24 and 48 h duration to young and mature plants, respectively, led to a much reduced signal in M cells, whereas, little or no change was detected in BS cells. The cellular level changes in SPS expression were also seen at the tissue level as judged by Northern and Western blot analyses as well as in the estimates of enzyme activity. Based on our collective data, we suggest that SPS in BS cells is engaged in at least two distinctive modes of sucrose biosynthesis in maize. First, in young leaves, the BS-SPS may play a major role in the early biosynthesis of sucrose. It is likely that carbon fixation in BS cells may precede that of M cells because Calvin cycle is unique to the BS cells. Second, because there were no changes in SPS levels in BS cells in dark treatment, we suggest that the enzyme may also play a critical role in nonphotosynthetic biosynthesis of sucrose through starch turnover processes, as starch is strictly confined to the BS cells in maize leaf. Light-responsiveness of SPS in M cells suggests that the enzyme in these cells had a major role in photosynthetic sucrose biosynthesis.

Carbon Partitioning in *Coleus blumei* During Salinity Stress

Glena Gilbert, Michelle Gadush, Clyde Wilson, and Monica A. Madore

Department of Botany and Plant Sciences, University of California, Riverside, CA 92521-0124 (G.G.; M.G.; M.A.M.); and USDA Salinity Lab, Riverside, CA 92501, USA (C.W.)

A variegated cultivar of *Coleus blumei*, a species that synthesizes and translocates sugars of the raffinose oligosaccharide family, was subjected to salinity stress to investigate the effects of stress on carbon partitioning. Although shoot growth in the "Fairway" cultivar was substantially reduced by salt treatment, the plants grew and survived for prolonged periods and set seed normally. The white, nonphotosynthetic tissue in the leaves was maintained even though severe carbon limitations were being imposed. One initial response of *Coleus* to salinity stress is an increase in total pools of amino acids in the sink and source tissues, particularly those which are phloem mobile (e.g. asparagine, serine, and glutamine). Another response of *Coleus* to salinity stress is a great reduction in starch reserves, which may reflect increased diversion of carbon to the sink tissues. However, correlated with the decrease in starch is an increased level of raffinose oligosaccharides with a high degree of polymerization (DP > 5) and a cyclitol. We believe that the accumulation of both the high DP oligosaccharides and the cyclitol are adaptive responses to salt stress. By synthesizing high DP raffinose oligosaccharides, the osmotic contribution of these sugars to vacuolar osmotic potential is reduced significantly, so carbon fixed by photosynthesis could be stored without adding to the already high osmotic potential of the vacuole caused by salt accumulation.

Hypothetical Pathway of Citric Acid Accumulation in the Fruits of Citrus

Camilo Canel

Department of Botany and Plant Sciences,
University of California, Riverside, CA 92521-0124, USA

A single-copy gene encoding the enzyme citrate synthase (CS) has been found in the citrus genome. Transcription of the *cit* gene in juice cells gives rise to a single species of mRNA encoding a mitochondrial enzyme. Because CS is the only known biosynthetic source of citrate, its mitochondrial localization in juice cells indicates that the accumulating citrate is synthesized in the mitochondria. Similar levels of *cit* transcript were detected in the juice tissues of fruits at stages of development corresponding to the periods before, during, and after citric acid accumulation; this absence of transcriptional regulation of *cit* indicates that the pathway is not regulated through the activity of CS, provided that *cit* mRNA levels are proportional to CS activity. Transport of citrate across the tonoplast of citrus juice cells is driven by energy released during hydrolysis of ATP. Citrate transport appears to be directly mediated by a tonoplast ATPase, since no evidence of the involvement of a trans-tonoplast electrochemical gradient was obtained. Based on these results as well as on existing knowledge about the control for the TCA cycle, and previous observations of the processes of carboxylate transport in plant mitochondria, a hypothetical pathway of citric acid accumulation is proposed.

Accumulation of Transcripts for Invertase and Sucrose Synthase in Mycorrhizal Roots of Dark Red Kidney Bean

K. A. Blee and A. J. Anderson

Department of Biology, Utah State University, Logan, UT, USA

A cDNA corresponding to a predicted peptide of 653 amino acids has been isolated from a lambda Zap II library of dark red kidney bean. The deduced amino acid sequence shows homology to invertase sequences from other plant species. When the cDNA was used as a probe on Northern blots containing total RNA from sterile-grown bean seedlings, a single message band was identified. Southern blots containing bean genomic DNA also reveal hybridizing bands when probed with the cDNA. These potential invertase cDNA, along with a soybean sucrose-synthase cDNA, has been used as probes to investigate transcript accumulations of these enzymes in bean roots colonized by the vesicular-arbuscular mycorrhizal fungus *Glomus intraradices*. The mycorrhizal fungus utilizes carbon from the plant, and altered flux may occur upon root colonization. Northern blots of total RNA from noncolonized control bean roots versus mycorrhizal bean roots from three experiments indicate no change in sucrose synthase mRNA accumulation. The same blots, when reprobed, show that accumulation of the invertase message may be reduced in colonized roots.

INDEX